Discovering Algebra
An Investigative Approach

Solutions Manual

DISCOVERING

MATHEMATICS

D1088581

Key Curriculum Press
Innovators in Mathematics Education

Teacher's Materials Project Editor: Joan Lewis

Editor: Stacey Miceli

Project Manager: Shannon Miller

Editorial Assistants: Christopher David, Heather Dever

Accuracy Checker: Dudley Brooks

Production Editor: Jacqueline Gamble

Copy Editors: Robert Fiske, Margaret Moore, Mary Roybal

Editorial Production Manager: Deborah Cogan

Production Director: Diana Jean Parks

Production Coordinator: Ann Rothenbuhler

Text Designer: Jenny Somerville

Art Editor: Jason Luz

Composition, Technical Art, Prepress: Interactive Composition Corporation

Art and Design Coordinator: Caroline Ayres

Cover Designer: Jill Kongabel

Printer: Data Reproductions

Executive Editor: Casey FitzSimons

Publisher: Steven Rasmussen

Key Curriculum Press
1150 65th Street
Emeryville, CA 94608
(510) 595-7000
editorial@keypress.com
http://www.keypress.com

Printed in the United States of America
10 9 8 7 6 5 4 3   07 06 05 04 03   ISBN 1-55953-341-2

Contents

Chapter 3

Chapter 4

Chapter 5

Chapter 6

Chapter 7

Chapter 8

Chapter 9

Chapter 10

Chapter 11

Introduction

The *Solutions Manual* for *Discovering Algebra: An Investigative Approach* contains solutions to the exercises at the end of each lesson and to the Improving Your Reasoning Skills, Improving Your Visual Thinking Skills, Improving Your Geometry Skills, and Take Another Look features. You can find solutions for the Investigations from the student text in the *Teacher's Edition*.

The solutions in this *Solutions Manual* are more complete than those offered as annotations in the *Teacher's Edition* or in the selected answers in the back of the student book. Although complete solutions for the problems are provided here, keep in mind that often there is more than one method students might use to solve a particular problem. Also, the answers will vary for some problems, depending on assumptions that students make. For problems that could have many different answers, a sample solution is given.

Refer to these solutions when your students have difficulty solving a problem and need some assistance in determining a possible approach toward solving it. You might also want to provide a copy of certain solutions for students who have been absent for an extended period of time.

CHAPTER 0

LESSON 0.1

EXERCISES

1. a. $\frac{1}{16} + \frac{1}{16}$ or $2 \cdot \frac{1}{16}$; total area $= \frac{2}{16}$ or $\frac{1}{8}$

b. $\frac{1}{64} + \frac{1}{64} + \frac{1}{64}$ or $3 \cdot \frac{1}{64}$; total area $= \frac{3}{64}$

c. $\frac{1}{25} + \frac{1}{25} + \frac{1}{25} + \frac{1}{25} + \frac{1}{25} + \frac{1}{25} + \frac{1}{25} + \frac{1}{25} +$

$\frac{1}{25} + \frac{1}{25} + \frac{1}{25} + \frac{1}{25} + \frac{1}{25} + \frac{1}{25} + \frac{1}{25}$ or

$15 \cdot \frac{1}{25}$; total area $= \frac{15}{25}$ or $\frac{3}{5}$

d. $\frac{1}{625} + \frac{1}{625} + \frac{1}{625} + \frac{1}{625} + \frac{1}{625} + \frac{1}{625} + \frac{1}{625}$

or $7 \cdot \frac{1}{625}$; total area $= \frac{7}{625}$

2. a. $\frac{1}{4} + \frac{1}{16} = \frac{4}{16} + \frac{1}{16} = \frac{5}{16}$

b. $\frac{2}{16} + \frac{3}{64} = \frac{8}{64} + \frac{3}{64} = \frac{11}{64}$

c. $9 \cdot \frac{1}{81} = \frac{9}{81} = \frac{1}{9}$

d. $\frac{1}{9} + \frac{2}{81} = \frac{9}{81} + \frac{2}{81} = \frac{11}{81}$

3. a.

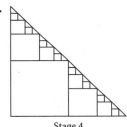

Stage 4

b. The area of the square is half the area of the Stage 0 triangle. So, the area of the square is 32.

c. At Stage 1, the area of each small triangle is 16. The area of each smallest square at Stage 2 is half this area, or 8. So, the total area of the squares at Stage 2 is 8 + 8 + 32, which equals 48.

d. At Stage 2, the area of each smallest triangle is 4. The area of each smallest square at Stage 3 is half this area, or 2. So, the total area of the squares at Stage 3 is 2 + 2 + 2 + 2 + 8 + 8 + 32, which equals 56.

4. a. $\frac{1}{3} + \frac{2}{9} = \frac{3}{9} + \frac{2}{9} = \frac{5}{9}$

b. $\frac{3}{4} + \frac{1}{2} + \frac{1}{3} = \frac{9}{12} + \frac{6}{12} + \frac{4}{12} = \frac{19}{12}$

c. $\frac{2}{5} \cdot \frac{3}{7} = \frac{6}{35}$

d. $2 - \frac{4}{9} = \frac{18}{9} - \frac{4}{9} = \frac{14}{9} = 1\frac{5}{9}$

5. Several answers are possible for each problem. Samples are shown.

a.

b.

c.

d.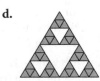

6. Answers will vary. Students should mention that the figure is created by a recursive process and that smaller parts are similar to the whole figure.

7. a. Answers will vary. Possible description: Divide each side of the square into thirds and connect those points with lines parallel to the sides. A square is formed in the middle. Trace around the square and then erase the other lines. To get the next stage, do the same thing in all eight squares formed around the middle square.

b.

Stage 3

c. The hole at Stage 1 has an area of $\frac{1}{9}$. At Stage 2, each of the 8 new holes has an area of $\frac{1}{9} \cdot \frac{1}{9}$ or $\frac{1}{81}$, so the combined area of the holes at Stage 2 is $\frac{1}{9} + \left(8 \cdot \frac{1}{81}\right) = \frac{9}{81} + \frac{8}{81} = \frac{17}{81}$. At Stage 3, each of the 64 new holes has an area of $\frac{1}{9} \cdot \frac{1}{81}$ or $\frac{1}{729}$, so the combined area of the holes at Stage 3 is $\frac{17}{81} + \left(64 \cdot \frac{1}{729}\right) = \frac{153}{729} + \frac{64}{729} = \frac{217}{729}$.

d. At each stage, the area of the carpet is 1 minus the combined area of the holes. The area of the carpet at Stage 1 is $1 - \frac{1}{9} = \frac{8}{9}$. The area of the carpet at Stage 2 is $1 - \frac{17}{81} = \frac{64}{81}$. The area of the carpet at Stage 3 is $1 - \frac{217}{729} = \frac{512}{729}$.

8. a. The large triangle is divided into four equal-size smaller triangles. Because the area of the large triangle is 8, the area of each smaller triangle is $8 \div 4 = 2$.

b. $\frac{1}{4}$; $8 \cdot \frac{1}{4} = 2$

c. There is no difference. Dividing by 4 is the same as multiplying by its reciprocal, $\frac{1}{4}$.

d. Together, the three shaded triangles make up $\frac{3}{4}$ of the total area. Because the total area is 8, the area of the shaded triangles is $8 \cdot \frac{3}{4}$, or 6.

9. a. Each smallest triangle makes up $\frac{1}{16}$ of the total area. Because nine smallest triangles are shaded, $\frac{9}{16}$ of the area is shaded.

b. Answers will vary. Here are two possibilities: Because the large triangle has area 12 and $\frac{9}{16}$ of the triangle is shaded, the total shaded area is $12 \cdot \frac{9}{16}$. Or, because the large triangle could be divided into 16 equal-size smallest triangles, each with area $\frac{12}{16}$ or $\frac{3}{4}$, and because 9 smallest triangles are shaded, the total area shaded is $9 \cdot \frac{3}{4}$. Both these expressions are equal to $\frac{27}{4}$ or $6\frac{3}{4}$.

10. a. $\frac{1}{9}$

b. Each small triangle is $\frac{1}{9}$ of a medium triangle, so its area is $\frac{1}{81}$ of the original triangle.

c. The total shaded area is $\left(\frac{4}{9} \cdot 24\right) + \left(\frac{3}{81} \cdot 24\right)$ $= \frac{96}{9} + \frac{72}{81} = \frac{96}{9} + \frac{8}{9} = \frac{104}{9} = 11\frac{5}{9}$. Another way to calculate this is $24 \cdot \left(\frac{4}{9} + \frac{3}{81}\right) = 24 \cdot \left(\frac{36}{81} + \frac{3}{81}\right)$ $= 24 \cdot \left(\frac{39}{81}\right) = \frac{936}{81} = \frac{104}{9}$.

11. Answers will vary, but should be equivalent to those shown.

a. The Stage 0 triangle has area 32. At each stage, the area of the smallest triangle is $\frac{1}{4}$ the area of the smallest triangle at the previous stage. So, at Stage 2, the area is $\frac{1}{4}$ of $\frac{1}{4}$ of 32.

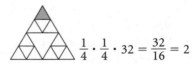
$\frac{1}{4} \cdot \frac{1}{4} \cdot 32 = \frac{32}{16} = 2$

b. The area of one smallest Stage 3 triangle is $\frac{1}{4}$ of $\frac{1}{4}$ of $\frac{1}{4}$ of 32. So, the area of three smallest Stage 3 triangles is $\frac{3}{4}$ of $\frac{1}{4}$ of $\frac{1}{4}$ of 32.

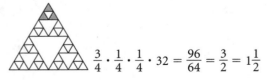
$\frac{3}{4} \cdot \frac{1}{4} \cdot \frac{1}{4} \cdot 32 = \frac{96}{64} = \frac{3}{2} = 1\frac{1}{2}$

c. $\frac{1}{4}$ of $\frac{1}{4}$ of $\frac{1}{4}$ of 32 is the area of one Stage 3 triangle. because $\frac{1}{2}$ is twice as much as $\frac{1}{4}$, $\frac{1}{2}$ of $\frac{1}{2}$ of $\frac{1}{4}$ of 32 is four times the area of one Stage 3 triangle, so it is equal to the area of four Stage 3 triangles.

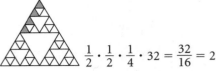
$\frac{1}{2} \cdot \frac{1}{2} \cdot \frac{1}{4} \cdot 32 = \frac{32}{16} = 2$

12. $\frac{1}{4} + \frac{1}{16} + \frac{1}{32} = \frac{8}{32} + \frac{2}{32} + \frac{1}{32} = \frac{11}{32}$

13. $1 - \frac{11}{32} = \frac{32}{32} - \frac{11}{32} = \frac{21}{32}$

LESSON 0.2

EXERCISES

1. a. 5^4 **b.** 7^5 **c.** 3^7 **d.** 2^3

2. a. $3 \times 3 \times 3 \times 3$; $3 \cdot 3 \cdot 3 \cdot 3$; $3(3)(3)(3)$

b. $5 \times 5 \times 5 \times 5 \times 5 \times 5$; $5 \cdot 5 \cdot 5 \cdot 5 \cdot 5 \cdot 5$; $5(5)(5)(5)(5)(5)$

c. $\frac{1}{2} \times \frac{1}{2} \times \frac{1}{2}$; $\frac{1}{2} \cdot \frac{1}{2} \cdot \frac{1}{2}$; $\frac{1}{2}\left(\frac{1}{2}\right)\left(\frac{1}{2}\right)$

3. a. 3^3 **b.** 2^5

c. 5^4 or 25^2 **d.** 7^3

4. a. $\frac{2}{3} \cdot 12 = \frac{24}{3} = 8$

b. $\frac{1}{3} + \frac{3}{5} = \frac{5}{15} + \frac{9}{15} = \frac{14}{15}$

c. $\frac{3}{4} - \frac{1}{8} = \frac{6}{8} - \frac{1}{8} = \frac{5}{8}$

d. $5 - \frac{2}{7} = \frac{35}{7} - \frac{2}{7} = \frac{33}{7}$ or $4\frac{5}{7}$

e. $\frac{1}{4} \cdot \frac{1}{4} \cdot 8 = \frac{8}{16} = \frac{1}{2}$

f. $\frac{3}{64} + \frac{3}{16} + \frac{3}{4} = \frac{3}{64} + \frac{12}{64} + \frac{48}{64} = \frac{63}{64}$

5. a. At Stage 2, two new branches are added to each of the two Stage 1 branches, so there are a total of 2^2 or four new branches. At Stage 3, two branches are added to the end of each of the Stage 2 branches, so there are a total of $2 \cdot 2^2$ or 2^3 or eight new branches.

b. Stage 0 has one branch. To find the number of new branches at each stage, you multiply the number at the previous stage by 2. By Stage 5, you will have done this five times. So, the total number of new branches at Stage 5 is 2^5.

6. a. At Stage 2, five new branches are added to each of the five new Stage 1 branches, so there are a total of 5^2 or 25 new branches.

b. There are five new branches at Stage 3 for every new branch at Stage 2 for a total of $5 \cdot 5^2$ or 5^3 or 125 branches.

c. Stage 0 has one branch. To find the number of new branches at each stage, you multiply the number at the previous stage by 5. By Stage 5, you will have done this five times. So, the total number of new branches at Stage 5 is 5^5.

7. a. Each stage has 8 times as many square holes as the previous stage, so Stage 3 has $8 \cdot 8$ or 64 new square holes.

b. Stage 4 would have $8 \cdot 64$ or 512 new square holes.

c. 8^2; 8^3

d. At Stage 7, there would be 8^6 or 262,144 new holes.

e. The exponent is always one less than the stage number.

f. According to the pattern, the Stage 1 figure should have 8^0 holes. $8^0 = 1$, so the pattern does work.

8. a. Stage 1 is made up of 5 segments (three along the long vertical segment, plus the two branches). At Stage 2, two new branches are added to each of these segments, for a total of $2 \cdot 5$ or 10 branches.

b. Stage 2 is made up of 25 segments. At Stage 3, two new branches are added to each of these segments, for a total of $2 \cdot 25$ or 50 branches.

c. At Stage 3, there are $2 \cdot 5^2$ new branches; at Stage 4, there are $2 \cdot 5^3$ new branches; and at Stage 5, there are $2 \cdot 5^4$ new branches.

d. At each stage, each segment from the previous stage is replaced by 5 new segments. At each stage, two branches are added to each segment from the *previous* stage.

9. a, b.

Stage number	Area of one shaded triangle	Total area of the shaded triangle
0	1	1
1	$\frac{1}{4} \cdot 1 = \frac{1}{4}$	$\frac{3}{4}$
2	$\frac{1}{4} \cdot \frac{1}{4} = \frac{1}{16}$	$9 \cdot \frac{1}{16}$ or $\frac{3}{4} \cdot \frac{3}{4} = \frac{9}{16}$
3	$\frac{1}{4} \cdot \frac{1}{16} = \frac{1}{64}$	$27 \cdot \frac{1}{64}$ or $\frac{3}{4} \cdot \frac{9}{16} = \frac{27}{64}$

c. Answers will vary. The area of one shaded triangle at each stage is $\frac{1}{4}$ the area of one shaded triangle at

the previous stage. The total area of the shaded triangles at each stage is $\frac{3}{4}$ the shaded area at the previous stage.

10. $2 \cdot 2 \cdot 2 \cdot 2 \cdot 2 \cdot 2 \cdot 2 \cdot 2 = 2^8 = \$256.00$

11. Answers will vary. One possibility: The restaurant had $\frac{3}{4}$ of a pie left. Five people wanted pie. After cutting the pie into fifths, how much did each person get? $\frac{3}{20}$.

12. a. $\frac{1}{4} + \frac{1}{16} + \frac{1}{64} = \frac{16}{64} + \frac{4}{64} + \frac{1}{64} = \frac{21}{64}$

b. $\frac{1}{4} + \frac{2}{16} + \frac{5}{64} = \frac{16}{64} + \frac{8}{16} + \frac{5}{64} = \frac{29}{64}$

LESSON 0.3

EXERCISES

1. a. $\frac{125}{8}$; 15.63   **b.** $\frac{25}{9}$; 2.78

  c. $\frac{2401}{81}$; 29.64   **d.** $\frac{729}{64}$; 11.39

2. $\frac{5^2}{3^2} - \frac{5}{3} = \frac{25}{9} - \frac{5}{3} = \frac{25}{9} - \frac{15}{9} = \frac{10}{9}$; or, using the rounded decimal values, $2.78 - 1.67 = 1.11$.

3. $\left(\frac{5}{3}\right)^4 \approx 7.72.$ $\left(\frac{5}{3}\right)^5 \approx 12.86.$ The Stage 5 figure is the first figure with a total length of more than 10.

4. a. $\frac{1}{5} + \frac{3}{4} = \frac{4}{20} + \frac{15}{20} = \frac{19}{20}$

b. $3^2 + 2^4 = 9 + 16 = 25$

c. $\frac{2}{3} \cdot \left(\frac{6}{5}\right)^2 = \frac{2}{3} \cdot \frac{36}{25} = \frac{72}{75} = \frac{24}{25}$

d. $4^3 - \frac{2}{5} = 64 - \frac{2}{5} = 63\frac{3}{5}$

5. a.

Stage number	Total length		
	Multiplication form	Exponent form	Decimal form
2	$5 \cdot 5 \cdot \frac{1}{4} \cdot \frac{1}{4} = \frac{25}{16}$	$5^2 \cdot \left(\frac{1}{4}\right)^2$	1.56
3	$5 \cdot 5 \cdot 5 \cdot \frac{1}{4} \cdot \frac{1}{4} \cdot \frac{1}{4}$ $= \frac{125}{64}$	$5^3 \cdot \left(\frac{1}{4}\right)^3$ $= \left(\frac{5}{4}\right)^3$	1.95

b. $\left(\frac{5}{4}\right)^4 \approx 2.44$; $\left(\frac{5}{4}\right)^5 \approx 3.05$. So, the figure at Stage 5 is the first to be longer than 3. $\left(\frac{5}{4}\right)^{10} \approx 9.31$; $\left(\frac{5}{4}\right)^{11} \approx 11.64$. So the figure at Stage 11 is the first to be longer than 10.

6. a. Note that each stage has six times as many segments as the previous stage, and each segment is $\frac{1}{4}$ the length of the segments in the previous stage. (*See table at bottom of page.*)

 b. Because $\left(\frac{3}{2}\right)^5 = \frac{243}{32}$, Stage 5 has length $\frac{243}{32}$.

 c. $\left(\frac{6}{4}\right)^{11} \approx 86.50$; $\left(\frac{6}{4}\right)^{12} \approx 129.75$. So the figure at Stage 11 has a length closest to 100.

7. a. Note that each stage has seven times as many segments as the previous stage, and each segment is $\frac{1}{3}$ the length of the segments in the previous stage. (*See table at bottom of page.*)

 b. Because $\left(\frac{7}{3}\right)^5 = \frac{16{,}807}{243}$, Stage 5 has length $\frac{16{,}807}{243}$.

 c. No. Stage 6 has a length of slightly more than 161, and Stage 7 has a length of over 376. There is no stage between these two stages.

8. a.

	Total length		
Stage number	Expanded form	Exponent form	Decimal form
2	$8 \cdot 8 \cdot \frac{1}{3} \cdot \frac{1}{3} = \frac{64}{9}$	$8^2 \cdot \left(\frac{1}{3}\right)^2$ $= \left(\frac{8}{3}\right)^2$	7.11
3	$8 \cdot 8 \cdot 8 \cdot \frac{1}{3} \cdot \frac{1}{3} \cdot \frac{1}{3}$ $= \frac{512}{27}$	$8^3 \cdot \left(\frac{1}{3}\right)^3$ $= \left(\frac{8}{3}\right)^3$	18.96

 b. Estimates will vary. The actual value is $\left(\frac{8}{3}\right)^4$, or about 50.

 c. Answers may vary. On many calculators, Stage 23 is the last to be shown without resorting to scientific notation.

9. 2.8

10. $\frac{8}{9} - \frac{12}{9} = \frac{8}{3} - \frac{4}{3} = \frac{4}{3} = 1\frac{1}{3}$

11. a. 4

 b. 16

 c. The 16 segments drawn at Stage 3 divide the figure into 64 pieces. In Stage 4, a segment would be drawn across each of these pieces, so 64 new segments would be drawn.

 d. $4^1, 4^2, 4^3$

 e. In general, the exponent is one less than the stage number. This holds true for Stage 1 because $4^0 = 1$, and 1 new segment is added at Stage 1.

IMPROVING YOUR REASONING SKILLS

The polygon with "an infinite number of sides" is the circle, and the area between the inscribed polygon and the circle approaches 0 as the number of sides increases. Although the process shown for generating regular polygons isn't recursive (no stage builds on the previous one), it could be made so, by repeatedly doubling the number of sides. Some students may believe that the resulting circle is a fractal because it's the result of an infinite sequence of recursive operations, others that it's not a fractal because it's not self-similar.

Lesson 0.3, Exercise 6.a.

	Total length		
Stage number	Expanded form	Exponent form	Decimal form
2	$6 \cdot 6 \cdot \frac{1}{4} \cdot \frac{1}{4} = \frac{36}{16} = \frac{9}{4}$	$6^2 \cdot \left(\frac{1}{4}\right)^2 = \left(\frac{6}{4}\right)^2 = \left(\frac{3}{2}\right)^2$	2.25
3	$6 \cdot 6 \cdot 6 \cdot \frac{1}{4} \cdot \frac{1}{4} \cdot \frac{1}{4} = \frac{216}{64} = \frac{27}{8}$	$6^3 \cdot \left(\frac{1}{4}\right)^3 = \left(\frac{6}{4}\right)^3 = \left(\frac{3}{2}\right)^3$	3.38

Lesson 0.3, Exercise 7.a.

	Total length		
Stage number	Expanded form	Exponent form	Decimal form
2	$7 \cdot 7 \cdot \frac{1}{3} \cdot \frac{1}{3} = \frac{49}{9}$	$7^2 \cdot \left(\frac{1}{3}\right)^2 = \left(\frac{7}{3}\right)^2$	5.44
3	$7 \cdot 7 \cdot 7 \cdot \frac{1}{3} \cdot \frac{1}{3} \cdot \frac{1}{3} = \frac{343}{27}$	$7^3 \cdot \left(\frac{1}{3}\right)^3 = \left(\frac{7}{3}\right)^3$	12.7
4	$7 \cdot 7 \cdot 7 \cdot 7 \cdot \frac{1}{3} \cdot \frac{1}{3} \cdot \frac{1}{3} \cdot \frac{1}{3} = \frac{2401}{81}$	$7^4 \cdot \left(\frac{1}{3}\right)^4 = \left(\frac{7}{3}\right)^4$	29.64

Discovering Algebra Solutions Manual
©2002 Key Curriculum Press

Exercises

1. a. $-4 + 7 = 3$

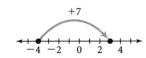

b. $5 + (-8) = -3$

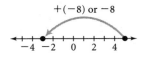

c. $-2 - 5 = -7$

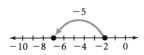

d. $-6 - (-3) = -3$

2. a. $-2 \cdot 5 = -10$

b. $6 \cdot (-4) = -24$

c. $-3 \cdot (-4) = 12$

d. $-12 \div 3 = -4$

e. $36 \div (-6) = -6$

f. $-50 \div (-5) = 10$

3. a. $5 \cdot -4 - 2 \cdot (-6) = -20 - (-12)$
$= -20 + 12 = -8$

b. $3 + (-4) \cdot 7 = 3 + (-28) = -25$

c. $-2 - 5 \cdot (6 + (-3)) = -2 - 5 \cdot 3$
$= -2 - 15 = -17$

d. $(-3 - 5) \cdot (-2) + 9 \cdot (-3)$
$= -8 \cdot (-2) + (-27) = 16 + (-27) = -11$

4. Answers will vary. Students may talk of "numbers without their signs" instead of "absolute values." Possible answers:

a. Subtract the number with the smaller absolute value from the number with the larger absolute value. Give the result the sign of the number with the larger absolute value.

b. Add the absolute values. Make the result negative.

c. Add the opposite of the negative number to the positive number.

d. Subtracting a negative number is the same as adding a positive number, so the problem actually involves adding a negative number and a positive number. See the answer to 4a.

e. Multiply the absolute values. Make the result negative.

f. Multiply the absolute values.

g. Divide the absolute values. Make the result negative.

h. Divide the absolute values.

5. a. In the first recursion, he made a mistake when finding $-0.2 \cdot 2$. He should have gotten -0.4, not 0.4. In the second recursion, he used the wrong value (-3.6 instead of -4.4) because of his previous error. His arithmetic was also incorrect because $-0.2 \cdot (-3.6) = 0.72$, not -0.72.

b. $-0.2 \cdot 2 - 4 = -0.4 - 4 = -4.4$
$-0.2 \cdot (-4.4) - 4 = 0.88 - 4 = -3.12$
$-0.2 \cdot (-3.12) - 4 = 0.624 - 4 = -3.376$
$-0.2 \cdot (-3.376) - 4 = 0.6752 - 4 = -3.3248$

c. $-0.2 \cdot (-1) - 4 = 0.2 - 4 = -3.8$
$-0.2 \cdot (-3.8) - 4 = 0.76 - 4 = -3.24$
$-0.2 \cdot (-3.24) - 4 = 0.648 - 4 = -3.352$

d. Yes. The calculations in 1b and c seem to be approaching a value close to -3.3.

6. a. (*See table at bottom of page.*)

b. Answers may vary, but probably will be about -2.222.

c. Entering -2.222222222222 as a starting value in the calculator returns the same value as an answer.

7. a.

Starting value	2	−1	10
First recursion	−3	3	−19
Second recursion	7	−5	39
Third recursion	−13	11	−77

b. The values get farther and farther apart with each recursion. The expression does not reach an attractor value.

Lesson 0.4, Exercise 6.a.

Starting value	2	−1	10
First recursion	$0.1 \cdot (2) - 2 = -1.8$	$0.1 \cdot (-1) - 2 = -2.1$	$0.1 \cdot (10) - 2 = -1$
Second recursion	$0.1 \cdot (-1.8) - 2 = -2.18$	$0.1 \cdot (-2.1) - 2 = -2.21$	$0.1 \cdot (-1) - 2 = -2.1$
Third recursion	$0.1 \cdot (-2.18) - 2 = -2.218$	$0.1 \cdot (-2.21) - 2 = -2.221$	$0.1 \cdot (-2.1) - 2 = -2.21$

8. a. i. 12   **ii.** -16 **iii.** -8

b. The attractor value is twice the constant term (if you rewrite the expression as addition). For example, in the expression $0.5 \cdot \square + 3$, the constant term is 3, and the attractor value is $2 \cdot 3 = 6$. In the expression $0.5 \cdot \square - 4$, the constant term is -4, and the attractor value is $2 \cdot (-4) = 8$. In general, for an expression in the form $coefficient \cdot \square + constant\ term$, the attractor value is $\frac{constant\ term}{1 - coefficient}$.

c. Many answers are possible. One choice is $0.5 \cdot \square + 3$.

9. a. i. 7.5   **ii.** -10 **iii.** 6.25

b. The attractor value is 1.25 times the constant (if you rewrite the expression as addition). For example, in the expression $0.2 \cdot \square - 8$, the constant term is -8 and the attractor value is $1.25 \cdot (-8)$ or -10. In general, for an expression in the form $coefficient \cdot \square + constant\ term$, the attractor value is $\frac{constant\ term}{1 - coefficient}$.

c. Many answers are possible. One choice is $0.2 \cdot \square + 1.8$.

10. All these processes involve repeating a process. Each time the result of one repetition becomes the starting value or figure for the next repetition.

11. $4 - 12 \div 4 \cdot \frac{1}{2} - 5^2$

$= 4 - 12 \div 4 \cdot \frac{1}{2} - 25$ Evaluate the exponents first.

$= 4 - 3 \cdot \frac{1}{2} - 25$ Divide.

$= 4 - \frac{3}{2} - 25$ Multiply.

$= \frac{8}{2} - \frac{3}{2} - \frac{50}{2}$ Rewrite with a common denominator.

$= -\frac{45}{2} = -22\frac{1}{2}$ Subtract.

12. $(-3 \cdot -4) - (-4 \cdot 2) = 12 - (-8) = 12 + 8 = 20$

LESSON 0.5

EXERCISES

1. a. 8.0 cm   **b.** 4.3 cm   **c.** 7.2 cm

2. a. The segment should be 2.8 cm long.

b. The segment should be 5.7 cm long.

c. The segment should be 5.08 cm long, or about 5.1 cm.

3. a–c. Answers will vary but should look proportional to this.

d. Points D and B are closest together. This relationship does not change with the length of the original segment.

4. a. $-2 + 5 - (-7) = 3 - (-7) = 3 + 7 = 10$

b. $(-3)^2 - (-2)^3 = 9 - (-8) = 9 + 8 = 17$

c. $\frac{3}{5} + \frac{-2}{3} = \frac{9}{15} + \frac{-10}{15} = \frac{-1}{15}$

d. $-0.2 \cdot 20 + 15 = -4 + 15 = 11$

5. The resulting figure should resemble a right-angle Sierpiński triangle.

6. a–b. Answers will vary.

c.

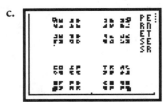

d. The resulting figure resembles the Sierpiński carpet from Exercise 7 of Lesson 0.1.

e. Answers will vary. Because there are six numbers on a die and only four corners, you could ignore rolls of 5 or 6 and move toward the corner 1, 2, 3, or 4 depending on the roll of the die.

7. a. This game fills the entire square.

b. This game creates a small Sierpiński triangle at each corner of the triangle.

c. This game creates four small Sierpiński carpets, one at each corner of the square.

d. This game creates a pattern like the Sierpiński triangle. It is difficult to see this figure clearly on the calculator screen, but if you let the program run for a very long time, you'll begin to see the pattern below.

8. Answers will vary. One possibility is to use a die and ignore rolls of 6 and then use the others to indicate the five corners. Another possibility is to use five playing cards and choose one to indicate the move. The answer should describe a process by which all corners are equally likely to be chosen.

9. Point should divide segment into an 8-cm and a 4-cm segment.

10. a. i. 2   **ii.** 4   **iii.** -6

b. Answers will vary. The attractor value is $\frac{2}{3}$ of the constant.

c. Answers will vary. One possibility: $-0.5 \cdot \square - 15$.

11. Each stage has 6 times as many segments as the previous stage, and each segment is $\frac{1}{4}$ as long as the segments in the previous stage. (*See table at bottom of page.*)

CHAPTER 0 Review

EXERCISES

1. a. 1 **b.** 3 **c.** 9 **d.** 27

  e. 81 **f.** 6561 **g.** 531,441 **h.** 1

  i. $\frac{1}{3}$ **j.** $\frac{1}{9}$ **k.** $\frac{1}{27}$ **l.** $\frac{1}{81}$

  m. $\frac{1}{6561}$ **n.** $\frac{1}{531,441}$

2. a. iii **b.** v **c.** ii

  d. iv **e.** i

3. a. $2 \cdot (24 + 12) = 2 \cdot 36 = 72$

  b. $2 + 24 \cdot 12 = 2 + 288 = 290$

  c. $2 - 24 + 12 = -22 + 12 = -10$

  d. $(2 + 24) \cdot 12 = 26 \cdot 12 = 312$

  e. $(2 + 24) \div 12 = 26 \div 12 = \frac{13}{6} = 2.1\overline{6}$

  f. $2 - (24 + 12) = 2 - 36 = -34$

4. a. $\frac{1}{3} \times \frac{1}{3} \times \frac{1}{3}$ **b.** $\frac{2}{3} \times \frac{2}{3} \times \frac{2}{3} \times \frac{2}{3}$

  c. 1.2×1.2

  d. $16 \times 16 \times 16 \times 16 \times 16$

  e. $2 \times 2 \times 2 \times 2 \times 2 \times 2 \times 2$

5. a. $\frac{1}{16} + \frac{1}{16} + \frac{1}{16} = \frac{3}{16}$

  b. $\frac{1}{16} + \frac{1}{16} + \frac{1}{4} = \frac{3}{8}$

  c. $\frac{1}{9} + \frac{1}{9} + \frac{1}{81} + \frac{1}{81} = \frac{20}{81}$

  d. $\frac{1}{4} + \frac{1}{16} + \frac{1}{64} + \frac{1}{64} = \frac{22}{64}$ or $\frac{11}{32}$

6. a.

Stage 3

At each stage, add a branch at the midpoint of the branch added at the previous stage. The length of the new branch should be half the length of the previous branch, and it should be rotated 45° counterclockwise from the midpoint of previous branch.

b.

Stage 3

Replace the "right" half of each segment from the previous stage with a "bottomless" equilateral triangle.

c.

Stage 3

Cross each segment from the previous stage at its midpoint with a centered perpendicular segment of the same length.

d.

Stage 3

Lesson 0.5, Exercise 11.

Stage number	Total length		
	Multiplication form	**Exponent form**	**Decimal form**
0	1	1^0	1
1	$6 \cdot \frac{1}{4}$	$6^1 \cdot \left(\frac{1}{4}\right)^1 = \left(\frac{6}{4}\right)^1 = \left(\frac{3}{2}\right)^1$	1.5
2	$6 \cdot 6 \cdot \frac{1}{4} \cdot \frac{1}{4}$	$6^2 \cdot \left(\frac{1}{4}\right)^2 = \left(\frac{6}{4}\right)^2 = \left(\frac{3}{2}\right)^2$	2.25
3	$6 \cdot 6 \cdot 6 \cdot \frac{1}{4} \cdot \frac{1}{4} \cdot \frac{1}{4}$	$6^3 \cdot \left(\frac{1}{4}\right)^3 = \left(\frac{6}{4}\right)^3 = \left(\frac{3}{2}\right)^3$	3.38
4	$6 \cdot 6 \cdot 6 \cdot 6 \cdot \frac{1}{4} \cdot \frac{1}{4} \cdot \frac{1}{4} \cdot \frac{1}{4}$	$6^4 \cdot \left(\frac{1}{4}\right)^4 = \left(\frac{6}{4}\right)^4 = \left(\frac{3}{2}\right)^4$	5.06

Each unshaded square is divided horizontally and vertically to create four congruent squares; the bottom right square is shaded.

7. a. Each stage has seven times as many segments as the previous stage, and each segment is $\frac{1}{5}$ the length of segments in the previous stage.

Stage number	Total length		
	Multiplication form	Exponent form	Decimal form
0	1	1^0	1
1	$7 \cdot \frac{1}{5}$	$7^1 \cdot \left(\frac{1}{5}\right)^1 = \left(\frac{7}{5}\right)^1$	1.4
2	$7 \cdot 7 \cdot \frac{1}{5} \cdot \frac{1}{5}$	$7^2 \cdot \left(\frac{1}{5}\right)^2 = \left(\frac{7}{5}\right)^2$	1.96

b. $\left(\frac{7}{5}\right)^{20} \approx 836.68$

8. No matter what value you start with, the result approaches 5, so the attractor is 5.

TAKE ANOTHER LOOK

The behavior of numbers raised to a power depends on the kinds of numbers involved.

Number in box	Exponent of 3 (or any odd integer greater than 1)	Exponent of 4 (or any even integer greater than zero)
Positive number greater than 1	bigger	bigger
Negative number less than -1	smaller (negative yet farther from zero)	bigger (becomes positive)
Zero or 1	stays the same	stays the same
-1	stays the same	bigger (becomes 1)
Positive fraction between 0 and 1	smaller (positive yet closer to zero)	smaller (positive yet closer to zero)
Negative fraction between 0 and -1	bigger (negative yet closer to zero)	bigger (becomes positive)

The statement "If the denominator of a fraction increases, the value of the fraction decreases" is true for positive fractions written with both numerator and denominator positive. For negative fractions—written with only the numerator negative—increasing the denominator makes the magnitude of the fraction decrease, thereby moving it closer to zero. Because the fraction moves to the right along the number line, it becomes greater.

For $\frac{\bigcirc}{\square^3}$ to be smaller than $\square^3$ the numerator would have to be less than $\square^6$.

For $\frac{\bigcirc}{\square^3}$ to be greater than $\square^3$, the numerator would need to be greater than $\square^6$. For $\frac{\bigcirc}{\square^4}$, the numerator would be compared to $\square^8$.

LESSON 1.1

EXERCISES

1. Max: 93 bpm; min: 64 bpm; range: $93 - 64 = 29$ bpm.

2. The categories in this problem are the elements (note the chemical abbreviations are used in the graph below). Percentages are shown on the vertical axis. The height of each bar represents the percentage for that element.

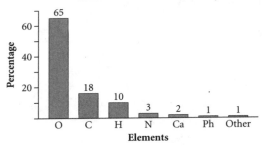

Elements in the Human Body

3. a. Uranus (There are 21 named satellites.)

b. Mercury and Venus have no satellites.

c. $17 - 8 = 9$ more satellites.

d. $18 \div 2 = 9$ times as many satellites.

4. a. Draw a number line to represent the times. Your number line will need to include values from at least 1 (the minimum time) to 15 (the maximum time). Make a column of dots over each time to represent the number of students who take that much time to get to school. For example, because two people spend 3 minutes traveling to school, there are two dots over the number 3.

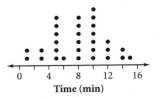

Travel Time to School

b. To find the total number of students, count the dots. There are 30 students in the class.

c. To find the combined time, multiply each time by the number of students who take that long to get to school. Then, add the results: $2 \cdot 1 + 2 \cdot 3 + 6 \cdot 5 + 1 \cdot 6 + 6 \cdot 8 + 7 \cdot 10 + 3 \cdot 12 + 2 \cdot 14 + 1 \cdot 15 = 241$. So, the combined time is 241 minutes, or 4 hours and 1 minute.

d. To find the average, divide the combined time by the number of students. The average is $\frac{241}{30} \approx 8$ minutes.

5. a. 80 bpm (the number with the tallest column of dots)

  b. $93 - 64 = 29$ bpm

  c. Answers will vary. She probably counted her pulse rates for one full minute.

  d. Any whole number could occur, not just multiples of four.

  e. A full minute, sometimes longer, to ensure accuracy.

6. a. Graph iii is the best match. The values in graphs ii and iv are too large. Graph i has some values of 0, which cannot be correct because at least one person (the student) must live in each student's home.

  b. Graph ii is the best match. The values in graphs i and iii are too small. The values in graph iv seem too large. The shortest person represented in that graph is 5 ft 8 in., the tallest person is 6 ft 5 in., and more than half the students are over 6 ft tall!

  c. Graph iv is the best match. The values in the other graphs are too low.

  d. Graph i is the best match. The values in the other graphs are too large.

7. Knowing there are 3 students in the R&B category, you can see that there are 2 in Country, 5 in Rap, and 7 in Pop/Rock. That leaves 3 in Classical to reach the known total of 20 students.

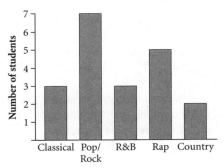

Favorite Types of Music

8. A bar graph because the information falls into categories, is not numeric data, and cannot be scaled on a number line.

9. a. 10^4 **b.** $2^3 \cdot 5^6$ **c.** $\dfrac{3^6}{8^3}$

10. a. $7 + (3 \cdot 2) - 4 = 7 + 6 - 4 = 9$

  b. $8 + 2 - 4 \cdot 12 \div 16 = 8 + 2 - 48 \div 16$
  $= 8 + 2 - 3 = 7$

  c. $1 - 2 \cdot 3 + 4 \div 5 = 1 - 6 + 0.8 = -5 + 0.8$
  $= -4.2$

  d. $1 - (2 \cdot 3 + 4) \div 5 = 1 - (6 + 4) \div 5$
  $= 1 - 10 \div 5 = 1 - 2 = -1$

  e. $1^2 \cdot 3 + (4 \div 5) = 1^2 \cdot 3 + 0.8 = 1 \cdot 3 + 0.8$
  $= 3 + 0.8 = 3.8$

11. a. Double 225 until you go past 4050. Double 1 the same number of times.

Doubles of 225	450	900	1800	3600	7200
Doubles of 1	2	4	8	16	32

  Find doubles of 225 that add to 4050: $450 + 3600 = 4050$. Then, add the corresponding doubles of 1: $2 + 16 = 18$. So, $4050 \div 225 = 18$.

  b. Double 6 until you get past 57.

Doubles of 6	6	12	24	48	96
Doubles of 1	1	2	4	8	16

  Look for doubles of 6 that add to 57. There is no combination that works. The closest you can get is $6 + 48 = 54$. You need 3 more to get to 57. Since 3 is half of 6, find half of 1 as well. Add these values to the table:

3	6	12	24	48	96
1/2	1	2	4	8	16

  Because $3 + 6 + 48 = 57$, you can find the quotient by adding the corresponding "doubles" of 1: $0.5 + 1 + 8 = 9.5$. So, $57 \div 6 = 9.5$.

IMPROVING YOUR REASONING SKILLS

Perhaps JoAnn's graph illustrates low temperatures better, since negative values fall under the axis; her choice of scale adds some distortion to the values. However, the side-by-side feature of Janet's graph allows easy comparison between high and low temperatures.

LESSON 1.2

EXERCISES

1. a. To find the mean, add the values and divide by the number of values. The sum is 54, and there are 9 values. So, the mean is $54 \div 9 = 6$.
To find the median, list the values in order: 1, 3, 5, 5, 6, 7, 8, 9, 10. The median is the middle value, which is 6.
The mode is 5, the value that occurs most often.

  b. The mean is $51 \div 10$ or 5.1. Order the list to find the median: 1, 2, 3, 3, 4, 6, 7, 8, 8, 9. The median is the average of the middle two numbers (4 and 6), or 5. The modes are 3 and 8.

  c. The mean is $82 \div 8 = 10.25$. Order the list to find the median: 2, 5, 6, 7, 11, 12, 18, 21. The median is 9. There is no mode.

  d. Mean: 17.5; median: 20; mode: 20

2. a. Read the data values from the graph. The number of dots above a number indicate the number of times that number occurs in the data set. So, the values are 1, 1, 1, 2, 2, 2, 3, 4, 5, 6, 6, 6, 8, 9, 9. The mean of this data is $\frac{65}{15} \approx 4.3$. The median is 4. There is no mode because there are too many most common values.

   b. Mean: $\frac{53}{15} \approx 3.5$; median: 2; modes: 1 and 2

3. a. To find the number of students, just count the dots. Twenty student responses are shown.

   b. Range = maximum − minimum = 8 − 0 = 8

   c. 1 (the number with the tallest column of dots)

4. a. Mean = $\frac{145 + 137 + 161 + 205 + 310}{5} = \frac{958}{5}$
   = 191.6 ft; median: 161 ft; no mode

   b. Mean: 181.2 ft; median: 155 ft; no mode

5. The average cost = $\frac{\text{total bill}}{\text{number of items}}$, so you can find the total bill by multiplying the average cost by the number of items. This gives you $16 \cdot 1.14 = 18.24$, making the total bill $18.24.

6. a. Mean: 67.15 feet; median: 66 feet; no mode

   b. Because the median and mean are close, either would be a good choice.

7. The first three members averaged 53 seconds each, so together, they took 53(3) or 159 seconds. The total time for the whole team must be 50(5) or 250 seconds. The two remaining members must have a total of 250 − 159 or 91 seconds. So the last two people must average 91 ÷ 2 or 45.5 seconds each.

8. The mean, 83.8, is lower than all but one of his scores. The median, 88, is more representative.

9. a. The mean weight = $\frac{\text{total weight}}{\text{number of fish}}$; you can find the total weight by multiplying the mean weight by the number of fish. So, the total weight is $1527.4 \cdot 10$ or 15,274 pounds.

   b. Five of the fish caught weigh 1449 pounds or less, and five weigh 1449 pounds or more.

   c. Maximum = minimum + range = 991 + 1673 = 2664. So, the maximum weight is 2664 pounds.

10. Answers will vary. Sample answers are provided.

   a. When the five data values are listed in order, the third value must be 12. Because the mean of the five values is 19, the total value must be $19 \cdot 5$ or 95. So, the remaining values must add to 95 − 12 or 83, and there must be two values less than 12 and two values greater than 12. One possibility is {8, 10, 12, 32, 33} years.

   b. When the six values are listed in order, the mean of the two middle values is 4, and the value 5 must occur most often. One possibility is {2, 3, 3, 5, 5, 5} people.

   c. {7, 14, 20, 21, 24, 27, 27} points

11. a. (*See graph at bottom of page.*)

   b. Mean: 33.95; median: 30; mode: 29

   c. Either the mode or the median is probably best. The mean is distorted by one extremely high value.

12. a. Because the data is numeric, a dot plot may be most appropriate. However, if each value were translated into years (divide by 12), you could make a bar graph or pictograph with ages as categories.

   b. Answers may vary. (*See graph at bottom of page.*)

13. a. 12 cm   **b.** 8 cm   **c.** 2.4 cm

LESSON 1.3

EXERCISES

1. a. The minimum is 5 and the maximum is 50. The median is the middle value, 23. The first quartile (Q1) is 10, the middle value in the first half of the data. The third quartile (Q3) is 37, the middle

Lesson 1.2, Exercise 11.a.

Highest-Paid Athletes

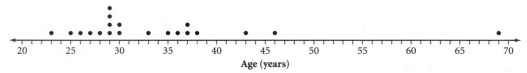

Age (years)

Lesson 1.2, Exercise 12.b.

Student Ages

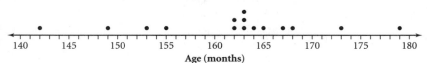

Age (months)

value in the second half. So, the five-number
summary is 5, 10, 23, 37, 50.

Q1   Median   Q3
↓   ↓   ↓
5 5 8 10 14 16 22 23 32 32 37 37 44 45 50

b. The minimum is 10 and the maximum is 50.
Because there are an even number of values, the
median is the number halfway between the two
middle values, 30 and 33. So the median is 31.5.
The first quartile (Q1) is 22, the middle value in
the first half of the data, and the third quartile
(Q3) is 37, the middle value in the second half.
The five-number summary is 10, 22, 31.5, 37, 50.

Q1   Median   Q3
↓   ↓   ↓
10 15 20 22 25 30 30 33 34 36 37 41 47 50

c. 14, 22.5, 26, 41, 47. The values are listed in order
below with the location of the median and
quartiles indicated.

Q1   Median   Q3
↓   ↓   ↓
14 16 20 25 26 26 26 33 37 40 42 44 47

d. 5, 10, 19, 34.5, 47. The values are listed in order
below with the location of the median and
quartiles indicated.

Q1   Median   Q3
↓   ↓   ↓
5 5 9 11 16 17 21 32 34 35 43 47

2. a. i. There are 20 data values. Listed in order, they are
0, 0, 0, 1, 1, 1, 1, 1, 1, 1, 2, 2, 2, 3, 3, 3, 3, 4, 5, 7.
The median is the value halfway between the
tenth and eleventh values, which are 1 and 2.
The first quartile is median of the 10 values in
the first half of the data. So, it is the number
halfway between the fifth and sixth values,
which are 1 and 1. The third quartile is the
median of the 10 values in the second half of the
data, so it is the number halfway between the
fifteenth and sixteenth values, which are 3 and 3.

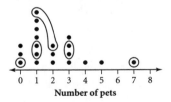

Number of pets

ii. (*See graph at bottom of page.*)

b. i. 0, 1, 1.5, 3, 7   **ii.** 64, 75, 80, 86, 93

3. The five-number summary is 1, 4, 6, 7, 9. To create a
box plot, make dots over the minimum and
maximum values. Draw vertical segments over the
median and quartiles. Draw a box with ends at
the first and third quartiles. Draw horizontal
segments that extend from each end of the box to
the minimum and maximum values.

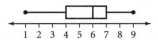

4. Choices a and d are both possible. Both have the
five-number summary shown in the box plot.
Choice b has the correct minimum, median, third
quartile, and maximum, but the wrong first quartile.
Choice c has the correct minimum, first quartile,
median, and maximum, but the wrong third quartile.

5. a. Answers will vary. Quartiles are the boundaries
dividing a data set into four groups, or quarters,
with approximately the same number of values.

    b. The range

    c. The interquartile range, or IQR

    d. Outliers are at or near the minimum and
maximum values, which are the endpoints of
the whiskers.

6. a. Answers will vary. The prediction should be less
than the mean.

    b. Because the mean of the four scores is 25.5, the
total must be 4 · 25.5, or 102. The sum of the three
scores Stu knows is 79, so the third score must be
103 − 79, or 23 points.

    c. The four scores are 23, 23, 27, and 29. The
five-number summary for this data set is
23, 23, 25, 28, 29.

    d. Answers will vary. Because there are only four
values, a five-number summary may be
inappropriate—the values themselves illustrate
the spread of the data.

7. a. 151, 426, 644, 1020, 1305

    b. There is no mode for either data set. The mean for
the Bulls is about 675 points, and the mean for the
Raptors is about 715 points; the medians are 416
points and 644 points, respectively. The Chicago
mean is much higher than its median because of
Michael Jordan's total points. The fact that the

Lesson 1.3, Exercise 2. a. ii.

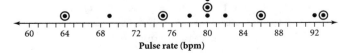

Pulse rate (bpm)

Raptors' mean and median values are higher than the Bulls' indicates that, on average, individual Toronto players scored more points than individual Chicago players.

c. The median probably best represents the total-points-scored data for the Bulls because the mean is heavily influenced by Michael Jordan's value, which is an outlier. Students can justify choosing either the mean or the median for the Raptors.

d. The minimum value is the same for both teams, but the range is much greater for the Bulls. The IQR (indicated by the length of the box) is about the same for both teams. Half of the Bulls scored more than 416 points, while three-quarters of the Raptors scored more than 416 points.

e. Without Jordan, the range of the data is much smaller, and the box is a little shorter. If Jordan's points scored are eliminated, the Raptors have the higher-scoring players. There is more variation in the number of points scored by individual Raptors than for individual Bulls.

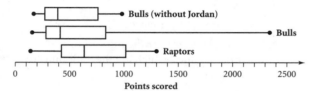

8. a. Answers will vary. For men, the mean salary is approximately $639.56, and the five-number summary is 342, 495, 629, 718.5, 1001; for women, the mean salary is approximately $466.69, and the five-number summary is 288, 353, 445, 563.5, 708.

Median Weekly Earnings, 2000

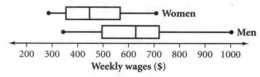

b. Women received less pay than men for the same type of work.

c. The box plots highlight the discrepancy in pay and spread of the data. However, dollar amount comparisons within a single profession are possible only in the table.

d. Answers will vary. The table shows that women are not paid as much as men, so people interested in gender equity are asking for equal pay for equal work.

9. a. 35 feet

b. No. We cannot read the fifth value from the graph. We can see that the median—which is between the fifth and sixth value—is 17.5 and that the first quartile—which is the third value—is 11. So, we do

know that the length of the king cobra is greater than or equal to 11 ft and less than or equal to 17.5 ft.

c. 65 mi/hr

d. The ten longest snakes vary in length from about 8 ft to 35 ft. About half of these snakes range in length from about 11 ft to 25 ft. Running speeds of the ten fastest mammals range from 42 mi/hr to 65 mi/hr. About half of the speeds are between 43 mi/hr and 50 mi/hr. The cheetah runs much faster than about three-fourths of the other fastest mammals.

e. No, because the units of these data sets are different.

f. The median is halfway between the fifth and sixth values. Because these values are the same, the median must be equal to these values. From the graph, we can see that the median is about 47. So, the fifth and sixth fastest mammals can run about 47 mi/hr.

10. a. $1.5(841 - 288) = 829.5$

b. $288 - 829.5 = -541.5$

c. $841 + 829.5 = 1670.5$

d. An outlier would have to score fewer than -541.5 points or more than 1670.5 points. Michael Jordan is an outlier.

11. When the ages are listed in order, the third value is 14. The total of all ages must be $5 \cdot 22$ or 110 years. One possibility is {4, 10, 14, 39, 43}.

12. a. 2 million $\cdot$ number of paw prints = 2 million $\cdot$ 33 = 66 million

b. There are four more paw prints next to "Cat." Each paw print represents 2 million animals. So, there are $4 \cdot 2$ million or 8 million more cats than dogs.

c. There are 11 million parakeets, and there would be one paw print for every 2 million. So, there would be 11 million ÷ 2 million or $5\frac{1}{2}$ paw prints.

LESSON 1.4

EXERCISES

1. a. To find the number of people surveyed, add the heights of the bars. For the matinee, the sum is $3 + 4 + 4 + 6 + 4 + 5 + 2 + 1$, or 29. For the evening performance, the sum is $2 + 6 + 8 + 7 + 6 + 1$, or 30.

b. Matinee **c.** None

d. Any 15-year-olds surveyed would be in the age 10–20 bar. You can't determine exactly how many (if any) of those four respondents were exactly 15 years old. You can only say for certain that the number is less than or equal to 4.

2. a. Possible graphs:

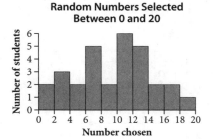

Random Numbers Selected
Between 0 and 20

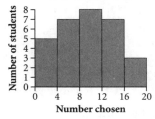

Random Numbers Selected
Between 0 and 20

b. Answers will vary. Students tend to choose numbers in the middle of the range.

c. 1, 6, 10, 12, 18

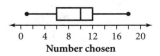

Random Numbers Selected
Between 0 and 20

d. 7 and 12

3. a. To find the number of countries represented, add the bar heights: $1 + 1 + 4 + 3 + 7 + 17 + 18 = 51$.

b. Approximately one fourth of the countries had a female life expectancy between approximately 81 and 83 years.

c. 2

d. There are no bins to the right of 85 in the histogram. Also, the maximum point in the box plot is located at approximately 83 years.

4.

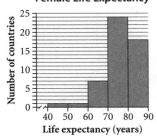

Female Life Expectancy

5. a. Minimum: 6.0 cm; maximum: 8.5 cm; range: 2.5 cm.

b. Put the ones digits in the stem. Use the tenths digits as the leaves.

Ring Finger Length

```
6 | 0  5  5
7 | 0  0  0  5
8 | 5
```

Key

6 | 0 means 6.0 cm

6. a. $24 \cdot 10{,}000$, or 240,000 cars

b. Three models sold for between 80,000 and 119,999 cars, inclusive.

c. [80000, 440000, 40000, 0, 7, 1]

d.

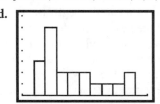

e. An approximate five-number summary is 110000, 131000, 179000, 275000, 430000. The actual five-number summary is 113843, 131385.5, 179029.5, 274017.5, 429575.

f.

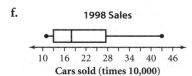

1998 Sales

7. Answers will vary.

a. With a bin width of 1, the bar heights should be about the same (because each number has the same chance of being rolled) with about 16 or 17 in each of six bars.

b. There will probably be a few short bars at the ends for students who estimated poorly and then taller bars near the middle for students whose estimates were closer to the actual measurements.

c. The horizontal axis should show the range of ages for students in the school. The heights of the bars should be about the same. There may be a few students who are younger or older than most of the rest of the students, so there could be shorter bars on the ends.

d. The combined height of the first two bars (2–3 and 3–4) should be a little less than 25. The combined height of the next four bars (4–5, 5–6, 6–7, 7–8) should be a little more than 25. The last two bars (8–9 and 9–10) should each have a height of 25.

8. a. The minimum is 1, the maximum is 9, and the median and both quartiles are 7. The data set must be {1, 7, 7, 7, 7, 7, 7, 9}.

b. Answers will vary. Each value must be greater than or equal to 5 and less than 6. One possible data set is {5, 5, 5, 5, 5, 5, 5, 5}.

c. Because there is one value in each bar, there is one value greater than or equal to 1 but less than 2, one value greater than or equal to 2 but less than 3, and so on. One possible data set is {1, 2, 3, 4, 5, 6, 7, 8}.

d. The minimum and Q1 are both 2, and the maximum and Q3 are both 4. The median is equal to either 2 or 4. There are two possible data sets: {2, 2, 2, 2, 2, 4, 4, 4} or {2, 2, 2, 4, 4, 4, 4, 4}.

9. a. Answers will vary. You could give the top two students A's, and the next seven (down to 15 points) B's. Those students with 9 to 15 points would get C's, and the bottom three students would get D's. This scheme allows those students who score in the center to get a C.

b. Using the grading scheme described above, the student gets an A.

c. Answers will vary.

10. a. Look at the lowest stem value, 15, and read the lowest leaf, 0. This value represents the lowest price, $1.50.

b. Chips priced $1.75 and $1.79.

c. Stem values from 15 through 19 represent the chips priced at $1.99 or less. So, to find the number of bags priced less than $2, count the leaves on those stems. There are 14 bags priced less than $2.

d. Look for the leaf that occurs the most times on a single stem. The leaf 9 occurs five times on the 19 stem, so the most common price is $1.99.

e. $2.59 − $1.50 = $1.09

11. (*See graph at bottom of page.*)

12. Answers will vary. The **bold** values are fixed. One possibility is {**64**, 70, 74, 80, **82, 82, 82, 82, 95**}.

LESSON 1.5

Activity Day
(No answers for this lesson.)

LESSON 1.6

EXERCISES

1.

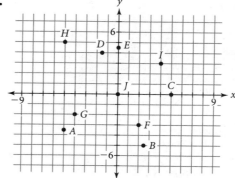

2. a. Positive *x*-axis
   b. Quadrant II
   c. Quadrant I
   d. Quadrant III
   e. The origin
   f. Negative *y*-axis

3. All work is done on the calculator.

4. Answers may vary slightly.

a. On the curve, find the point with *time* value 2. The *distance* value for the point is about 2. The walker was 2 m from the sensor.

b. The lowest point on the curve has the smallest distance value. This point has a *time* coordinate of about 5. So the walker is closest to the sensor after about 5 sec.

c. About 2.7 m

d. Look for "flat" portions of the curve, where the distance value does not change for a period of time. The walker stopped for about one second between 4.5 and 5.5 seconds and paused at the beginning between 0 and 1 seconds.

5. a. $A(-7, -4)$, $B(0, -2)$, $C(3, 6)$, $D(0, 3)$, $E(4, -4)$, $F(-2, -6)$, $G(4, 0)$, $H(7, 1)$, $I(-5, 2)$, and $J(-5, 4)$

b.

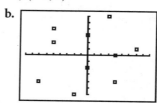

Lesson 1.4, Exercise 11

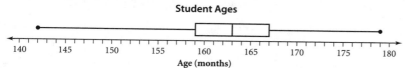

Student Ages

Age (months)

Discovering Algebra Solutions Manual
©2002 Key Curriculum Press

c. *B*, *D*, and *G*

d. I: *C* and *H*; II: *I* and *J*; III: *A* and *F*; IV: *E*

6. Scatter plot descriptions will vary. However, the location scenarios should include information such as (*positive, positive*) in Quadrant I; (*negative, positive*) in Quadrant II; (*negative, negative*) in Quadrant III; (*positive, negative*) in Quadrant IV; (0, *any number*) on *y*-axis; (*any number*, 0) on *x*-axis, and (0, 0) as the origin.

7. **a.** Approximate answers (the second coordinates are in millions):

(1984, 280), (1985, 320), (1986, 340), (1987, 415), (1988, 450), (1989, 445), (1990, 442), (1991, 360), (1992, 366), (1993, 340), (1994, 345), (1995, 273), (1996, 225), (1997, 173), (1998, 159), (1999, 142).

b. Window [1984, 1999, 1, 100, 500, 50]

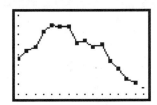

c. Answers will vary. Shipments increased until 1988 and then decreased except for a slight increase in 1992 and 1994. The introduction of compact discs may have influenced the decrease.

8. **a.** Years elapsed are {0, 5, 10, 15, 20, 25, 30, 35, 36, 37, 38}.

b.

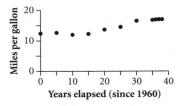

c.

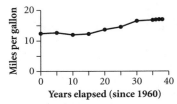

d. Approximately 14.6 mpg

e.

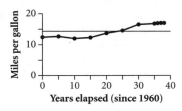

The horizontal line lets you see which data points are above the mean and which are below the mean.

f. Answers will vary.

9. **a.** $(-1.5, 2.6)$, $(-3, 0)$, $(-1.5, -2.6)$, $(1.5, -2.6)$

b. Answers will vary.

10. **a.** 8:06 (The speed drops suddenly at this point.)

b. 40 mi/hr   **c.** 12 min

d. Answers will vary. It seems unrealistic that Xavier's dad never fully stopped during the trip.

11. **a.** The **bold** values are fixed. One possibility is {**5, 12**, 14, **15**, 20, **30, 47**}.

b. The **bold** values are fixed. One possibility is {**5**, 10, **12**, 13, 14, 16, 20, **30**, 40, **47**}.

c. The **bold** values are fixed. One possibility is {**5**, 10, 12, 12, 13, 14, 16, 20, 28, 32, 40, **47**}.

12. **a.** The five-number summary is 428, 490, 527, 555.5, 643.

b.

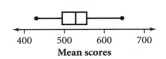

c. The greatest spread is between the third quartile and the maximum, or the right whisker. The least spread occurs between the median and the third quartile.

d. IQR = 65.5

e. Between first quartile and median: Latvia, United States, Norway, England, New Zealand, Sweden
Between median and third quartile: Czech Republic, Belgium, Hong Kong, Japan, Korea, Singapore

IMPROVING YOUR REASONING SKILLS

The weather glyphs show three variables: cloud coverage, wind direction, and wind speed; time could be considered a fourth variable. Time is definitely a numeric variable, and wind direction is definitely categorical. Cloud coverage and wind speed, however, could be argued as either numerical or categorical.

Cloud coverage could be three categories, or be assigned a percentage (0%, 50%, 100%), or be assigned a degree number (1, 2, 3). Wind speed is even more complex because although a specific numeric wind speed would be measured (e.g., 6 knots), each is then placed in a categorical bin (e.g., 3–7 knots). A variety of graphs can display this data, but it may be hard to find a single type of graph to display all the information.

LESSON 1.7

EXERCISES

1. a. Actual number of dinosaurs; estimated number of dinosaurs.

   b. Window: [0, 70, 10, −10, 60, 10]. (The lower Ymin value allows trace numbers to appear on the calculator screen without interfering with plotted points.)

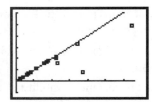

   c. $y = x$

   d. No. In no case is the estimated number of dinosaurs more than the actual number.

   e. Yes. For five species, the estimated count is less than the actual count.

2. a. The points below the line—*B, C, E, F,* and *J*—represent Lucia's estimates.

   b. The points above the line—*A, D, G, H,* and *I*—represent Malcolm's estimates.

3. Overestimates are points for which the *y*-coordinate is greater than the *x*-coordinate. These points are *B, C, D, E,* and *G*. Underestimates are points for which the *y*-coordinate is less than the *x*-coordinate. These points are *A, F, H,* and *I*.

4. a. Possible approximations are

Time	0	0.5	1.0	1.5	2.0
Distance	0	0.5	0.8	1.4	2.1

Time	2.5	3.0	3.5	4.0	4.5
Distance	2.7	3.0	3.6	3.9	4.25

   b. Answers will vary. A minimum window is [0, 5, 1, 0, 5, 1]

   c. $y = x$

   d. Increasing

5. a. Answers will vary. The more the rubber band is stretched, the farther it flies.

   b. Answers will vary between 400 and 600 cm. For a point with *x*-coordinate 15 to fit the pattern in this graph, it would need to have a *y*-coordinate between 400 and 600.

   c. Answers will vary between 7 and 12 cm. For a point with *y*-coordinate 400 to fit the pattern in this graph, it would need to have an *x*-coordinate between 7 and 12.

6. a. For such a point, the actual price is 12 and the estimated price is 16. The point is *A* (12, 16).

   b. For such a point, the actual price is 18 and the estimated price would be 13. The point is *B* (18, 13).

   c. Point *C* is an overestimate of $2, point *D* an overestimate of $5, and point *E* an overestimate of $2.

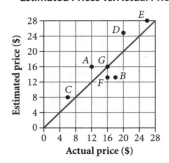

Estimated Prices vs. Actual Prices

   d. See graph for 6c.

   e. On a horizontal line through the estimate $16 on the vertical axis

   f. On a vertical line through the actual $16 on the horizontal axis

   g. They are points on the line shown. These points indicate points for which *estimate = actual price.*

7. a. It shows the differences between the estimated number of each species and the actual count. This helps identify overestimates and underestimates.

   b. Window: [0, 60, 10, −40, 10, 10]

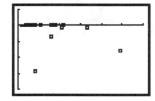

   c. 5; for the points below the *x*-axis, the *y*-coordinate, estimated number − actual number, is less than 0, so the estimated number is less than the actual number. They represent underestimates.

d. (8, −29); the 8 is the estimated number of velociraptors; the number of velociraptors was underestimated by 29.

8. a. (−4, 1) **b.** (−2, −5) **c.** (1, 5)

d. Plotted points will vary. In general, they lie on the line that bisects Quadrant II and Quadrant IV. The equation $y = -x$ fits these points.

9. a. Because more points are above the line than below it, more states had students with higher verbal scores than mathematics scores.

b. The national average is an average of all students, not an average of the state averages. So, for example, if states with higher math scores had larger student populations taking the test, the average of the math scores for all U.S. students could be higher than the average of the verbal scores.

10. a. About 1 m/sec, because the distances in meters are about equal to the times in seconds.

b. Between 0.5 and 1.0, between 2.5 and 3.0, between 3.5 and 4.0, between 4.0 and 4.5. For these intervals, the change in the distance values is less than the change in the time values.

c. Between 1.0 and 1.5, between 1.5 and 2.0, between 2.0 and 2.5. For these intervals, the change in the distance values is greater than the change in the time values.

d. Between 0 and 0.5, between 3.0 and 3.5. For these intervals, the change in the distance values is about equal to the change in the time values.

11. Answers will vary.

a. The median must be equal to one of the quartiles. One possible answer is {1, 3, 3, 3, 4, 5, 6}.

b. The first and third quartiles must be the same. One possible answer is {1, 4, 4, 4, 4, 4, 7}.

c. The minimum value must be less than $Q1 - 1.5 \cdot IQR$. One possible answer is {1, 6, 6, 7, 7, 8, 9}.

d. The third quartile and the maximum value must be the same. One possible answer is {1, 2, 3, 4, 5, 6, 6}.

12. a. The data values need to be organized in increasing order. The key should show an actual value from the data set.

b.

```
13 | 5  8
14 | 2  6  7  9
15 | 2  5  7  7  8  8
16 | 2  2  4  4  5  8
17 | 1  3  3  3  6
18 | 2  4
```

Key
_____

13 | 5 means 13.5 cm

c. $18.4 - 13.5 = 4.9$ cm

LESSON 1.8

EXERCISES

1. Matrix [A] shows the 1992 statistics. Row 2 represents Randall Cunningham. Column 3 represents the number of touchdown passes. So, the entry in row 2, column 3, of matrix [A] tells you that Randall Cunningham threw 19 touchdown passes in 1992.

2. Steve Young made 322 pass completions in 1998.

3. 3×4

4. Answers will vary.

5. $\begin{bmatrix} 788 & 489 & 35 & 19 \\ 809 & 492 & 53 & 21 \\ 919 & 590 & 61 & 19 \end{bmatrix}$

This matrix gives the totals from the two years.

6. Yes. This result should always be true if the matrices have the same dimensions.

7. $\begin{bmatrix} -158 & -115 & -11 & -9 \\ 41 & 26 & 15 & -1 \\ 115 & 54 & 11 & 5 \end{bmatrix}$

This matrix gives the difference between the 1998 totals and the 1992 totals.

8. $([A] + [B]) \cdot \left(\frac{1}{2}\right)$

9. a. $\begin{bmatrix} 8 & -5 & 4.5 \\ -6 & 9.5 & 5 \end{bmatrix}$ Add corresponding entries.

b. $\begin{bmatrix} -3 & 4 & -2.5 \\ 2 & -6 & -4 \end{bmatrix}$ Change each entry in [A] to its opposite.

c. $\begin{bmatrix} 15 & -3 & 6 \\ -12 & 10.5 & 3 \end{bmatrix}$ Multiply each entry in [A] by 3.

d. $\begin{bmatrix} 4 & -2.5 & 2.25 \\ -3 & 4.75 & 2.5 \end{bmatrix}$ Add corresponding entries and then multiply each result by $\frac{1}{2}$.

10. $[B] = \begin{bmatrix} -2 & 0 \\ 6 & -11.6 \\ 4.25 & 7.5 \end{bmatrix} - \begin{bmatrix} 2.8 & 2.4 \\ 2.5 & -9.4 \\ 1 & 6 \end{bmatrix}$

$= \begin{bmatrix} -4.8 & -2.4 \\ 3.5 & -2.2 \\ 3.25 & 1.5 \end{bmatrix}$

11. Answers will vary. Possible problem: Find the labor costs of building an item using 16 hours billed at $5.25 per hour and 30 hours billed at $8.75 per hour. The product is

$[5.25 \quad 8.75] \cdot \begin{bmatrix} 16 \\ 30 \end{bmatrix} = [5.25 \cdot 16 + 8.75 \cdot 30]$

$= [84 + 262.50] = [346.50]$.

12. a. Quantity matrix: $\begin{bmatrix} 74 & 25 & 37 \\ 32 & 38 & 16 \\ 120 & 52 & 34 \end{bmatrix}$

Profit matrix: $\begin{bmatrix} 0.90 \\ 1.25 \\ 2.15 \end{bmatrix}$

The number of columns in the quantity matrix must be the same as the number of rows in the profit matrix.

b. Atlanta profit:
74($0.90) + 25($1.25) + 37($2.15) = $177.40

Decatur profit:
32($0.90) + 38($1.25) + 16($2.15) = $110.70

Athens profit:
120($0.90) + 52($1.25) + 34($2.15) = $246.10

c. $\begin{bmatrix} 177.40 \\ 110.70 \\ 246.10 \end{bmatrix}$; 3×1

d. The answer matrix gives the profit at each location.

Location	Profit
Atlanta	$177.40
Decatur	$110.70
Athens	$246.10

e. The error message—ERR: DIM MISMATCH— means that the dimensions of the matrices in the product don't match.

13. a. Answers will vary. The minimum must be 0 and the maximum must be 7. Also, the data value 2 must occur more frequently than any other. A sample solution is {0, 1, 2, 2, 2, 2, 3, 4, 6, 7}.

b. Answers will vary. The minimum must be 22.2 and the maximum must be 30.4. No values in the list should be repeated. A sample solution is {22.2, 24.5, 25.1, 26.2, 28.3, 28.7, 29.4, 30.4}.

14. a. The 40 leaves to the left of the stem represent Mrs. Shapiro's students. The 41 leaves to the right represent Mr. Chin's students. So, there are 40 students in Mrs. Shapiro's class and 41 in Mr. Chin's class.

b. Mrs. Shapiro's: $1.35; Mr. Chin's: $1.25.

c. 13

d. In Mrs. Shapiro's class, one student had $1.35 and one student had $1.30.

e. Answers will vary. Based on the stem plot, you might expect Mrs. Shapiro's class to have more money. There are more students with more than a dollar in her class and more with less than 50¢ in Mr. Chin's class.

f. Mr. Chin's: $20.34; Mrs. Shapiro's: $24.96.

CHAPTER 1 Review

EXERCISES

1. a. Mean: 41.5; divide the sum of the numbers by 14. Median: 40; list the numbers in order and find the mean of the two middle numbers. Mode: 36; find the number that occurs most often.

b. 27, 36, 40, 46, 58

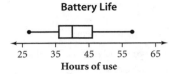

Battery Life

25 35 45 55 65
Hours of use

2. The five-number summary gives us five of the seven values. We need only fill in the blanks in this ordered data set {9, 11, –?–, 16, –?–, 21, 22}. Because the mean of the seven values is 16, the sum of the values must be 7 · 16 = 112. The values we have so far have a sum of 79, so the missing values must add to 112 − 79 or 33. The values 14 and 19 add to 33, so one possible data set is {9, 11, 14, 16, 19, 21, 22}.

3. a.

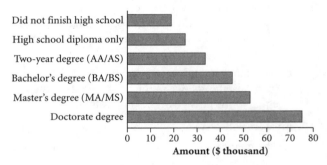

Mean Annual Wages, 1998

Did not finish high school
High school diploma only
Two-year degree (AA/AS)
Bachelor's degree (BA/BS)
Master's degree (MA/MS)
Doctorate degree

0 10 20 30 40 50 60 70 80
Amount ($ thousand)

b. Greatest difference: from a master's degree to a doctorate; smallest difference: from not finishing high school to a high school diploma.

4. a. **Top College Career Scorers**

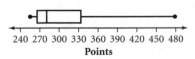

240 270 300 330 360 390 420 450 480
Points

b. The IQR is 70. For a data value to be considered an outlier, it must be more than 70(1.5) or 105 units away from the lower or upper quartile. The maximum value, 479, is greater than 333 + 105, or 438, so it is an outlier.

c. The mean (311.8) and the median (282.5) best represent what is typical. Only two of the values are less than the mode (263), so it is not a typical value.

5. a. Mean ≈ 154; median $= 121$; there is no mode.

b. Bin widths may vary.

Pages Read in Current Book

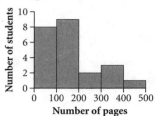

Pages Read in Current Book

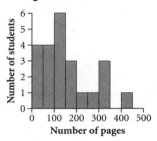

c. **Pages Read in Current Book**

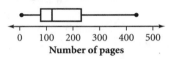

d. Answers will vary. Possible answer: Most of the students questioned had read fewer than 200 pages, with a fairly even distribution between 0 and 200.

6. a. **Invention Dates**

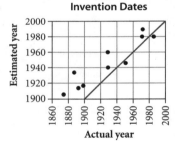

b. **Invention Dates**

c. $y = x$, where x represents actual year and y represents estimated year.

7. a. $\begin{bmatrix} 5.00 & 8.00 \\ 3.50 & 4.75 \\ 3.50 & 4.00 \end{bmatrix}$, $\begin{bmatrix} 0.50 & 0.75 \\ 0.50 & 0.25 \\ 0.50 & 0.25 \end{bmatrix}$, $\begin{bmatrix} 43 & 81 & 37 \end{bmatrix}$

b. Add the matrix of current prices and the matrix of price increases.

$$\begin{bmatrix} 5.00 & 8.00 \\ 3.50 & 4.75 \\ 3.50 & 4.00 \end{bmatrix} + \begin{bmatrix} 0.50 & 0.75 \\ 0.50 & 0.75 \\ 0.50 & 0.25 \end{bmatrix} = \begin{bmatrix} 5.50 & 8.75 \\ 4.00 & 5.00 \\ 4.00 & 4.25 \end{bmatrix}$$

c. Multiply the attendance matrix by the new price matrix calculated in 7b.

$$\begin{bmatrix} 43 & 81 & 37 \end{bmatrix} \begin{bmatrix} 5.50 & 8.75 \\ 4.00 & 5.00 \\ 4.00 & 4.25 \end{bmatrix} = \begin{bmatrix} 708.5 & 938.5 \end{bmatrix}$$

The revenue from a matinee will be $708.50. The revenue from an evening show will be $938.50.

8. a. Kayo was jogging fastest between points A and B because she covered a lot of distance in a short period of time.

b. Kayo was not moving; perhaps she was resting.

c. A possible answer is, Kayo started out jogging fast but had to rest for a few minutes. Then she jogged much slower until she had to rest again. She finally got the energy to jog all the way home at a steady pace without stopping.

9. a. 2,820,000

b. (*See graph at bottom of page.*)

Chapter 1 Review, Exercise 9. b.

The Ten Most Populated U.S. Cities, 1998

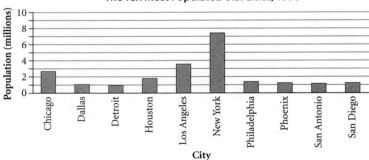

c. The Ten Most Populated
U.S. Cities, 1998

0	97
1	08 11 20 22 44 79
2	82
3	60
4	
5	
6	
7	42

Key

2 | 82 means 2.82 million

d. The Ten Most Populated
U.S. Cities, 1998

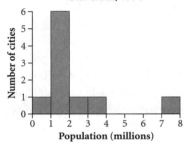

e. The bar graph shows how each city compares to
the others, since they are identified by name. The
stem plot shows the distribution of values as well
as the actual values. The histogram shows the
distribution and a definite clustering between
1 and 2 million, but it does not show individual
cities or populations.

10. a. Mean = 416.875 minutes

b. Median = 425 minutes   **c.** Mode = 480 minutes

TAKE ANOTHER LOOK

The picture bar graph uses both a broken vertical axis
(starting at 15) and pictures with decreasing area to
exaggerate the decline of green space. The normal bar
graph, on the other hand, measures only acres and
neglects the ratio to the increasing population, which
the first bar graph does. Therefore, both of the bar
graphs are engineered to persuade. Answers will depend
on whether you think acres per person or total acres is a
better measure.

CHAPTER 2

LESSON 2.1

EXERCISES

1. Estimates will vary. Actual values are given below.

a. 0.875   **b.** 0.65   **c.** 2.6   **d.** 2.08

2. a. There are fourteen 9th graders $(9 + 3 + 2)$. Nine
of the 9th graders have brown eyes, so the ratio
is $\frac{9}{14}$.

b. $\frac{11}{20}$ **c.** $\frac{4}{3}$ **d.** $\frac{3}{30}$ or $\frac{1}{10}$

3. a. $\frac{240 \text{ miles}}{1 \text{ hour}}$

b. 10 ppm means 10 parts per million—in this case,
10 parts capsaicin to 1,000,000 parts water. This
can be written $\frac{10 \text{ parts capsaicin}}{1,000,000 \text{ parts water}}$ or $\frac{1 \text{ capsaicin}}{100,000 \text{ water}}$.

c. $\frac{350 \text{ women-owned firms}}{1000 \text{ firms}}$ or $\frac{7 \text{ women-owned firms}}{20 \text{ firms}}$

d. $\frac{35,500 \text{ dollars}}{1 \text{ person}}$

4. a. $\frac{5}{2} = \frac{25}{10}, \frac{2}{10} = \frac{5}{25}, \frac{25}{5} = \frac{10}{2}$

b. $\frac{7}{3} = \frac{28}{12}, \frac{3}{12} = \frac{7}{28}, \frac{28}{7} = \frac{12}{3}$

c. $\frac{20}{16} = \frac{15}{12}, \frac{15}{20} = \frac{12}{16}, \frac{16}{12} = \frac{20}{15}$

5. a.

$$\frac{24}{40} = \frac{T}{30}$$

$$30 \cdot \frac{24}{40} = \frac{T}{30} \cdot 30 \qquad \text{Multiply both sides by 30.}$$

$$30 \cdot \frac{24}{40} = T \qquad \frac{30}{30} \text{ is equivalent to 1.}$$

$$18 = T \qquad \text{Multiply and divide.}$$

b. $R = 28$

c.

$$\frac{52}{91} = \frac{42}{S}$$

$$\frac{91}{52} = \frac{S}{42} \qquad \text{Invert both sides.}$$

$$42 \cdot \frac{91}{52} = \frac{S}{42} \cdot 42 \qquad \text{Multiply both sides by 42.}$$

$$42 \cdot \frac{91}{52} = S \qquad \frac{42}{42} \text{ is equivalent to 1.}$$

$$73.5 = S \qquad \text{Multiply and divide.}$$

d. $x = 2.1$

e.

$$\frac{M}{16} = \frac{87}{232}$$

$$16 \cdot \frac{M}{16} = \frac{87}{232} \cdot 16 \qquad \text{Multiply both sides by 16.}$$

$$M = \frac{87}{232} \cdot 16 \qquad \frac{16}{16} \text{ is equivalent to 1.}$$

$$M = 6 \qquad \text{Multiply and divide.}$$

f.

$$\frac{6}{n} = \frac{62}{217}$$

$$\frac{n}{6} = \frac{217}{62} \qquad \text{Invert both sides.}$$

$$6 \cdot \frac{n}{6} = \frac{217}{62} \cdot 6 \qquad \text{Multiply both sides by 6.}$$

$$n = \frac{217}{62} \cdot 6 \qquad \frac{6}{6} \text{ is equivalent to 1.}$$

$$n = 21 \qquad \text{Multiply and divide.}$$

g. $c = 31.2$

h. $W = 9$

6. a. The ratio of the amount the ant can carry to the ant's weight would be equal to the ratio of the amount the student could carry to the student's weight. Let x be the amount the student could carry, and then write and solve a proportion.

$$\frac{4\text{ g}}{1.5\text{ g}} = \frac{x\text{ kg}}{55\text{ kg}}$$

$$55 \cdot \frac{4}{1.5} = \frac{x}{55} \cdot 55 \qquad \text{Multiply both sides by 55.}$$

$$55 \cdot \frac{4}{1.5} = x \qquad \frac{55}{55} \text{ is equivalent to 1.}$$

$$146.\overline{6} = x \qquad \text{Multiply and divide.}$$

The student could carry about 147 kg (about 323 lb). (Note: The proportion above is only one possibility. In this, and other parts of this exercise, there are several proportions that also lead to the correct solution. For example, the ratio of the ant's weight to the student's weight is equal to the ratio of the amount the ant can carry to the amount the student can carry.)

b. The ratio of the ant's stride to the ant's length would be equal to the ratio of the student's stride to the student's height. Let x be the length of the student's stride, and then write and solve a proportion.

$$\frac{0.84\text{ cm}}{1.27\text{ cm}} = \frac{x\text{ m}}{1.65\text{ m}}$$

$$1.65 \cdot \frac{0.84}{1.27} = \frac{x}{1.65} \cdot 1.65 \qquad \text{Multiply both sides by 1.65.}$$

$$1.65 \cdot \frac{0.84}{1.27} = x \qquad \frac{1.65}{1.65} \text{ is equivalent to 1.}$$

$$1.09 \approx x \qquad \text{Multiply and divide.}$$

The student would have strides about 1.09 m long.

c. The ratio of the distance the ant travels to the ant's length would be equal to the ratio of the distance the student travels to the student's height. Let x be the distance the student travels, and then write and solve a proportion.

$$\frac{0.4\text{ km}}{0.0127\text{ km}} = \frac{x\text{ km}}{1.65\text{ km}} \qquad \begin{array}{l}\text{Change cm to km so}\\ \text{both parts of left ratio}\\ \text{are in the same unit.}\end{array}$$

$$1.65 \cdot \frac{0.4}{0.0127} = \frac{x}{1.65} \cdot 1.65 \qquad \begin{array}{l}\text{Multiply both sides}\\ \text{by 1.65.}\end{array}$$

$$1.65 \cdot \frac{0.4}{0.0127} = x \qquad \frac{1.65}{1.65} \text{ is equivalent to 1.}$$

$$52 \approx x \qquad \text{Multiply and divide.}$$

The student would travel about 52 km (about 32 mi).

7. a. If 15% is withheld, then Jeremy gets to keep 100% − 15% or 85%.

b. 85% means 85 out of 100. So the ratio of Jeremy's hourly take-home wage t to his hourly wage is equal to $\frac{85}{100}$. You can find the value of t by writing and solving a proportion.

$$\frac{t}{7.38} = \frac{85}{100}$$

$$7.38 \cdot \frac{t}{7.38} = \frac{85}{100} \cdot 7.38 \qquad \begin{array}{l}\text{Multiply both sides}\\ \text{by 7.38.}\end{array}$$

$$t = \frac{85}{100} \cdot 7.38 \qquad \frac{7.38}{7.38} \text{ is equivalent to 1.}$$

$$t = 6.273 \qquad \text{Multiply and divide.}$$

Jeremy's hourly take-home pay is $6.27.

8. Use P to represent the number of people in the resort area during the summer. Then, set up a proportion, making sure both ratios make the same comparison.

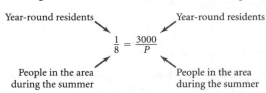

To solve this proportion, invert both ratios and then multiply both sides by 3000. The number of people in the area during the summer is 24,000.

9. No matter how many servings you make, the ratio of cups of oatmeal to servings is $\frac{1}{3}$. To find the amount of oatmeal m needed for 2 servings, you can solve the proportion $\frac{1}{3} = \frac{m}{2}$. Multiplying both sides by 2, you get $m = \frac{2}{3}$ cup. You need four times as much water as oatmeal, so you need $4 \cdot \frac{2}{3}$ or $\frac{8}{3}$ or $2\frac{2}{3}$ cups of water.

You can use the same strategy to find the amounts for 5 servings, or you can just add the amounts for 2 servings to the amounts for 3 servings. For 5 servings, you need $4 + 2\frac{2}{3} = 6\frac{2}{3}$ cups water and $1 + \frac{2}{3} = 1\frac{2}{3}$ cups oatmeal.

10. a. 3 carbon, 6 hydrogen, 1 oxygen

b. You will need 3(470) or 1410 atoms of carbon and 6(470) or 2820 atoms of hydrogen.

c. 500 molecules; use all the hydrogen atoms, 1500 carbon atoms, and 500 oxygen atoms.

11. Reading from the plot, the values are 2, 2, 4, 4, 4, 5, 5, 6, 6, 6, 6, 8, 8, 10, 10, 10, 10, 11, 11, 11, 15, 15, 16, 17. The median of these 24 values is 8, the mean of the twelfth and thirteenth values (8 and 8). Q1 is 5, the mean of the sixth and seventh values (5 and 5). Q2 is 11, the mean of the eighteenth and nineteenth values (11 and 11).

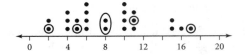

12. Mean: $97 million; median: $52 million; mode: $45 million. The very high incomes of George Lucas and Oprah Winfrey make the mean much higher than the median. The mode just happens to be the lowest income.

13. a. $5 \cdot -4 + 8 = -20 + 8 = -12$

  b. $-12 \div (7 - 4) = -12 \div 3 = -4$

  c. $-3 - 6 \cdot 25 \div 30 = -3 - 150 \div 30 = -3 - 5 = -8$

  d. $18\,(-3) \div 81 = -\frac{2}{3}$

LESSON 2.2

EXERCISES

1. Sample answers:

  a. In this proportion 24 is the part, w is the whole, and 32 is the percent. So the proportion represents this question: 32% of what number is 24?

  b. In this proportion, t is the part, 450 is the whole, and 48 is the percent. So the proportion represents this question: 48% of 450 is what number?

  c. In this proportion, 98 is the part, 117 is the whole, and n is the percent. So the proportion represents this question: What percent of 117 is 98?

2. Different variables will be used.

  a. In general, a percent question can be expressed by a proportion in the form $\frac{\text{part}}{\text{whole}} = \frac{\text{percent}}{100}$. In this question, we are given the percent, 125, and the part, 80. If we let d represent the whole, we can write the proportion $\frac{80}{d} = \frac{125}{100}$.

  b. In this question, we are given the percent, 0.25, and the whole, 46. If we let k represent the part, we can write the proportion $\frac{k}{46} = \frac{0.25}{100}$.

  c. In this question, we are given the part, 72, and the whole, 470. If we let r represent the percent, we can write the proportion $\frac{72}{470} = \frac{r}{100}$.

3. The ratio of twelfth graders to all students is equal to 17% or $\frac{17}{100}$. To find the number of twelfth graders x, write and solve a proportion.

$$\frac{x}{1582} = \frac{17}{100}$$

$$1582 \cdot \frac{x}{1582} = \frac{17}{100} \cdot 1582 \quad \text{Multiply both sides by 1582.}$$

$$x = \frac{17}{100} \cdot 1582 \quad \frac{1582}{1582} \text{ is equivalent to 1.}$$

$$x = 268.94 \quad \text{Multiply and divide.}$$

There are 269 twelfth graders.

4. a. The ratio of tagged fish in the sample to total fish in the sample is $\frac{5}{75}$. This is approximately equal to the ratio of tagged fish in the lake, 250, to total fish in the lake, f. So, to estimate the number of fish in the lake, solve this proportion $\frac{5}{75} = \frac{250}{f}$.

$$\frac{5}{75} = \frac{250}{f}$$

$$\frac{75}{5} = \frac{f}{250} \quad \text{Invert both sides.}$$

$$250 \cdot \frac{75}{5} = \frac{f}{250} \cdot 250 \quad \text{Multiply both sides by 250.}$$

$$250 \cdot \frac{75}{5} = f \quad \frac{250}{250} \text{ is equivalent to 1.}$$

$$3750 = f \quad \text{Multiply and divide.}$$

There are about 3750 fish in the lake.

  b. The ratio of tagged fish in the sample to total fish in the sample should be about equal to $\frac{250}{5500}$ (the ratio of tagged fish in the lake to total fish in the lake). So, solve the proportion $\frac{250}{5500} = \frac{15}{f}$ to find the number of fish in the sample. There are about 330 fish in the sample.

5. a. Marie has won more than half of the games so far, so she should win more than 6 of the next 12 games.

  b. $\frac{28 \text{ games won by Maria}}{28 + 19 \text{ total games}} = \frac{M}{12}$; $M = 7.15$. So Marie should win 7 games.

  c. $\frac{19}{47} = \frac{30}{G}$ (Both ratios express the ratio of Tracy's wins to games played.); $G \approx 74$; they would need to play about 74 games.

6. a. Slightly fewer than 600 pieces. Sixteen ounces is almost ten times 1.69 ounces.

  b. $\frac{60 \text{ candy pieces}}{1.69 \text{ ounces}} = \frac{N \text{ pieces}}{16 \text{ ounces}}$; there are about 568 candies in a 1-pound bag.

  c. $\frac{1,000,000}{568} \approx 1761$ pounds

7. $\frac{\text{errors found by first librarian}}{\text{total errors}} = \frac{\text{errors found by both librarians}}{\text{errors found by second librarian}}$, so if E is the total number of errors, then $\frac{43}{E} = \frac{35}{62} \cdot E \approx 76$; so there are about 76 errors in the dictionary.

8. a. $\frac{5}{3}$ **b.** $\frac{5}{8}$ **c.** $\frac{3}{8}$

9. a. 1 sulfur atom, 2 hydrogen atoms, and 4 oxygen atoms

  b. There is 1 sulfur atom for every 2 hydrogen atoms, so it would take 100 sulfur atoms to combine with 200 hydrogen atoms. There are 4 oxygen atoms for every 2 hydrogen atoms. So, it would take 400 oxygen atoms to combine with 200 hydrogen atoms.

  c. Use all 400 atoms of oxygen, 200 atoms of hydrogen, and 100 atoms of sulfur to make 100 molecules of sulfuric acid.

10. a. When the ages are ordered, the median is between the 21st and 22nd values. Looking at the bar heights, you can see that both values are in the bin 54–56. So, the median age is 54 or 55.

b. $2 + 3 + 3 = 8$

c. Younger than 42, 44, 45, 66, 67, older than 69.

d.

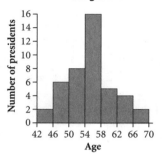

Presidents' Ages at Inauguration

11. $12 - 2 \cdot 6 - 3 = 12 - 12 - 3 = 0 - 3 = -3$. Matt is correct. Marta and Miguel did not use the order of operations. Marta did the operations from left to right, and Miguel did the subtractions before he multiplied. In the order of operations, multiplication comes first.

IMPROVING YOUR REASONING SKILLS

To see why the percentage of juice in the water is the same as the percentage of the water in the juice, think about particular amounts of liquid, such as 10 ounces of each with 1 ounce being transferred. Or use a deck of playing cards. Start with a pile of ten red cards and a pile of ten black cards. Pull out any number of red cards and mix them among the black cards. Then pull out the same number of cards from the mixed pile and put them into the red pile. Keep track of how many of each color are moving, and try it with extreme cases.

LESSON 2.3

EXERCISES

1. a. $x = 49.4$ **b.** $x = 40$

c. $x \approx 216$ **d.** $x = 583.\overline{3}$

2. A conversion factor is a ratio that tells you how two units are related. In 1a, the ratio $\frac{1 \text{ meter}}{3.25 \text{ feet}}$ is the conversion factor. It tells you that 1 meter is equivalent to 3.25 feet. To find out how many feet are in 50 meters, you can solve the proportion $\frac{1 \text{ meter}}{3.25 \text{ feet}} = \frac{50 \text{ meters}}{x \text{ feet}}$, or you can use dimensional analysis:

$$50 \; \cancel{\text{meters}} \cdot \frac{3.25 \text{ feet}}{1 \; \cancel{\text{meter}}} = 162.5 \text{ feet}$$

There are 162.5 feet in 50 meters.

3. a. $\frac{50 \; \cancel{\text{m}}}{1 \; \cancel{\text{sec}}} \cdot \frac{1 \text{ km}}{1000 \; \cancel{\text{m}}} \cdot \frac{60 \; \cancel{\text{sec}}}{1 \; \cancel{\text{min}}} \cdot \frac{60 \; \cancel{\text{min}}}{1 \text{ hr}} = 180 \text{ km/hr}$

b. $0.025 \; \cancel{\text{day}} \cdot \frac{24 \; \cancel{\text{hr}}}{1 \; \cancel{\text{day}}} \cdot \frac{60 \; \cancel{\text{min}}}{1 \; \cancel{\text{hr}}} \cdot \frac{60 \; \cancel{\text{sec}}}{1 \; \cancel{\text{min}}} = 2160 \text{ sec}$

c. $1200 \; \cancel{\text{oz}} \cdot \frac{1 \; \cancel{\text{lb}}}{16 \; \cancel{\text{oz}}} \cdot \frac{1 \text{ ton}}{2000 \; \cancel{\text{lb}}} = 0.0375 \text{ ton}$

4. In each part, the ratio of ounces to grams is equal to 1 to 28.4 (or, equivalently, the ratio of grams to ounces is 28.4 to 1).

a. $\frac{8 \text{ oz}}{x \text{ g}} = \frac{1 \text{ oz}}{28.4 \text{ g}}$; 227 g

b. $\frac{x \text{ oz}}{50 \text{ g}} = \frac{1 \text{ oz}}{28.4 \text{ g}}$; 1.76 oz

c. $\frac{160 \text{ oz}}{x \text{ g}} = \frac{1 \text{ oz}}{28.4 \text{ g}}$; 4544 g

d. $\frac{x \text{ oz}}{100 \text{ g}} = \frac{1 \text{ oz}}{28.4 \text{ g}}$; 3.52 oz

5. In each part, the ratio of centimeters to inches is equal to 2.54 to 1 (or, equivalently, the ratio of inches to centimeters is 1 to 2.54).

a. $\frac{x \text{ cm}}{62.5 \text{ in.}} = \frac{2.54 \text{ cm}}{1 \text{ in.}}$; 158.8 cm

b. $\frac{x \text{ cm}}{96 \text{ in.}} = \frac{2.54 \text{ cm}}{1 \text{ in.}}$; 244 cm

c. $\frac{12 \text{ cm}}{x \text{ in.}} = \frac{2.54 \text{ cm}}{1 \text{ in.}}$; 4.72 in.

d. $\frac{3.25 \text{ cm}}{x \text{ in.}} = \frac{2.54 \text{ cm}}{1 \text{ in.}}$; about 1.28 in.

6. If you divide each meter value by the yard value and round to the nearest tenth, you get 0.9. So, 0.9 meter is equal to about 1 yard. You can use the conversion factor $\frac{0.9 \text{ meter}}{1 \text{ yard}}$ to answer 6a–6d.

a. Solve this proportion $\frac{0.9 \text{ meter}}{1 \text{ yard}} = \frac{x \text{ meter}}{100 \text{ yards}}$. A football field is about 90 meters long.

b. Solve this proportion $\frac{0.9 \text{ meter}}{1 \text{ yard}} = \frac{200 \text{ meters}}{x \text{ yards}}$. The exit is about 222 yards away.

c. Solve this proportion $\frac{0.9 \text{ meter}}{1 \text{ yard}} = \frac{100 \text{ meters}}{x \text{ yards}}$, or just find half of the answer to 6c. A 100-meter dash is about 111 yards long.

d. Solve this proportion $\frac{0.9 \text{ meter}}{1 \text{ yard}} = \frac{x \text{ meters}}{15 \text{ yards}}$. You should buy 13.5 meters of fabric if you need 15 yards.

7. a.

Yards	1	2	3	4	5
Feet	3	6	9	12	15

b. 3

c. Because there are 3 feet in every yard, the ratio of feet f to yards y is 3 to 1. You can write this as the proportion $\frac{f}{y} = \frac{3}{1}$.

d. i. 450 feet   **ii.** 128 yards

8. a. Divide each feet value by the corresponding rod value. 1 rod ≈ 16.5 feet, so you can use the ratio $\frac{16.5 \text{ ft}}{1 \text{ rod}}$ to convert between rods and feet.

    b. i. 57.75 feet   **ii.** 0.9 rod

9. a. To make 120 servings, you need 120 · 8 or 960 ounces of lemonade. One can of concentrate makes 64 ounces, so to make 960 ounces, you need 960 ÷ 64 or 15 cans of concentrate.

    b. Since 12 ounces of concentrate makes 64 ounces of lemonade, you need $\frac{12}{64}$ or 0.1875 ounces to make 1 ounce of lemonade.

    c. $\dfrac{\text{number of ounces of concentrate}}{\text{number of ounces of lemonade}} = \dfrac{12}{64}$

    d. $\dfrac{16}{L} = \dfrac{12}{64}$; $L \approx 85$ oz

10. $120 \text{ ml} \cdot \dfrac{1 \text{ liter}}{1000 \text{ ml}} \cdot \dfrac{1.06 \text{ qt}}{1 \text{ liter}} \cdot \dfrac{4 \text{ cups}}{1 \text{ qt}} = 0.5088$ cup or about $\frac{1}{2}$ cup

11. The Math Club has $\frac{3}{5}$ of the 20 students. If the profits are divided in proportion to the number of students in the clubs, the Math Club would get $\frac{3}{5}$ · 480 or $288, leaving $480 − $288 or $192 for the Chess Club.

12. a.

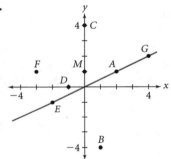

    b. E, A, G

    c. List the x-values in order: −3, −2, −1, 0, 1, 2, 4. The median x-value is 0. List the y-values in order: −4, −1, 0, 1, 1, 2, 4. The median y-value is 1. So point M has coordinates (0, 1).

13. Because only five values are represented in the plot, they must correspond to the values in the five-number summary, 10 cm, 22 cm, 33 cm, 41 cm, 46 cm.

From the first bullet, you know that the pygmy kingfisher has length 10 cm and the laughing kookaburra has length 46 cm.

The mean length of the five birds is 30.4. So, the second bullet indicates that the belted kingfisher is 30.4 + 2.6, or 33 cm long. This leaves 22 cm and 41 cm.

Because the ringed kingfisher's length is closer to the median than the green kingfisher, the ringed kingfisher has length 41 cm, and the green kingfisher has length 22 cm.

IMPROVING YOUR VISUAL THINKING SKILLS

Two pentominos are considered the same if either can be flipped over (reflected) or turned (rotated) to match the other. The 12 distinct, or unique, pentominos are often named after letters of the alphabet they resemble. Of these, the F, L, N, T, W, X, Y, and Z pentominos fold into an open box.

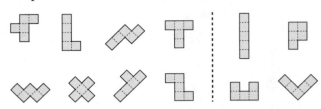

LESSON 2.4

EXERCISES

1. a. False. If the picture is enlarged by 150%, its new width and height are 100% + 150% or 250% of its original width and height.

    b. True. The new height and width are 250% or 2.5 times the original height and width.

    c. False. The original height and width are each multiplied by 2.5, so the new area is multiplied by 2.5^2 or 6.25.

    d. True. See the explanation in part c.

2. a. $\dfrac{108}{100}$ **b.** $\dfrac{89}{100}$

    c. $\dfrac{1125}{1000}$ or $\dfrac{112.5}{100}$ **d.** $\dfrac{9{,}375}{10{,}000}$ or $\dfrac{93.75}{100}$

    e. $\dfrac{100 + x}{100}$ **f.** $\dfrac{100 - y}{100}$

3. If the population grows by 1.1% each year, then the population for a given year is 101.1% (100 + 1.1) of the previous year's population. So, you can find the population p for a given year, by solving a proportion of the form

$$\frac{p}{\text{previous year's population}} = \frac{101.1}{100}$$

So, because the 2000 population is 274,700,000, you can find the 2001 population p by solving $\frac{p}{274{,}700{,}000} = \frac{101.1}{100}$. The 2001 population is 277,722,000. Starting with the 2001 population, you can calculate that the 2002 population is 280,777,000. Starting with the 2002 population, you can calculate that the 2003 population is 283,865,000.

4. Let J be the amount Justin needs to pay. Since Justin agreed to pay 70%, solve this proportion $\frac{J}{2649} = \frac{70}{100}$ to find J. Justin needs to pay $1,854.30.

5. a. The total population for the five countries listed is 2,949,043,000. If P is the percentage this total is of the world population, then you can find P by solving this proportion $\frac{2,949,043,000}{6,080,142,000} = \frac{P}{100}$. The combined population of the five listed countries is about 49% of the world's population.

b. Between 1990 and 2000, the population increased by 1,014,004,000 − 850,558,000, or 163,446,000. To find the percent increase, solve this proportion $\frac{163,446,000}{850,558,000} = \frac{P}{100}$. The population increased by about 19%.

c. If the population increases by 10.8% from 2000 to 2010, then the 2010 population x will be 110.8% of the 2000 population. Find x by solving this proportion $\frac{x}{1,261,832,000} = \frac{110.8}{100}$. The 2010 population of China will be approximately 1,398,110,000.

6. The scholarship pays 36% of Raimy's expenses, so Raimy's family must pay 100% − 36%, or 64%. To find the amount they must pay, solve $\frac{x}{18,500} = \frac{64}{100}$. Her family must pay $11,840.

Raimy's parents will pay 35% of the $11,840, so Raimy is responsible for 100% − 35%, or 65%. If R is the amount Raimy must pay, then $\frac{x}{11,840} = \frac{65}{100}$. Raimy must pay $7,696.

7. a. Tamara's new hourly rate is 103.5% of her old rate. To find her new hourly rate, solve this proportion $\frac{x}{7.5} = \frac{103.5}{100}$. Her new hourly rate is $7.76.

b. Now her hourly rate is 100% − 3.5%, or 96.5% of $7.76 (the rate you calculated in 7a). To find her new rate, solve this proportion $\frac{x}{7.76} = \frac{96.5}{100}$. Now, her hourly rate is $7.49.

c. Her wage dropped by $0.01 per hour because the increase was calculated as 3.5% of $7.50, but the decrease was based on $7.76.

8. a. $3,115,200,000

b. The increase was 10,505.5 million − 3,115.2 million = 7390.3 million. To find the percentage of the 1992 revenue, solve this proportion $\frac{7390.3}{3115.2} = \frac{P}{100}$. The 1996 revenue is about 237% of the 1992 revenue.

c.

20th Century Fox	31.38%
MCA Universal	14.94%
Sony	21.32%
Time Warner	54.7%
Viacom	1306.9%

d. To find the 1993 revenue, solve this proportion $\frac{x}{3945} = \frac{150.9}{100}$. The 1993 revenue was $5,953.0 million. Now, find the percentage increase from 1993 to 1996 by solving this proportion $\frac{6103.0}{5953.0} = \frac{P}{100} \cdot P \approx 102.5$, indicating a 2.5% increase.

e. From 7d, the 1993 revenue was $5,953.0 million. The 1994 revenue was 100% − 14.8% or 85.2% of $5,953.0 million. So find the 1994 revenue by

solving this proportion $\frac{x}{5953.0} = \frac{85.2}{100}$. The 1994 revenue was $5,072.0 million. To find the percentage increase from 1994 to 1996, solve this proportion $\frac{6103.0}{5072.0} = \frac{P}{100}$. $P \approx 120.3$, indicating a 20.3% increase.

9. Only the first two digits of the values are known. Possible answer: {124, 127, 131, 134, 134, 137, 140, 142, 144, 146, 147, 148, 148, 151, 152, 153, 155, 156, 158, 158, 158, 160, 163, 165, 166, 168, 174, 174, 177}.

10. a. [0.5 1.5 2]

b. To multiply two matrices, the number of columns in the first matrix must equal the number of rows in the second. The ingredient matrix must be on the left, and the sizing matrix on the right, so you are multiplying a 7 × 1 matrix by a 1 × 3 matrix.

c.

Half	50% larger	Double
75	225	300
1	3	4
9	27	36
1.75	5.25	7
100	300	400
9.5	28.5	38
62.5	187.5	250

11. a.

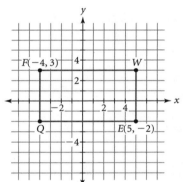

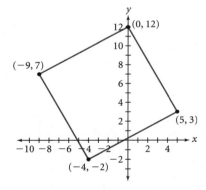

b. Possible answer: There are two squares and infinitely many rectangles that can be formed.

IMPROVING YOUR REASONING SKILLS

This problem can be solved in several ways. By working backwards, you will realize that some numbers won't work. For example, for each child and the dog to get one cookie at the end, there must have been 7 cookies when the last child gives one to the dog and takes one-third. But 7 is not two-thirds of any number, so each child must have gotten at least 2 in the end, and so on up to 7, the smallest number that works. Another approach is to create a function and put it into a graphing calculator. At the last split, the number of cookies each child will receive can be given by the formula $y = \frac{1}{3}\left(\frac{2}{3}\left(\frac{2}{3}\left(\frac{2}{3}(x-1)-1\right)-1\right)-1\right)$. Looking at the table for this equation, you see that 79 is the first value of x that gives an integral value for y (when $x = 79$, $y = 7$).

LESSON 2.5

EXERCISES

1. To find the number of people with Type O blood, find 43% of 75,000. Use a similar method to find the number of people with blood of each of the other types. Type AB = 3,750; Type B = 9,000; Type A = 30,000; Type O = 32,250.

2. c; the total of the values in 2c is 120. The values 12, 18, 24, 30, and 36 make up 10%, 15%, 20%, 25%, and 30% of this total, respectively. These percents match those in the graph.

3. No, the total height of all the bars must be 100%.

4.
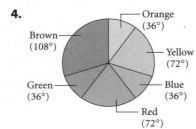
- Orange (36°)
- Yellow (72°)
- Blue (36°)
- Red (72°)
- Green (36°)
- Brown (108°)

5. a. There are a total of 58 candies. Convert each number to a percentage of the total. For example, to find the percentage for orange, solve this proportion $\frac{11}{58} = \frac{P}{100}$. Then, create a bar graph in which the vertical axis shows percentages.

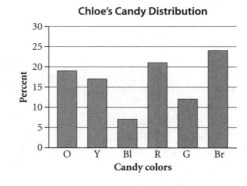

Chloe's Candy Distribution

b.
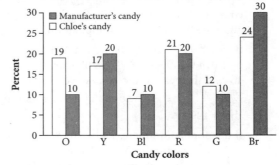

Comparing Chloe's Candy with the Manufacturer's

Answers will vary. Chloe's bag of candy had the same dominant color as the graph from the manufacturer, and her least frequent color was one of the least manufactured. But the distributions are not very close.

6. a. iii; in the circle graph, the A and D sections should be the largest, with D slightly larger than A. The B section should be about $\frac{2}{3}$ the size of the C section.

 b. i; the D section should be the largest, the B section should be the smallest, and the A and C sections should be the same size.

 c. iv; the C section should be the largest, then A, then D. B should be much smaller than the other sections.

 d. ii; the A section should be the largest, then D, then C, then B. B should be about half the size of D.

7. a. 9th: 27%; 10th: 26%; 11th: 25%; 12th: 22%.

 b. 9th: 189; 10th: 172; 11th: 170; 12th: 147. The total population before semester break was 676. After semester break, it is 678. So, the population has increased by 2 students. This is a 0.3% increase.

 c.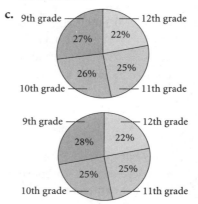

Proportionally, the ninth grade increased 1% and the tenth grade decreased 1%.

8. a. $-3 \cdot -7 \cdot (8 + -5) = -3 \cdot -7 \cdot 3 = 21 \cdot 3 = 63$

b. $(-5 - 7) \cdot -4 + 17 = -12 \cdot -4 + 17$
$= 48 + 17 = 65$

c. $6 + - 2 \cdot (7 + 9) = 6 + -2 \cdot 16 = 6 + -32$
$= -26$

d. $14 - (25 + 8 - 32) = 14 - 1 = 13$

e. $1 + 6 \cdot 5 - 11 = 1 + 30 - 11 = 20$

f. $33 + 5 \cdot -8 = 33 + -40 = -7$

9. a. If p is the pulses per second, then $\frac{p}{40} = \frac{4.5}{1}$. The anemometer should be giving off 180 pulses per second.

b. If s is the wind speed, then $\frac{84}{s} = \frac{4.5}{1}$. The wind speed is $18.\overline{6}$ meters per second.

10. a. Douglas had the largest percent of growth.

County	Change from 1990 to 1999	Percent change
Douglas	96,469	159.7
Forsyth	52,603	119.3
Elbert	10,111	104.8
Park	7,044	98.2
Henry	54,702	93.1

b. Los Angeles County grew by 466,825 people, a change of 5%.

c. Answers may vary. In terms of the number of people, Los Angeles County grew 4.8 times as much as Douglas did. However, the population of Douglas County increased by 159.7%, while Los Angeles country grew by only 5.3%. The percent change is probably a better representation of the growth of a county because it tells how the new population compares to the original population. For example, Los Angeles grew by many more people than Douglas, but because the increase was a relatively small percentage of the original population, the increase was probably more manageable from the point of view of the stress on the infrastructure—roads, schools, utilities.

LESSON 2.6

EXERCISES

1. a. Heads, tails   **b.** 1, 2, 3, 4, 5, 6

c. 2, 3, 4, 5, 6, 7, 8, 9, 10, 11, 12

d. A, B, C, D, E

2. a. The probability of selecting a particular type of candle is $\frac{\text{number of candles of that type}}{\text{total number of candles}}$. So for example, the probability of selecting a vanilla candle, P(V), is $\frac{4}{20}$ or 0.20. Here are the probabilities for selecting each of the other types: P(O) = 0.10; P(S) = 0.30; P(C) = 0.25; P(W) = 0.15.

b. P(S or V)
$= \frac{\text{number of strawberry} + \text{number of cinnamon}}{\text{total number of candles}}$
$= \frac{6 + 5}{20} = \frac{11}{20} = 0.55$

c. P(W or S or V) $= \frac{3 + 6 + 4}{20} = \frac{13}{20} = 0.65$

d. P(C) = 0.25. All probabilities would be the same as for the original pack because the ratios wouldn't change.

3. a. $\frac{\text{number in shaded area}}{\text{number in circle}} = \frac{27}{100} = 0.27$

b. P(landing in shaded area) = 0.25 because the shaded area makes up $\frac{1}{4}$ of the circle.

4. There are 16 possible ways the four coins could land: HHHH, HTHH, HHTH, HHHT, HTTH, HHTT, HTHT, HTTT, TTTT, THTT, TTHT, TTTH, THHT, TTHH, THTH, THHH. Since TTTT and HHHH are 2 of the 16 outcomes, the probability of getting four heads or four tails is $\frac{2}{16}$ or $\frac{1}{8}$.

5. Answers will vary. The probability for 5f is 0 or very nearly 0; the probability for 5g is 1.

6. The area of the rectangle is $77 \cdot 63$ or 4851. Since 137 of the 350 beans are in the shaded region, the ratio of the shaded area to the total area should be about $\frac{137}{350}$. Solving the proportion $\frac{a}{4851} = \frac{136}{350}$ gives a shaded area of about 1885, approximately 1900.

7. a. Finding and counting a litter is a trial; the outcomes are 1 cub, 2 cubs, 3 cubs, and 4 cubs.

b. No. If the outcomes were equally likely, then the number of litters of each size would be about the same, with about 9 litters of each size.

c. $\frac{\text{litters with three cubs}}{\text{total number of litters}} = \frac{22}{35} \approx 0.63$

8. a.

Student Responses

b. $\frac{\text{number of responses of 75\% or greater}}{\text{number of responses}} = \frac{5}{20} = \frac{1}{4}$

c. $\frac{3}{4}$ (15 out of 20) of responses are 50% or greater. So, you could expect that $\frac{3}{4}$ of the 4500 students, or 3375 students, would give estimates of 50% or greater.

9. a. $\frac{60°}{360°} = \frac{1}{6} \approx 17\%$

b. $\frac{90° + 165°}{360°} = \frac{255}{360} \approx 71\%$

c. $\frac{45° + 60°}{360°} = \frac{105}{360} \approx 29\%$

(The result of the previous contestant's spin does not affect the current contestant's spin.)

10. a. 1 to 12 is red, 13 to 30 is orange, 31 to 45 is yellow, 46 to 63 is green, 64 to 75 is light blue, and 76 to 100 is dark blue.

b. Answers will vary. For some calculators, a routine that works is—randInt(1,100,50).

c. Answers will vary. Sorting the list in ascending order is suggested.

d. Answers will vary.

11. Answers will vary. Possible answer: $(-4, 1), (-1, 3), (4, 3), (1, 1)$.

12. a. $\frac{0.5\text{ in.}}{1\text{ mo}} \cdot \frac{12\text{ mo}}{1\text{ yr}} \cdot \frac{2.54\text{ cm}}{1\text{ in.}} \cdot \frac{1\text{ m}}{100\text{ cm}} = 0.152$ m/yr

b. $\frac{1\text{ yr}}{0.1523\text{ m}} = \frac{x\text{ yr}}{1\text{ m}}$; about $6\frac{1}{2}$ yr

13. The hitter had 8 official at bats (the two walks and the sacrifice bunt do not count). Let h represent the number of hits he got. Because his batting average did not change, $\frac{h}{8} = 0.375$. Multiplying both sides by 8 gives $h = 3$. So, he got 3 hits.

LESSON 2.7

EXERCISES

1. Theoretical probability: $\frac{74}{180} \approx 0.411$; observed probability: $\frac{15}{50} = 0.30$. Possible answers: There are many possible reasons why the observed probabilities are different from the theoretical probability. Perhaps the method of selecting students was not random. For example, the results could be only from students who were participating in after-school activities or only from students in a particular class. Perhaps the question was worded in such a way that students were biased in their response or reluctant to answer honestly.

2. a. Of the estimated 3500 rainbow trout in the lake, 100 are tagged. So the probability of catching a tagged trout is $\frac{100}{3500}$ or 0.0286.

b. You have to assume that the population is 3500, it remains stable (no fish die and no new fish hatch), and the fish are well mixed.

c. Of the 100 trout she caught, 3 were tagged. So the observed probability of catching a tagged trout is $\frac{3}{100}$ or 0.03.

3. a. $\frac{15}{250} = 0.06$ **b.** $\frac{235}{250} = 0.94$ **c.** 0.06

4. Of the 126 squares, 32 are shaded. So, if points are plotted randomly, the ratio of points in the shaded region to total points should be about $\frac{32}{126}$. To find the number of points you would need to plot to get 25 points in the shaded region, you could solve the proportion $\frac{32}{126} = \frac{25}{t}$. The result is $t \approx 98$, so you would need to plot about 98 points.

5. a. H, H, T, H, H, T

b. Find the cumulative sum of list L1.

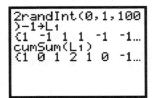

c. Even after many steps you may be close to 0.

d. With many trials, you might be farther from 0.

6. a. Answers will vary.

b. Answers will vary. Experience with a 9-mm-diameter head and a 6-mm point has indicated that the observed probability of "point up" is about 0.55.

c. In one actual experiment, there was no change between a hard surface and a soft one.

7. One possible routine is randInt(1,6). Assign students in order to groups 1 to 6, skip a number once that group is full.

8. The letter P

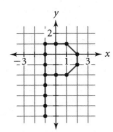

9. Solve the proportion $\frac{60}{t} = \frac{22}{84}$. There are about 229 chipmunks in the campground.

10. a. 64 **b.** $\frac{1}{36}$ **c.** $\frac{9}{16}$

d. 3^3 **e.** $\left(\frac{1}{5}\right)^3$ **f.** $\left(\frac{2}{9}\right)^2$ or $\frac{2^2}{3^4}$

11. Answers will vary. You could cover the rectangle with beans to find the total number of beans. Then find the number of beans that would cover the shaded region. Solve the proportion:

$$\frac{\text{number of beans in shaded region}}{\text{total number of beans}}$$
$$= \frac{\text{area of shaded region}}{150,000}$$

CHAPTER 2 Review

EXERCISES

1. a. $n = 8.75$　　**b.** $w = 84.6$　　**c.** $k = 5\frac{1}{6}$ or $5.1\overline{6}$

2. To find the number of students with each eye color, read the percentage from the graph and then find that percentage of 350. For example, the graph indicates that 30% of the 350 students have blue eyes. You can find the number of students with blue eyes by solving this proportion $\frac{x}{350} = \frac{30}{100}$. 105 students have blue eyes, approximately 52 or 53 have gray eyes, 70 have green eyes, and approximately 122 or 123 have brown eyes.

3. Possible answers:
$$\frac{7\,\text{bh}}{5\,\text{hr}} = \frac{30\,\text{bh}}{x\,\text{hr}}; \frac{7\,\text{bh}}{30\,\text{bh}} = \frac{5\,\text{hr}}{x\,\text{hr}}; \frac{5\,\text{hr}}{7\,\text{bh}} = \frac{x\,\text{hr}}{30\,\text{bh}};$$
$$\frac{30\,\text{bh}}{7\,\text{bh}} = \frac{x\,\text{hr}}{5\,\text{hr}}$$

4. a. Next year's tuition will be 103.7% of this year's tuition. So, for example, to find next year's tuition for the first school, solve this proportion $\frac{x}{2,860} = \frac{103.7}{100}$. Answers are rounded to the nearest $10.

This year	Next year
$2,860	$2,970
$3,580	$3,710
$8,240	$8,540
$9,460	$9,810
$11,420	$11,840
$22,500	$23,330
$26,780	$27,770

b. Enter this year's data into L1. Define L2 = 1.037 · L1.

5. a. Possible points include (2, 1), (3, 1.5), (4, 2), (5, 2.5), (6, 3), (7, 3.5), (8, 4).

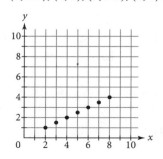

b. All points appear to lie on a line.

6. a. $20\ \cancel{\text{ells}} \cdot \dfrac{3.75\ \text{feet}}{1\ \cancel{\text{ell}}} = 75$ feet

b. $\dfrac{75\ \text{feet}}{12\ \cancel{\text{years}}} \cdot \dfrac{1\ \cancel{\text{year}}}{12\ \text{months}} \approx \dfrac{0.52\ \text{foot}}{1\ \text{month}}$
$= 0.52$ foot per month

7. a. 12.5 cm²; $\dfrac{12.5}{40} = 0.3125$

b. 32.5 cm²; $\dfrac{32.5}{45} = 0.7\overline{2}$

8. a. Find 85% of each price: $2.12; $1.61; $2.80.

b. Answers will vary; $\dfrac{85}{100} = \dfrac{\text{sale price}}{\text{original price}}$

c. To find the wholesale price, add 1 cent to the original price, and then take half: 1.25, 0.95, 1.65.

d. About 70%; you can find this percentage by solving a proportion of the form $\dfrac{\text{marked down price}}{\text{wholesale price}} = \dfrac{P}{100}$ for one of the bags of candy. Using the first bag, this is $\dfrac{\$2.12}{\$1.25} = \dfrac{P}{100}$; $P \approx 170$, so Sal made a 70% profit.

9. Answers will vary. If the politician is talking about the entire state, this cannot occur. All scores cannot be greater than the middle score. The probability is 0.

10. a. In each case, the net gain is $25 less than the amount won, so tickets must cost $25.

b. Probability you win $125 + probability you win $525 = 5% + 1% = 6%.

c. One person is $500 ahead, 5 people are $100 ahead, 10 people will be even, and 84 people will be $25 behind. This is a net loss of $1100, or $11 per person.

11. $\dfrac{\text{number of shih of millett}}{\text{total number of shih}}$ should be about equal to $\dfrac{\text{grains of millet in sample}}{\text{total grains in sample}}$. So, you can find the amount of millet m by solving this proportion $\dfrac{m}{1534} = \dfrac{28}{254}$. You have about 169 shih of millet and about $1534 - 169$ or 1365 shih of rice.

TAKE ANOTHER LOOK

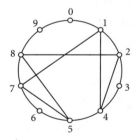

The pattern is symmetric. The pictures for all fractions with denominators of 7 look the same, but they start on different digits. To draw other interesting patterns, choose the denominator to be prime.

CHAPTER 3

LESSON 3.1

EXERCISES

1. a. $\frac{3 \text{ pounds}}{30 \text{ days}} = 0.1$ pound per day

b. $\frac{5 \text{ pounds}}{45 \text{ days}} = 0.\overline{1}$ pound per day

c. Crystal's cat eats more each day.

2. $\frac{240 \text{ miles}}{4 \text{ hours}} = 60$ miles per hour

3. a. $\frac{1 \text{ gallon}}{10 \text{ miles}} = 0.1$ gallon per mile

b. $\frac{0.1 \text{ gallon}}{1 \text{ mile}} \cdot 220 \text{ miles} = 22$ gallons

c. $\frac{10 \text{ miles}}{1 \text{ gallon}} \cdot 15 \text{ gallons} = 150$ miles

4. a. $\frac{12.5 \text{ gallons}}{350 \text{ miles}} \approx 0.036$ gallon per mile;
$\frac{0.036 \text{ gallon}}{1 \text{ mile}} \cdot 520 \text{ miles} = 18.72$ gallons

b. $\frac{225 \text{ miles}}{10.7 \text{ gallons}} \approx 21$ miles per gallon;
$\frac{21 \text{ miles}}{1 \text{ gallon}} \cdot 9 \text{ gallons} = 189$ miles

5. a. $\dfrac{24{,}901.55 \text{ miles}}{(2 \cdot 365 + 2 \cdot 30.4 + 2) \text{ days}}$
≈ 31.4 miles per day

b. $\frac{31.4 \text{ miles}}{1 \text{ day}} \cdot (1.5 \cdot 365) \text{ days} \approx 17{,}191.5$ miles

c. Let t represent the number of days, and then write and solve the proportion $\frac{1 \text{ day}}{31.4 \text{ miles}} = \frac{t}{60{,}000 \text{ miles}}$; $t \approx 1{,}911$ days or about 5.24 years.

6. a. More than 5¢ but less than 10¢. If the card were good for 50 minutes of calls, the cost would be $\frac{\$5.00}{50 \text{ minutes}} = \$0.10$ per minute. If the card were good for 100 minutes of calls, the cost would be $\frac{\$5.00}{100 \text{ minutes}} = \$0.05$ per minute. The actual per-minute cost must be between these two costs.

b. $\frac{\$5}{80 \text{ minutes}} \approx \$0.0625$ per minute or 6.25¢ per minute

c. The cost of a 15-minute call is $0.0625 \cdot 15$ or about \$0.94; so, after the call, the card would be worth \$5 − \$0.94 or about \$4.06.

d. Possible answer: The prepaid calling card, because it charges less per minute.

e. In the 7 days, she will make $7 \cdot 30$ or 210 minutes of calls. Because each card allows her to make 80 minutes of calls, she would need three cards.

7. a. \$2.49 per box, 42¢ per bar, \$2.99 per box, 25¢ per ounce

b. Yes; $\$2.49 \div 6 = \$0.415$, so the bars cost 42¢ each.

c. $\frac{2.99 \text{ dollars}}{1 \text{ box}} \cdot \frac{1 \text{ box}}{8 \text{ bars}} \cdot \frac{1 \text{ ounce}}{0.25 \text{ dollar}}$
$= \frac{2.99 \text{ ounces}}{2 \text{ bars}} = 1.495$ ounces per bar

d. $\frac{\$2.49}{10 \text{ ounces}} = \$0.249$ per ounce or approximately 25¢ per ounce

e. Possible answer: Both brands cost the same amount per ounce. Chewy Granola Bars cost less per bar (37¢ versus 42¢), but the bars are smaller. If Marie and Tracy prefer fewer, larger bars, they should buy Crunchy Granola Bars. If they prefer more, smaller bars, they should buy Chewy Granola Bars.

8. a. $\frac{425 \text{ miles}}{10.8 \text{ gallons}} \approx 39.4$ miles per gallon

b. $\frac{1 \text{ gallon}}{39.4 \text{ miles}} \cdot 750 \text{ miles} \approx 19$ gallons

c. $19 \text{ gallons} \cdot \frac{\$1.35}{1 \text{ gallon}} = \$25.65$

d. Portia's gas mileage is about 12% or 4.4 miles per gallon greater than the higher estimate; it is about 31% or 9.4 miles per gallon greater than the lower estimate.

9. a. Possible answers:
$\frac{20 \text{ pounds of food}}{1 \text{ week}}$; $\frac{\$36}{1 \text{ bag of food}}$;
$\frac{\$0.90}{1 \text{ pound of food}}$; $\frac{\$18}{1 \text{ week}}$

b. $\frac{36 \text{ dollars}}{2 \text{ weeks}} \cdot \frac{52 \text{ weeks}}{1 \text{ year}} = \frac{1872 \text{ dollars}}{2 \text{ years}}$
$= \$936$ per year

c. The ratio of pounds per week Tootsie eats (20) to Tootsie's weight (85) is equal to the ratio of the number of pounds per week Clara eats (f) to Clara's weight (60)—that is, $\frac{20}{85} = \frac{f}{60}$. Clara eats about 14 pounds of food per week.

d. Cathy's dog eats $14 \cdot 52$ or 728 pounds per year, which is $728 \div 40$ or 18.2 bags. At \$36 per bag, the yearly cost is $18.2 \cdot 36$ or \$655.20. So Cathy spends $936 - 655.20$ or \$280.80 less than Chris.

10. a.

$[-5, 40, 5, -1, 6, 1]$

Students should notice that the points are on a line.

b. The values in L₃ are all 0.13333, which represents $0.1\overline{3}$. This is the rate of speed in miles per minute.

c. $\frac{0.1\overline{3} \text{ mile}}{1 \text{ minute}} \cdot \frac{60 \text{ minutes}}{1 \text{ hour}} = 8$ miles per hour

11. a. $x = \frac{21}{5}$ or 4.2   **b.** $x = \frac{22}{9}$ or $2.\overline{4}$

c.
$$\frac{x}{c} = \frac{d}{e}$$
$$c \cdot \frac{x}{c} = \frac{d}{e} \cdot c \qquad \text{Multiply both sides by } c.$$
$$x = \frac{dc}{e} \qquad \frac{c}{c} \text{ is equal to 1.}$$

12. a. You can find the percent by solving the proportion $\frac{6,822,000}{25,779,000} = \frac{p}{100}$. About 26.5% of the foreign-born people in the United States were born in Asia.

b. You can find the number of people born in the Philippines by solving the proportion $\frac{x}{6,822,000} = \frac{16.6}{100}$. About 1,132,452 people were born in the Philippines.

13. a.

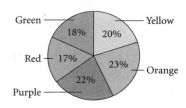

Jelly Beans in Small Bag

b.

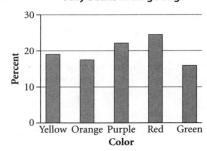

Jelly Beans in Large Bag

c. In the small bag, orange occurs most frequently and red least frequently; in the large bag, red occurs most frequently and green least frequently.

d. 85 pieces with one left over; no, because each color does not occur equally often

14. a. 10 : 9   **b.** 2 : 1   **c.** 1 : 15   **d.** 2 : 13

e. A sample bar graph is shown.

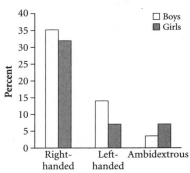

Hand Preference

IMPROVING YOUR REASONING SKILLS

Answers will vary. One method is to work with the reciprocals of the rates stated in the problem. The information about guests and dishes translates into three ratios: $\frac{1 \text{ dish}}{2 \text{ guests}}$, $\frac{1 \text{ dish}}{3 \text{ guests}}$, and $\frac{1 \text{ dish}}{4 \text{ guests}}$. To find the total number of dishes, rewrite the ratios with a common denominator of 12 guests and add: $\frac{6 \text{ dishes}}{12 \text{ guests}} + \frac{4 \text{ dishes}}{12 \text{ guests}} + \frac{3 \text{ dishes}}{12 \text{ guests}} = \frac{13 \text{ dishes}}{12 \text{ guests}}$. So there were 13 dishes for every 12 guests. There were 65 or $13 \cdot 5$ dishes in all, so there must have been $12 \cdot 5$ or 60 guests.

LESSON 3.2

EXERCISES

1. a. 40; find the y-value corresponding to an x-value of 25.

b. 75; find the x-value corresponding to a y-value of 120.

2. a. 88; scroll down to find the y-value corresponding to the x-value 55.

b. 281; scroll down to find the x-value corresponding to a y-value of about 450.

3. To change miles to kilometers, multiply by 1.6; to change kilometers to miles, divide by 1.6.

Distance (mi)	Distance (km)
2.8	4.5
7.8	12.5
650.0	1040.0
937.5	1500.0

4. a.
$$14 = 3.5x$$
$$\frac{14}{3.5} = \frac{3.5x}{3.5} \qquad \text{To isolate } x, \text{ divide both sides by 3.5.}$$
$$4 = x \qquad \text{Reduce.}$$

b. $x = 27.9$

c.
$$\frac{x}{7} = 0.375$$
$$7 \cdot \frac{x}{7} = 0.375 \cdot 7 \qquad \text{To isolate } x, \text{ multiply both sides by 7.}$$
$$x = 2.625 \qquad \text{Multiply and reduce.}$$

d.
$$\frac{12}{x} = 0.8$$
$$\frac{x}{12} = \frac{1}{0.8} \qquad \text{Invert both sides.}$$
$$12 \cdot \frac{x}{12} = \frac{1}{0.8} \cdot 12 \qquad \text{To isolate } x, \text{ multiply both sides by 12.}$$
$$x = 15 \qquad \text{Reduce.}$$

5. a. $c = 1.25(2.5) = 3.125$ or $3.13

   b. Substitute 5 for c to get $5 = 1.25f$. Then solve for f.

$$5 = 1.25f$$
$$\frac{5}{1.25} = \frac{1.25f}{1.25}$$
$$4 = f$$

   You can buy 4 yards of fabric for $5.

   c. $1.25

6. a.

Market A

Ears	7	14	21	28	35	42
Cost ($)	1.25	2.50	3.75	5.00	6.25	7.50

Market B

Ears	13	26	39	52	65	78
Cost ($)	2.75	5.50	8.25	11.00	13.75	16.50

   b. For Market A, the cost per ear is $1.25 ÷ 7 or $0.179. So, if x is the number of ears and y is the total cost in dollars, then $y = 0.179x$.

   For Market B, the cost per ear is $2.75 ÷ 13 or about $0.212. So, if x is the number of ears and y is the total cost in dollars, then $y = 0.212x$.

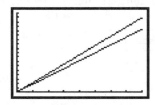

[0, 80, 10, 0, 18, 1]

   c. Market A: $0.18; Market B: $0.21; these are the constants of variation in the equations, rounded to the nearest tenth.

   d. The graph for the market with the lower rate is less steep than the graph for the market with the higher rate.

7. a.

Vegetable	Weight (kg)	Weight (lb)
Cabbage	56	123
Summer squash	49	108
Zucchini	29	64
Kohlrabi	28	62
Celery	21	46
Radish	13	28
Cucumber	9	20
Brussels sprout	8	18
Carrot	5	11

   b. Divide each pound value by the corresponding kilogram value and find the mean or median of the values. You should find that there are about 2.2 pounds per kilogram. So, if x is the number of kilograms and y is the number of pounds, then $y = 2.2x$.

   c. Solve $6.5 = 2.2x$. The pumpkin weighs about 2.95 kilograms.

   d. $y = 2.2 \cdot 3600 = 7920$. The elephant weighs 7920 pounds.

   e. 100 lb = 220 kg; 100 kg = $45.\overline{45}$ lb

8. a. Thu calculated $\frac{150}{93} = 1.61$, which is the number of kilometers per mile. In Thu's equation, x is the number of miles and y is the number of kilometers.

   b. Sabrina calculated $\frac{93}{150} = 0.62$, which is the number of miles per kilometer. In Sabrina's equation, x is the number of kilometers and y is the number of miles.

   c. Thu's equation may be more convenient because you can just multiply the number of miles by 1.61.

   d. Sabrina's equation is more convenient for converting kilometers to miles.

9. a. Answers will vary. A sample answer is to use the value of U.S. coins and bills in dollar denominations: {100, 50, 20, 10, 5, 1, 0.50, 0.25, 0.10, 0.05, 0.01}.

   b. Multiply the list by the exchange rate. For example, to convert to Japanese yen, multiply the list by 108.770. The result would be {10877, 5438.5, 2175.4, 1087.7, 543.85, 108.77, 54.385, 27.19, 10.88, 5.44, 1.09}.

   c. Divide list L_2 by the exchange rate to obtain the original values.

   d. Use dimensional analysis to find the number of liras per mark:

$$\frac{2119.150 \text{ liras}}{1 \text{ dollar}} \cdot \frac{1 \text{ dollar}}{2.140 \text{ marks}}$$
$$= 990.257 \text{ liras per mark}$$

   Then multiply the number of marks by this exchange rate.

   e. Answers will vary.

10. a. Because distance and time are directly proportional, the ratio of distance to time is a constant. I walk 3 miles in 1.5 hours, so the constant ratio is $\frac{3 \text{ miles}}{1.5 \text{ hours}}$ or 2 miles per hour. So in 1 hour I can walk 2 miles.

   b. 2 hours · 2 miles per hour = 4 miles

c. It takes 1 hour to walk 2 miles, so it would take 3 hours to walk 6 miles.

d.

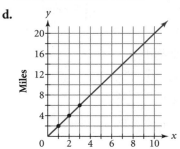

e. The constant of variation, 2 mi/hr, represents the constant walking speed.

f. $d = 2t$, where d is distance traveled in miles and t is travel time in hours

11. a. $\dfrac{130 \text{ km}}{1 \text{ hr}} \cdot \dfrac{1 \text{ mi}}{1.6 \text{ km}} = 81.25$ mi/hr

b. $\dfrac{25 \text{ mi}}{1 \text{ hr}} \cdot \dfrac{1.6 \text{ km}}{1 \text{ mi}} = 40$ k/hr

c. 65 miles per hour is 104 kilometers per hour. A speed limit sign might post 100 kilometers per hour.

12. a. To make \$12 per hour, she would need to earn \$36 for a 3-hour party. \$36 ÷ \$3.50 is 10.3, so she would have to entertain a minimum of 11 children.

b. Solve $\dfrac{0.6}{3.50} = \dfrac{p}{100}$; $p \approx 17$, so the cost of balloons and face paint per child is about 17% of the total cost per child.

c. Solve $\dfrac{0.6}{x} = \dfrac{10}{100}$; $x = 6$, so Cecile should charge \$6 per child.

13. a. Table 5's homework will be checked if Ms. Zany spins a 5 or a 10, so the probability that their homework will be checked is $\dfrac{2}{10}$ or $\dfrac{1}{5}$.

b. No; all the tables are equally likely to have their table number spun, and 9 or 10 being spun affects all tables equally.

IMPROVING YOUR REASONING SKILLS

The approximate ratios of °F to °C for each city are Athens, 2.87; Barcelona, 3.56; Buenos Aires, 4.73; Cairo, 2.71; Johannesburg, 3.93; Phoenix, 2.6; Rio de Janeiro, 3.08. These ratios are all different; the kilometers-to-miles

ratios in the investigation were all the same. Here is the graph of the data.

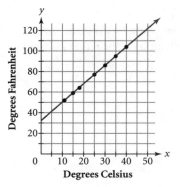

As in the other graphs in this lesson, the points lie on a straight line. However, this line does not pass through point (0, 0). In other words, 0°C is not equivalent to 0°F. So water does not freeze at 0°F. This relationship is not a direct variation because the ratio of the variables is not constant.

LESSON 3.3

EXERCISES

1. a. $y = \dfrac{1}{20}(15) = \dfrac{15}{20} = \dfrac{3}{4} = 0.75$

b. $y = \dfrac{1}{20}(40) = \dfrac{40}{20} = 2$

c.
$$5 = \dfrac{1}{20}x$$
$$20 \cdot 5 = \dfrac{1}{20}x \cdot 20 \qquad \text{Multiply both sides by 20.}$$
$$100 = x \qquad\qquad \text{Multiply and reduce.}$$

d.
$$5.4 = \dfrac{1}{20}x$$
$$20 \cdot 5.4 = \dfrac{1}{20}x \cdot 20 \qquad \text{Multiply both sides by 20.}$$
$$108 = x \qquad\qquad \text{Multiply and reduce.}$$

2. $\dfrac{x}{10} = \dfrac{15}{20}$ or $\dfrac{x}{15} = \dfrac{10}{20}$; $x = 7.5$ cm

3. a. Let l represent the lengths on the larger polygon, and let s represent the lengths on the smaller polygon. Because 8 cm on the larger polygon corresponds to 6 cm on the smaller one, $\dfrac{l}{s} = \dfrac{8}{6}$. Multiplying both sides by s gives the equation $l = \dfrac{8}{6}s$.

b. w is a side length on the larger polygon. The corresponding side length on the larger polygon is 7. So $w = \frac{8}{6}(7) = 9.\overline{3}$.

x is a side length on the smaller polygon. The corresponding side length on the larger polygon is 3. So, to find x, solve the equation $3 = \frac{8}{6}x$.

$$3 = \frac{8}{6}x$$
$$6 \cdot 3 = \frac{8}{6}x \cdot 6$$
$$18 = 8x$$
$$\frac{18}{8} = \frac{8x}{8}$$
$$2.25 = x$$

To find y, solve $8 = \frac{8}{6}y$; $y = 6$, $z = \frac{8}{6}(3) = 4$.

4. a. Convert 3 inches to 0.25 foot and then solve the proportion $\frac{0.25}{l} = \frac{1}{160}$; $l = 40$, so the length of the actual locomotive is 40 feet.

b. Solve the proportion $\frac{x}{40} = \frac{1}{87}$; $x \approx 0.46$, so the length of the model is 0.46 foot or about $5\frac{1}{2}$ inches.

5. a. Solve the proportion $\frac{2.8}{x} = \frac{1}{15}$; the towns are 42 miles apart.

b. Solve the proportion $\frac{x}{22} = \frac{1}{15}$; the towns should be about 1.5 inches apart on the map.

c. Solve the proportion $\frac{x}{47} = \frac{1}{15}$; the distance is a little over 3 inches on the map.

d. Solve the proportion $\frac{3.5}{x} = \frac{1}{15}$; the lake is about 52.5 miles across.

6. Rectangles i and iii are similar because corresponding angles are congruent and corresponding side lengths are proportional $\left(\frac{3}{6} = \frac{2}{4}\right)$. Rectangles iv and vi are similar because corresponding angles are congruent and corresponding side lengths are proportional $\left(\frac{2}{1} = \frac{4}{2}\right)$.

7. Rhombuses i and iii are similar, and rhombuses iv and v are similar. In each similar pair, corresponding sides are proportional (because all sides of a rhombus have equal length) and the angle measures are the same.

8. a. Answers will vary. One possibility is a square and a nonsquare rectangle.

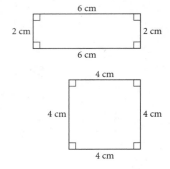

b. Answers will vary. One possibility is a rectangle and a parallelogram in which the ratio of the short side to the long side is the same for each shape.

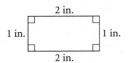

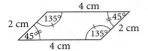

9. a.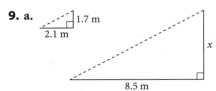

b. $\frac{1.7}{2.1} = \frac{x}{8.5}$; $x \approx 6.88$ or 6.9 meters

c. You could measure the length of the tree's shadow and write a proportion using a person's height and the length of his or her shadow.

10. a. x represents actual distance in miles, and y represents map distance in inches.

b. x represents map distance in inches, and y represents actual distance in miles.

c. Yes, it just depends on which variable is substituted; 4.7 inches represents 58.75 miles.

11. a. Possible answer: A sheet of notebook paper is about 28 cm long. To fit a scale drawing of the longest river (the Nile) on the paper, each centimeter would have to represent $6670 \div 28$ or about 238 kilometers. To make the scale easier to use and interpret, Tommy could use 1 cm = 250 km.

b. Answers will vary. Using the scale of 1 cm = 250 km, an equation would be $y = \frac{1}{250}x$, where x is the actual river length in kilometers and y is the scale-drawing length in centimeters. Approximations from a graph will vary based on window settings but should be around 26.7 cm, 25.8 cm, 25.2 cm, 23.9 cm, and 22.2 cm, respectively.

12. a.

Side length	Perimeter	Area
6	24	36
4	16	16
3	12	9
2	8	4
8	32	64

Discovering Algebra Solutions Manual
©2002 Key Curriculum Press

b. For the first two squares, the ratio of side lengths and the ratio of perimeters are both $\frac{3}{2}$. For any two squares in the table, the ratio of perimeters is the same as the ratio of side lengths.

c. For the first two squares, the ratio of side lengths is $\frac{3}{2}$ and the ratio of areas is $\frac{9}{4}$. So the ratio of areas is the square of the ratio of side lengths. This is true for any two squares in the table.

d. The perimeter of the larger square would be 5 times as long. The area of the larger square would be 25 times as great.

e. Answers may include the facts that the ratio of perimeters is the same as the ratio of side lengths and that the ratio of areas is the square of the ratio of side lengths.

13. a. $\frac{30}{100} = \frac{x}{24}$; $x \approx 7$ **b.** $\frac{30}{100} = \frac{p}{s}$

   c. $p = \frac{30}{100}s$ or $p = 0.3s$ **d.** *part = percent · total*

14. Using the general equation from 13d, $2874 = 0.74t$; $t = 3883.78$, so there are 3884 people in the town.

15. a. $\frac{\$12.98}{6 \text{ weeks}} \cdot \frac{1 \text{ week}}{7 \text{ days}} \approx \$0.31$ per day

   b. $\frac{7 \text{ pounds}}{6 \text{ weeks}} \cdot \frac{52 \text{ weeks}}{1 \text{ year}}$

   $= 60.\overline{6}$ or $60\frac{2}{3}$ pounds per year

   c. Together the cats eat $121.\overline{3}$ pounds per year. This is $121.\overline{3} \div 14$ or about 8.7 bags of food. It costs about $113 for 8.7 fourteen-pound bags. The owner will have to buy 9 bags and spend $116.82.

16. 11, 27.5, 47, 68.5, 85

17. P(mango flavored) $= \frac{4}{48}$ or $\frac{1}{12}$, or about 0.083

18. a. $(1 \cdot 1), (1 \cdot 3) + (2 \cdot 1), (2 \cdot 3)$; 156

   b. $(2 \cdot 1), (2 \cdot 4) + (1 \cdot 1), (1 \cdot 4)$; 294

   c. $(4 \cdot 3), (4 \cdot 1) + (2 \cdot 3), (2 \cdot 1)$; 12, 10, 2; the 10 carries into the next place to give 1302.

LESSON 3.4

EXERCISES

1. a. $y = \frac{15}{x}$ **b.** $y = \frac{35}{x}$ **c.** $y = \frac{3}{x}$

2. Because x and y are inversely proportional, their product is constant. When $x = 3$, $y = 4$, so the constant product is $3 \cdot 4$ or 12. In 2a–d, you need to find the value so that the coordinates have a product of 12.

   a. 3   **b.** 6   **c.** 12   **d.** 0.5

3. Answers will vary. For each point, the product of the coordinates must be 20. Possible points are $(4, 5), (2, 10), (5, 4), (10, 2)$, and $(2.5, 8)$. Here is a graph of the points and the equation made using the window $[0, 20, 2, 0, 20, 2]$.

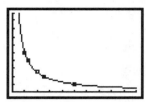

$[0, 20, 2, 0, 20, 2]$

4. a. 3 hr   **b.** 2 hr   **c.** 60 mph

5. This is not an inverse variation. The product of the quantities *time spent watching TV* and *time spent doing homework* is not a constant. It is an inverse relationship only in the sense that as one increases the other decreases, but the sum, not the product, is a constant. This is a relationship of the form $x + y = k$ or $y = k - x$, not an inverse variation of the form $xy = k$ or $y = \frac{k}{x}$.

6. a. Inverse variation; the x- and y-values have a constant product, 24; the equation is $y = \frac{24}{x}$ or $xy = 24$.

   b. Direct variation; the ratio of y to x is constant; the equation is $y = 12x$.

   c. Neither; it is not an inverse variation because some of the values are 0, and neither variable in an inverse variation can have the value 0; it is not a direct variation because the ratio of y to x is not constant $\left(\text{for example, } \frac{3.0}{3.0} = 1, \text{ while } \frac{1.5}{6} = 0.25\right)$.

   d. Inverse variation; the x- and y-values have a constant product, 19.5; the equation is $y = \frac{19.5}{x}$ or $xy = 19.5$.

7. a. If x is the distance and y is the force, then $y = \frac{935}{x}$. Substitute each given distance for x to find the corresponding force: $62.\overline{3}$ newtons, 93.5 newtons, and 187 newtons.

   b. As you move closer to the hinge, it takes more force to open the door. When you go from 15 cm to 10 cm, the required force increases by about 31.2 newtons. When you go from 10 cm to 5 cm, the required force increases by 93.5 newtons. As you move closer, the force needed increases more rapidly. When you get very close to the hinge, the force needed becomes extremely large.

c. The curve goes up very steeply near the *y*-axis.

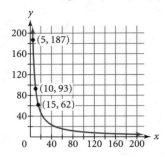

8. a. *Sid's weight · Sid's distance*
= *Emily's weight · Emily's distance*, so
65 · 4 = *Emily's weight* · 2.5;
Emily weighs 104 pounds.

b. Solve the equation 130 · 4 = 104 · *D* to find the distance Emily would have to sit from the center if the boys sit on the seat. Emily would have to sit 5 feet from the center. The distance from the center to the seat is only 4 feet, so she can't balance the two boys as long as they stay on the seat. However, if the boys move and Emily sits on the seat, it can be done. Solve 130 · *D* = 104 · 4 to find the distance the boys would then have to sit from the center. They must sit 3.2 feet from the center.

9. a. If the balance point is at the center, then the weight of an unknown object will be exactly the same as the weight that balances it on the other side. If the balance point is off-center, you must know the two distances and do some calculation.

b. 15 · *M* = 20 · 7; $M \approx 9.3$ kg

10. a. Answers will vary. In every case, the number of students times the amount should equal $10,000.

Number of students	Amount each needs to raise
100	$100
200	$50
250	$40
400	$25

b.

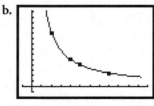

[−50, 600, 50, −10, 140, 10]

$$y = \frac{10,000}{x}$$

c. The graph should stop at *x* = 500 because there are only 500 students.

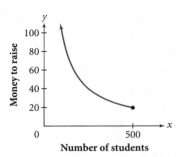

11. a. Answers will vary. On this graph, *x* represents frequency and *y* represents tube length. As the frequency increases, the tube length decreases; this appears to be an inverse relationship.

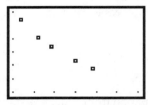

[400, 1000, 100, 30, 90, 10]

b. Possible answer: $y = \frac{37,227.1}{x}$, where 37,227.1 is the mean of the products of the frequencies and tube lengths

c. $y = \frac{37,227.1}{880.0}$; $y \approx 42.3$ cm

12. a. The product of the volume and the pressure is a constant. When the pressure is 1 atm, the volume is 1 liter, so the constant is 1 · 1, or 1. If the volume is 0.5 liter, the pressure must be 2 atm.

b. $0.25p = 1$; pressure is 4 atm.

c. $v · 10 = 1$; volume is 0.1 liter.

d. Answers will vary. You would have to increase the volume of the container. If you kept the same volume, you would have to suck some of the air out of the container.

e.

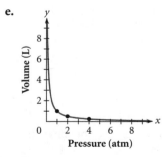

13. $s = 0.85p$; $s = 0.85(\$13.95)$; the sale price is $11.86.

14. a. Solve $\frac{5}{3} = \frac{2.5}{x}$; Mario's body should contain 1.5 pounds of phosphorus.

b. 2% of 130 pounds is 2.6 pounds, so Kyle's body should contain 2.6 pounds of calcium. To find the amount of phosphorus, solve the proportion $\frac{5}{3} = \frac{2.6}{x}$; Kyle's body should contain 1.56 pounds of phosphorus.

LESSON 3.5

Activity day (no answers for this lesson)

CHAPTER 3 Review

EXERCISES

1. a. $\frac{175 \text{ miles}}{13.5 \text{ gallons}}$, about 13 miles per gallon, or about 0.077 gallon per mile

b. 13 miles per gallon · 5 gallons = 65 miles

c. $\frac{1}{\frac{13 \text{ miles}}{\text{gallon}}} = \frac{0.077 \text{ gallons}}{\text{mile}}$; 0.077 gallon per mile · 100 miles = 7.7 gallons

2. a. $\frac{1 \text{ apartment}}{3 \text{ \sout{gallons}}}$ · 36 $\sout{\text{gallons}}$ = 12 apartments

b. $\frac{3 \text{ gallons}}{\sout{\text{apartment}}}$ · 24 $\sout{\text{apartments}}$ = 72 gallons

3. a. If x represents the weight in kilograms and y represents the weight in pounds, one equation is $y = 2.2x$ where 2.2 is the data set's mean ratio of pounds to kilograms.

b. Solve the equation $30 = 2.2x$. There are about 13.6 kilograms in 30 pounds.

c. $y = 2.2(25) = 55$. There are 55 pounds in 25 kilograms.

4. a. About 7.5 cm

b. The plant is growing about 1.5 cm per day. To reach a height of 25 cm will take $25 \div 1.5$ or about 17 days.

c. $H = 1.5 \cdot D$

5. a. Solve the proportion $\frac{1}{21} = \frac{x}{47}$. On the map, the towns are about 2.2 inches apart.

b. Solve the proportion $\frac{1}{21} = \frac{0.75}{x}$. The actual lake is 15.75 miles wide.

6. $x = 8, y = 6.5, z = 5.5, v = 4$. The 6-m side of the small figure corresponds to the 12-m side of the large figure. So the scale factor from the small figure to the large figure is 2. To find a missing side length on the large figure, multiply the corresponding side length on the small figure by 2. To find a missing side length on the small figure, multiply the corresponding side length on the large figure by $\frac{1}{2}$.

7. a. Because the product of the x- and y-values is about constant, it is an inverse variation.

b. One possibility: $y = \frac{45.5}{x}$, where 45.5 is the mean of the products

c. $y = \frac{45.5}{32}$; $y \approx 1.4$

8. a. Directly: $d = 50t$ **b.** Directly: $d = 1v$
c. Inversely: $100 = vt$, or $t = \frac{100}{v}$

9. a. Solve the equation $100 \cdot 3.2 = 80 \cdot D$. Robbie must be sitting 4 meters from the center.

b. To find the distance Robbie must sit from the center, solve the equation $100 \cdot 3.2 = 110 \cdot D$; Robbie can balance by sitting 2.9 meters from the center.

10. a. The product of the volume and the pressure is always $1.75 \cdot 1 = 1.75$. So, if the pressure is 0.8 atm, the volume is $1.75 \div 0.8$ or 2.1875 liters.

b. $1.75 \div 0.75$ or $2.\overline{3}$ atm

c. $y = \frac{1.75}{x}$

d.

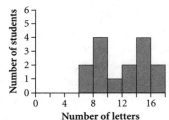

11. No, they won't fit. There are 2.54 cm in 1 inch, so 210 cm equals $210 \div 2.54$ or about 82.7 inches, which is about 6.89 feet.

12. a.

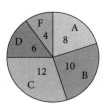

b. $P(8 \text{ or } 9) = \frac{4}{15}$

13. To find the number of degrees in each grade's section, solve a ratio of the form

$$\frac{\textit{number of students who got that grade}}{\textit{total number of students}}$$
$$= \frac{\textit{degrees in section}}{360}$$

Algebra Grades

14. a. $-3 \cdot 8 - 5 \cdot 6 = -24 - 30 = -54$

  b. $(-2 - (-4)) \cdot 8 - 11 = (-2 + 4) \cdot 8 - 11$
  $= 2 \cdot 8 - 11 = 16 - 11 = 5$

  c. $7 \cdot 8 + 4 \cdot (-12) = 56 + (-48) = 8$

  d. $11 - 3 \cdot 9 - 2 = 11 - 27 - 2 = -16 - 2 = -18$

15. a. About 1100.25 thousand (or 1.1 million) visitors

  b. 354, 465, 740, 1272, 3494

  c.

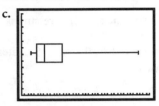

  [0, 4000, 100, 1, 12, 1]

  d. Yosemite; the number of guests exceeds 1272 by more than $1.5(1272 - 465)$.

16. a. $\frac{49}{99}$ **b.** $\frac{33}{99}$ or $\frac{1}{3}$ **c.** $\frac{19}{99}$ **d.** $\frac{9}{99}$ or $\frac{1}{11}$

17. Use Ohm's law to solve: $i = \frac{E}{R}$, where i is in amps, E is in volts, and R is in ohms. Because $i = 18$ when $R = 4$, the value of the constant E is $18 \cdot 4 = 72$. So the equation becomes $i = \frac{72}{R}$.

  a. 9 amperes   **b.** 6 ohms

18. a. $\frac{500}{6} \approx 83.3$ hours   **b.** $\frac{500}{0.75 \cdot 6} \approx 111.1$ hours

TAKE ANOTHER LOOK

Answers for the first three graphs: $k = 1$, $k < 1 \left(= \frac{1}{2}\right)$, and $k > 1 (= 2)$. In the fourth graph, $k < 0 (= -1)$ because the quotient $\frac{y}{x}$ is negative for every point on the graph. In the last graph pair, the first set of lines is symmetric across $y = x$; the k-values are reciprocals $\left(3 \text{ and } \frac{1}{3}\right)$. The second set of lines is perpendicular; the k-values are negative reciprocals $\left(-3, \frac{1}{3}\right)$. The geometric relationship can be confirmed with similar triangles. If $k = 0$, the graph is the x-axis. By the definition of a direct variation, $y = 0$ is a direct variation. Nothing is varying, so $y = 0$ would not usually be called a direct variation.

CHAPTER 4

LESSON 4.1

EXERCISES

1. a. $\frac{-27 + 39}{4} = \frac{12}{4} = 3$

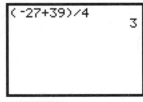

b. $2 + (-3)(4) = 2 - 12 = -10$

c. $\frac{3}{4} - \frac{1}{2} = \frac{3}{4} - \frac{2}{4} = \frac{1}{4}$

d. $\frac{12}{4 - 6} = \frac{12}{-2} = -6$

2. a. $-4(13 - 2 \cdot 3^2) = -4(13 - 2 \cdot 9)$
  $= -4(13 - 18) = -4(-5) = 20$

  b.

```
-4(13-2*3²)
                    20
```

3. a. $2L + 2W$

  b. $2(L + W) = 2(15 + 4) = 38; 2L + 2W$
  $= 2 \cdot 15 + 2 \cdot 4 = 38$

4. Procedure 1: Start with 8075 and subtract 3 times the sum of 37 and 5.

Procedure 2: Start with 8075. Subtract the product of 3 and 37. Then subtract the product of 3 and 5.

$8075 - 3(37 + 5)$	Rewrite the Procedure 1
$= 8075 + (-3)(37 + 5)$	expression.
$= 8075 + (-3)(37)$	Apply the distributive
$\quad + (-3)(5)$	property.
$= 8075 - 3 \cdot 27 - 3 \cdot 5$	Rewrite to get the Procedure 2
	expression.

5. a. $84

  b. Find the total number of hours and then multiply by 7. Or find 7 times the number of hours for each day and then add the results. The distributive property shows that these methods are equivalent: $7(4 + 3 + 5) = 7 \cdot 4 + 7 \cdot 3 + 7 \cdot 5$.

6. a. Think of 15% as 10% + 5%. 10% of $36 is $3.60; 5% is half of that, or $1.80, so the total tip is $5.40. Written out, the calculation looks like this:

$(0.10 + 0.05)36$	Distribute 36 over
$= 0.10(36) + 0.05(36)$	$0.10 + 0.05$.
$= 3.60 + 1.80$	Multiply.
$= 5.40$	Add.

  b. Because 10% of $21 is $2.10 and 5% of $21 is $1.05, 15% of $21 is $3.15.

  c. Because 10% of $48.50 is $4.85 and 5% of $48.50 is $2.43, 15% of $48.50 is $7.28.

7. a.

$\frac{15}{100} = \frac{x}{36}$	
$36 \cdot \frac{15}{100} = \frac{x}{36} \cdot 36$	Multiply both sides by 36.
$36 \cdot \frac{15}{100} = x$	$\frac{36}{36}$ is equivalent to 1.
$5.4 = x$	Multiply and divide.

The tip would be $5.40.

b. Solve the proportion $\frac{15}{100} = \frac{x}{21}$. The tip would be $3.15.

c. Solve the proportion $\frac{15}{100} = \frac{x}{48.50}$. The tip would be $7.28

8. Seija. Peter incorrectly added before multiplying.

9. a. First multiply 16 times 4.5. Then add 9.

   b. First divide 18 by 3. Then add 15.

   c. First square 6. Then add -5. Then multiply by 4. Then subtract the result from 3.

10. a. $((5 + 9)3 - 6)/3 - 5 = 7$

   b. $((8 + 9)3 - 6)/3 - 8 = 7$

   c. $((25 + 9)3 - 6)/3 - 25 = 7$

   d. $((2 + 9)3 - 6)/3 - 2 = 7$

   e. Expressions will vary. The answer is 7.

   f. Possible answer: The answer is always 7. This is because the original expression, $\frac{(5 + 9)3 - 6}{3} - 5$, can be simplified to $5 + 9 - 2 - 5$. The 5 is subtracted from itself, leaving $9 - 2$. The same thing happens when any number is used in place of 5. For example, $\frac{(8 + 9)3 - 6}{3} - 8$ $= 8 + 9 - 2 - 8 = 9 - 2$, and $\frac{(25 + 9)3 - 6}{3} - 25$ $= 25 + 9 - 2 - 25 = 9 - 2$.

11. a. Possible answers:

   $(3 + 2)(5) - 7 = 18$. First add 3 and 2 to get 5. Then multiply by 5 to get 25. Then subtract 7 to get 18.

   $3(2) + 5 + 7 = 18$. Multiply 3 times 2 to get 6. Then add 5 to get 11. Then add 7 to get 18.

   b. $8 - 5(6 - 7) = 13$. First subtract 7 from 6 to get -1. Then multiply by 5 to get -5. Then subtract this result from 8 to get 13.

12. a. $3L_1 - 12.6$; $\{-21.6, 0.9, 17.4\}$

```
{-3,4.5,10}→L1
       {-3 4.5 10}
3(L1-4.2)
       {-21.6 .9 17.4}
3L1-12.6
       {-21.6 .9 17.4}
```

   b. $3L_1 + 1.4$; $\{-7.6, 14.9, 31.4\}$

```
{-3,4.5,10}→L1
       {-3 4.5 10}
14+3(L1-4.2)
       {-7.6 14.9 31.4}
3L1+1.4
       {-7.6 14.9 31.4}
```

   c. $-3L_1 + 26.6$; $\{35.6, 13.1, -3.4\}$

```
{-3,4.5,10}→L1
       {-3 4.5 10}
14-3(L1-4.2)
       {35.6 13.1 -3.4}
-3L1+26.6
       {35.6 13.1 -3.4}
```

13. $\frac{(6 + 3) \cdot 4^2}{8 + 2} - 9 = 5.4$

14. Possible solutions:

   $1 + 2 + 3 + 4 + 5 + 6 + 7 + 8 \cdot 9 = 100$;

   $-1 + 2 + 3 + 4 \cdot 5 \cdot 6 - 7 - 8 - 9 = 100$;

   $12 + 34 + 5 \cdot 6 + 7 + 8 + 9 = 100$

15. a. Here is the scatter plot (the line is added in 15c):

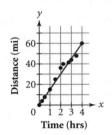

Distance Traveled

   b. The cyclist traveled 60 miles in 4 hours, so the average speed was $60 \div 4$ or 15 mi/hr.

   c. $y = 15x$, where x is the time in hours and y is the distance in miles

   d. From 1 hour to 2.25 hours and from 3.5 hours to 4 hours, the cyclist's speed is greater than the average speed, indicating that he or she may be traveling downhill. From 2.25 hours to 3.5 hours, the cyclist's speed is less than the average speed, indicating that he or she may be traveling uphill.

16. a.

Length (in.)	Width (in.)
1	24
2	12
3	8
4	6
6	4
8	3
12	2
24	1

b. Possible Boxes

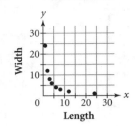

c. Indirect variation; the product of the length and the width equals a constant.

d. $l \cdot w = 24$ or $w = \frac{24}{l}$. Yes, the situation requires the dimensions to be whole numbers of inches.

17. The 20% discount is $2.59. The 8% tax on $10.36 is $0.83. The 15% tip on $12.95 is $1.94. The total is $12.95 − $2.59 + $0.83 + $1.94 or $13.13.

LESSON 4.2

EXERCISES

1. a. $-4 + (-8) = -12$

b. $(-4)(-8) = 32$

c. $-2(3 + 9) = -2(12) = -24$

d. $5 + (-6)(-5) = 5 + 30 = 35$

e. $(-3)(-5) + (-2) = 15 + (-2) = 13$

f. $\frac{-15}{3} + 8 = -5 + 8 = 3$

g. $\frac{23 - 3(4 - 9)}{-2} = \frac{23 - 3(-5)}{-2} = \frac{23 + 15}{-2}$
$= \frac{38}{-2} = -19$

h. $\frac{-4(7 + (-8))}{8} - 6.5 = \frac{-4(-1)}{8} - 6.5$
$= \frac{4}{8} - 6.5 = 0.5 - 6.5 = -6$

i. $\frac{6(2 \cdot 4 - 5) - 2)}{-4} = \frac{6(8 - 5) - 2}{-4}$
$= \frac{6(3) - 2}{-4} = \frac{18 - 2}{-4} = \frac{16}{-4} = -4$

2. No, this isn't correct. Sondro should have used parentheses:

$(75 + 81 + 71 + 78 + 83)/5 = 77.6$

3. a. $2(6) + 3 = 12 + 3 = 15$

b. $2(6 + 3) = 2(9) = 18$

c. $5(6) - 13 = 30 - 13 = 17$

d. $\frac{6 + 9}{3} = \frac{15}{3} = 5$

4. a. $x = 15$. Order of operations: Start with x. Subtract 3. Divide by 2. The result is 6. Working backward: Start with 6. Multiply by 2. Add 3. The result is 15.

Equation: $\frac{x - 3}{2} = 6$ Work backward

Operations on x	Undo operations	$x = 15$
$- 3$	$+ 3 \leftarrow$	12
$\div 2$	$\cdot 2 \leftarrow$	6

b. $x = 5$. Order of operations: Start with x. Multiply by 3. Add 7. The result is 22. Working backward: Start with 22. Subtract 7. Divide by 3. The result is 5.

Equation: $3x + 7 = 22$ Work backward

Operations on x	Undo operations	$x = 5$
$\cdot 3$	$\div 3 \leftarrow$	15
$+ 7$	$- 7 \leftarrow$	22

c. $x = 6$. Order of operations. Start with x. Divide by 6. Subtract 20. The result is -19. Working backward: Start with -19. Add 20. Multiply by 6. The result is 6.

Equation: $\frac{x}{6} - 20 = -19$ Work backward

Operations on x	Undo operations	$x = 6$
$\div 6$	$\cdot 6 \leftarrow$	1
$- 20$	$+ 20 \leftarrow$	-19

5. a. The instructions indicate that the sum of 2 and 3 should be multiplied by 4. In Juwan's expression, $2 + 3 \cdot 4 - 5$, only the 3 is multiplied by 4.

b. $(2 + 3)4 - 5$ or $4(2 + 3) - 5$

6. Justine could start with 33 and work backward, undoing each operation: Start with 33. Add 2 to get 35. Divide by 5 to get 7. Quentin picked 7.

7.

Description	Claudia's sequence	Al's sequence
Pick the starting number.	-8.6	x
Add 5.	-3.6	$x + 5$
Multiply by 4.	-14.4	$4(x + 5)$
Subtract 12.	-26.4	$4(x + 5) - 12$
Divide by 4.	-6.6	$\frac{4(x + 5) - 12}{4}$
Subtract the original number.	2	$\frac{4(x + 5) - 12}{4} - x$

8. a. 1. Pick a number.
2. Subtract 3.
3. Multiply your result by 2.
4. Add 4.
5. Divide by 2.
7. Add 4.

b. Stages 6 and 7; the original number has been subtracted.

c. Sample answer for the list {4, 11}:

```
{4,11}
              {4  11}
Ans-3
              {1   8}
Ans*2
              {2  16}
```

```
Ans+4
              {6  20}
Ans/2
              {3  10}
```

```
Ans-L1
              {-1  -1}
Ans+4
              {3   3}
```

d. $\dfrac{2(n-3)+4}{2} - n + 4$

9. a. Number Trick 1: Multiply by 2. Multiply by 3. Add 6. Divide by 3. Subtract your original number. Subtract your original number again.

b. Number Trick 2: Pick the starting number. Add 2. Multiply by 3. Add 9. Subtract 15. Multiply by 2. Divide by 6 (you should have your original number).

10. a. Pick a number. Subtract 5. Multiply by 4. Add 8. Divide by 2. Subtract the original number. Add 6.

b. Solutions will vary. The trick always produces the original number.

11. Answers will vary. Sample answer:

a. Pick a number. Subtract 3. Multiply by 2. Add 10. Divide by 2. Subtract the original number. Subtract 6.

b. I started with x and started applying operations. I subtracted 3, then multiplied by 2, and then subtracted 10. Because I multiplied by 2, I knew I had to undo this by dividing by 2, so I added this step. Then I subtracted the original number so the final result would not be affected by the starting number chosen. I tested my trick, and I always ended up with 2. I added the step "Subtract 6" so everyone would get −4.

c. $\dfrac{2(x-3)+10}{2} - x - 6$

12. a. 3

b. Start with 3 and see if you get the answer 3.

c. 15

d. The final result is always the original number.

13. Sample answer: Pick a number. Add 5. Multiply by 4. Divide by 2. Subtract the original number. Subtract 10.

14. a. 8.8   **b.** 15

c. I undid the operations shown in reverse order: I multiplied by 5, then added 12, then divided by 2, then subtracted 10.

d. $\dfrac{2(x+10)-12}{5}$

e. $\dfrac{2(x+10)-12}{5} = 0$. To solve this equation, work backward: Multiply by 5 to get 0. Add 12 to get 12. Divide by 2 to get 6. Subtract 10 to get −4. To check, use −4 as a starting number and work forward: Add 10 to get 6. Multiply by 2 to get 12. Subtract 12 to get 0. Divide by 5 to get 0.

15. a. 25. Add 7. Multiply by 5. Divide by 3.

b. Start with −18. Multiply by 3 to get −54. Divide by 5 to get −10.8. Subtract 7 to get −17.8.

16. a. $x = -2.4$. Start with 8. Subtract 4.2 to get 3.8. Multiply by 2.5 to get 9.5. Divide by 5 to get 1.9. Subtract 4.3 to get −2.4.

b. $x = 23.6$. Start with 5.4. Add 4.3 to get 9.7. Multiply by 5 to get 48.5. Divide by 2.5 to get 19.4. Add 4.2 to get 23.6.

17. a. To find the speed in miles per hour, solve the proportion $\frac{x}{200} = \frac{1}{87}$. The car travels about 2.3 miles per hour. To convert this speed to feet per second, you can use dimensional analysis:

$$\dfrac{2.3 \text{ miles}}{1 \text{ hour}} \cdot \dfrac{1 \text{ hour}}{60 \text{ minutes}} \cdot \dfrac{5280 \text{ feet}}{1 \text{ mile}} \approx 202 \text{ ft/min}$$

b. To convert to centimeters per second, use dimensional analysis:

$$\dfrac{202.3 \text{ feet}}{1 \text{ minute}} \cdot \dfrac{12 \text{ inches}}{1 \text{ foot}} \cdot \dfrac{2.54 \text{ centimeters}}{1 \text{ inch}} \cdot \dfrac{1 \text{ minute}}{60 \text{ seconds}} \approx 103 \text{ cm/sec}$$

18. Yes, this method works for any two numbers. To see why, use the distributive property to simplify the right side of the equation:

$ab = 10b - (10-a)b$	Original equation.
$= 10b - (10b - ab)$	Distribute the b to $10 - a$.
$= 10b - 10b + ab$	Distribute the minus sign to $10b - ab$.
$= ab$	Subtract $10b - 10b$.

Sample student answer:

$$9 \cdot 6 = 10 \cdot 6 - (10 - 9) \cdot 6$$
$$= 10 \cdot 6 - 1 \cdot 6$$
$$= 60 - 6$$
$$= 54$$

This method works best when it converts multiplying large numbers to multiplying small numbers. It would not be useful for calculating $3 \cdot 4$, for example.

19. a. $\frac{3}{4} + \frac{2}{3} + \frac{1}{2} = \frac{23}{12}$ or $1\frac{11}{12}$ cups

   b. $\frac{3}{4}(\$6.98) + \frac{2}{3}(\$7.98) + \frac{1}{2}(\$4.98) = \$13.05$

LESSON 4.3

EXERCISES

1. a. 15   **b.** -16 **c.** -5

2. a. $3L_1 + 6$; {12, 21, 24}

   b. $-24 + 4L_2$; {$-38.4, -26, 24$}

   c. $-7L_1 + 21$; {7, -14, -21}

3. a.

Figure #	Perimeter
1	5
2	8
3	11
4	14
5	17

   b. 5 ENTER, Ans + 3 ENTER, ENTER, . . .

   c. Figure 10 has a perimeter of 32.

   d. Figure 15 has a perimeter of 47.

4. $-14.2, -10.5, -6.8, -3.1, 0.6, 4.3$

5. a. 3 ENTER, Ans + 6 ENTER, ENTER, . . . ;
   10th term = 57

   b. 1.7 ENTER, Ans − 0.5 ENTER, ENTER, . . . ;
   10th term = -2.8

   c. -3 ENTER, Ans * -2 ENTER, ENTER, . . . ;
   10th term = 1536

   d. 384 ENTER, Ans/2 ENTER, ENTER, . . . ;
   10th term = 0.75

6. a. 0 ENTER, Ans + 12.35 ENTER, ENTER, ... The
   starting value is 0, the height of ground level (the
   first floor). The rule "+12.35" adds the average
   floor height of each of the next 85 floors
   ($1050 \div 85 \approx 12.35$).

   b. 1050 ENTER, Ans + 10.875 ENTER, ENTER, ... The
   starting value is the height of the 86th floor. The
   rule "+10.875" adds the average floor height of
   floors 86 through 102 $\left(\frac{1224 - 1050}{102 - 86} = 10.875\right)$.

   c. When you are 531 feet above the ground, you are
   43 floors up from ground level and thus on the
   44th floor.

   d. 1093.5 feet; 94th floor

7. a. Possible explanation: The smallest square has an
   area of 1. The next larger white square has an area
   of 4, which is 3 more than the smallest square. The
   next larger gray square has an area of 9, which is 5
   more than the 4-unit white square.

   b. 1 ENTER, Ans + 2 ENTER, ENTER, . . .

   c. 17, which is the value of the 9th term in
   the sequence

   d. 39

   e. The 48th term is 95. Students might press ENTER
   48 times or compute $2(48) - 1$.

8. a. The table for six figures of the L-shaped puzzle
   pieces is

Figure	Toothpicks	Perimeter	Area
1	8	8	3
2	14	12	6
3	20	16	9
4	26	20	12
5	32	24	15
6	38	28	18

   b. Number of toothpicks: 8 ENTER,
   Ans + 6 ENTER, ENTER, . . .
   Perimeter: 8 ENTER, Ans + 4 ENTER, ENTER, . . .
   Area: 3 ENTER, Ans + 3 ENTER, ENTER, . . .

   c. Figure 10 has 62 toothpicks, a perimeter of 44, and
   an area of 30.

   d. Figure 25, made from 152 toothpicks, has a
   perimeter of 104 and an area of 75.

9. a. 4 meters

   b. The height of the 25th floor is 101 m. (One way to
   find this is to notice that the height of each floor is
   4 times the floor number, plus 1.) Moving from the
   25th floor to the basement, the height decreases by
   4 m with each floor. So the recursive routine is
   101 ENTER, Ans − 4 ENTER, ENTER, ... The 19th
   term represents the height of the seventh floor.
   The height is 29 meters.

   c. 26

   d. $-3 + 4(-4) = -19$ meters = 19 meters
   underground

10. a. -4 ENTER, Ans +12 ENTER, ENTER, . . . , or
   -16 ENTER, Ans + 12 ENTER, ENTER, . . .
   -4 ENTER, Ans · -2 ENTER, ENTER, . . . , or
   2 ENTER, Ans · -2 ENTER, ENTER, . . .

b. For the first routine given in 10a, the sequence is
$\{-16, -4, 8, 20, 32, 44, 56, \ldots\}$. For the second
routine, the sequence is
$\{2, -4, 8, -16, 32, -64, 128, \ldots\}$.

c. More numbers in the sequence

11. a. $17 \cdot 7 = 119$

b. 14 (namely, $7 \cdot 15 = 105$ through $7 \cdot 28 = 196$)

c. Possible answer: There are 14 multiples of 7
between 100 and 200, and 14 multiples of 7
between 200 and 300 (namely, $7 \cdot 29 = 203$
through $7 \cdot 42 = 294$). However, there are
15 multiples of 7 between 300 and 400 (namely,
$7 \cdot 43 = 301$ through $7 \cdot 57 = 399$).

d. Possible answer: Find $7 \cdot 1, 7 \cdot 2, 7 \cdot 3$, and so on.
Or start with 7 and add 7 repeatedly.

12. a. 6.8 ENTER, Ans + 1.5 ENTER, ENTER, ...

b. 7.2 ENTER, Ans + 1.5 ENTER, ENTER, ...

c. The starting terms differ. The rule is the same.

d.

Age (mo)	Weight of Baby A (lb)	Weight of Baby B (lb)
0	6.8	7.2
1	8.3	8.7
2	9.8	10.2
3	11.3	11.7
4	12.8	13.2
5	14.3	14.7
6	15.8	16.2

e. The starting weights are different, but for both
babies the weight increases by 1.5 pounds each
month. The weight of Baby B is always 0.4 pound
more than the weight of Baby A.

13. a. 1 ENTER, Ans · 3 ENTER, ENTER, ...; the 9th term is
6561.

b. 5 ENTER, Ans · (−1) ENTER, ENTER, ...; the 123rd
term is 5.

c. −16.2 ENTER, Ans + 1.4 ENTER, ENTER, ...; the
13th term is the first positive term.

d. −1 ENTER, Ans · (−2) ENTER, ENTER, ...; the 8th
term is the first to be greater than 100.

14. a. The top box plot represents Portland, the middle
one San Francisco, and the bottom one Seattle.

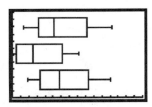

[0, 7, 0.5, 0, 12, 1]

Overall, San Francisco gets the least precipitation.
The Q1-value for San Francisco is less than the
minimum value of any of the other two cities,
indicating that during three months of the year
San Francisco gets less rain than the other two
cities get in any month. The maximum value in the
San Francisco plot is less than the Q3-value for
each of the other plots, indicating that for three
months of the year the average amount of
precipitation in Seattle and Portland is greater than
the average for any of the months in San Francisco.

b. You lose information about what time of year is
soggiest. A bar graph or scatter plot would show
trends over the months of the year more clearly.

15. a. $297.25

b. $4 \cdot 8(7.25) + 6 \cdot 1.5(7.25) = 232 + 65.25$
$= 297.25$, or $7.25(4 \cdot 8 + 6 \cdot 1.5) = 7.25(41)$
$= 297.25$

16. a. $\frac{3}{400}$ **b.** $\frac{397}{400}$ **c.** 0.75%

LESSON 4.4

EXERCISES

1. a. Negative; -1517 **b.** Positive; 472

c. Positive; $12.\overline{3}$ **d.** Positive; 326

e. Negative; $-3.\overline{3}$ **f.** Negative; -1464

2. a. 0.5, 1, 1.5, 2, 2.5, 3; 0.5 ENTER,
Ans + 0.5 ENTER, ENTER, ENTER, ENTER, ENTER

b. 4, 3, 2, 1, 0; 4 ENTER,
Ans −1 ENTER, ENTER, ENTER, ENTER

c. −1, −0.75, −0.5, −0.25, 0, 0.25; −1 ENTER,
Ans + 0.25 ENTER, ENTER, ENTER, ENTER, ENTER

d. −1.5, 0, 1.5, 3; −1.5 ENTER,
Ans + 1.5 ENTER, ENTER, ENTER

3. 2b:

x-coordinate	y-coordinate
0	4
1	3
2	2
3	1
4	0

2d:

x-coordinate	y-coordinate
0	−1.5
1	0
2	1.5
3	3

4. a.

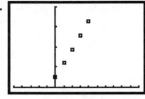

$[-5, 10, 1, 0, 40, 10]$

b.

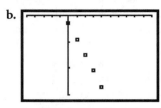

$[-5, 10, 1, 0, -30, 10]$

c. The starting point for each sequence lies on the *y*-axis. The *x*-coordinate of each starting point is 0.

d. For the recursive routine in 4a, the *y*-coordinates increase by 7. For the recursive routine in 4b, the *y*-coordinates decrease by 6.

5. a. $\dfrac{4 - 5(9 + 3)}{6} = \dfrac{4 - 5(12)}{6} = \dfrac{4 - 60}{6}$

$= \dfrac{-56}{6} = -9.\overline{3}$

b. $\dfrac{4 - 5(x + 3)}{6} = 12$; the order of operations is add 3, multiply by -5, add 4, divide by 6. To solve the equation, start with 12 and undo the operations in reverse order: Multiply by 6 to get 72, subtract 4 to get 68, divide by -5 to get -13.6, subtract 3 to get -16.6. So $x = -16.6$.

6. a. $\{0, 0\}$ ⏎ENTER⏎,
$\{\text{Ans}(1) + 1, \text{Ans}(2) + 2.54\}$ ⏎ENTER⏎, ⏎ENTER⏎, . . .

b.

In.	Cm
2	5.08
14	35.56
17	43.18

7. a. $\{0, 272\}$ ⏎ENTER⏎,
$\{\text{Ans}(1) + 1, \text{Ans}(2) - 68\}$ ⏎ENTER⏎, ⏎ENTER⏎, . . .

Time (hr)	Distance from San Antonio (mi)
0	272
1	204
2	136
3	68
4	0
5	-68

b.

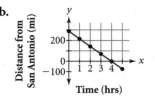

The line is added in 7e.

c. The starting value $\{0, 272\}$ is the *y*-intercept $(0, 272)$ of the graph.

d. On the graph, you move right 1 unit and down 68 units to get from one point to the next. In the recursive routine, you add 1 to the first number and subtract 68 from the second number.

e. The line represents the distance from San Antonio for any time between 0 and 5 hours. The points represent only distances at 1-hour intervals.

f. The car is within 100 miles of San Antonio after 2.53 hours have elapsed. Explanations will vary. Graphically, it is at, and after, the time which the line crosses the horizontal line $y = 100$.

g. The car takes 4 hours to reach San Antonio. Answers will vary. The answer is the fourth entry in the table. Graphically, it is where the line crosses the *x*-axis.

8. a. Possible answer: $\{1, 1.38\}$ ⏎ENTER⏎,
$\{\text{Ans}(1) + 1, \text{Ans}(2) + 0.36\}$ ⏎ENTER⏎, ⏎ENTER⏎, ...
The recursive routine keeps track of time and cost for each minute. Apply the routine until you get $\{7, 3.54\}$. A 7-minute call costs $3.54.

b. Possible answer: The graph should consist of points that lie on a line. It should include the point $(1, 1.38)$. Each subsequent point should be 1 unit to the right and 0.36 unit higher.

9. a.

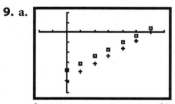

$[-10, 35, 5, -60, 20, 10]$

b. The points for each submarine appear to lie on a line. The points for the USS *Dallas* lie on a steeper line, indicating that it surfaces at a faster rate.

c. Yes; the lines show the depths of the submarines at every point in time, not just for multiples of 5 seconds.

d. The USS *Alabama* rises 4 feet above the surface of the water when surfacing.

10. a.

Tile Edges on Perimeter

Number of tiles	Triangle	Rhombus	Pentagon	Hexagon
1	3	4	5	6
2	4	6	8	10
3	5	8	11	14
4	6	10	14	18
5	7	12	17	22
6	8	14	20	26
7	9	16	23	30
8	10	18	26	34
9	11	20	29	38
10	12	22	32	42

b. Number of tiles:

1 [ENTER], Ans + 1 [ENTER], [ENTER], . . .

Triangle: 3 [ENTER], Ans + 1 [ENTER], [ENTER], . . .

Rhombus: 4 [ENTER], Ans + 2 [ENTER], [ENTER], . . .

Pentagon: 5 [ENTER], Ans + 3 [ENTER], [ENTER], . . .

Hexagon: 6 [ENTER], Ans + 4 [ENTER], [ENTER], . . .

To generate the sequences for all tiles simultaneously:

{1, 3, 4, 5, 6} [ENTER], {Ans(1) + 1, Ans(2) + 1, Ans(3) + 2, Ans(4) + 3, Ans(5) + 4} [ENTER], [ENTER], . . .

c. Triangle, 52; rhombus, 102; pentagon, 152; hexagon, 202

d.

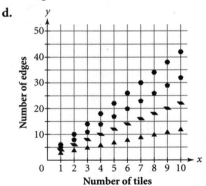

e. The points for each shape lie on a line. The leftmost point of each graph is (1, *number of sides the shape has*). The lines increase in steepness from the graph for the triangle tile to the graph for the hexagon tile.

f. No, because there must be a whole number of tiles and a whole number of edges.

11. a. Possible answer: The graph starts at (0, 5280). The points (0, 5280), (1, 4680), (2, 4080), and (3, 3480)

will lie on a line. From point (3, 3480) to point (8, −1520), the points will lie on a steeper line. The bicyclist ends up 1520 feet past you.

b.

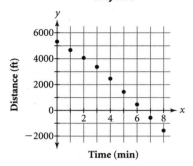

c. Answers will vary. Possible question: After how many minutes does the bicyclist pass you? Because the graph crosses the *x*-axis between 6 and 7, the bicyclist passes you after between 6 and 7 minutes.

12. a. $13.9\overline{3}$. Start with 7.2. Subtract 2.8 to get 4.4. Multiply by 3.2 to get 14.08. Add 5.4 to get 19.48. Divide by 1.2 to get $16.2\overline{3}$. Subtract 2.3 to get $13.9\overline{3}$.

b. To solve the equation $\frac{5.4 + 3.2(x - 2.8)}{1.2} - 2.3 = 3.8$, start with 3.8 and work backward, undoing the operations: Add 2.3 to get 6.1. Multiply by 1.2 to get 7.32. Subtract 5.4 to get 1.92. Divide by 3.2 to get 0.6. Add 2.8 to get 3.4. The solution is 3.4.

13. a. Subtract 32 from the Fahrenheit temperature. Multiply the difference by 5. Then divide the result by 9.

b. $F = \frac{9C}{5} + 32$; $C = \frac{5(F - 32)}{9}$

14. a. $\frac{1}{2}$ cup · $\frac{0.236 \text{ liter}}{1 \text{ cup}}$ = 0.118 liter, so Karen needs 0.118, or about $\frac{1}{8}$, liter of water.

$1\frac{1}{2}$ cups · $\frac{1 \text{ pound}}{4 \text{ cups}}$ · $\frac{454 \text{ grams}}{1 \text{ pound}}$ = 170.25 grams, so Karen needs 170.25, or about 170, grams of flour.

b. $C = \frac{5(425 - 32)}{9} = \frac{5(393)}{9} = \frac{1965}{9} = 218.\overline{3}$, so 425°F is about 220°C.

15. a.

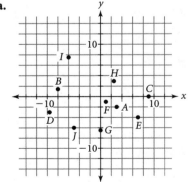

b. Quadrant I: *H*; Quadrant II: *B, I*; Quadrant III: *D, J*; Quadrant IV: *A, E, F*; *x*-axis: *C*; *y*-axis: *G*

c. If both coordinates are 0, the point is on the origin. If just the x-coordinate is 0, the point is on the y-axis. If just the y-coordinate is 0, the point is on the x-axis. If both coordinates are positive, the point is in Quadrant I. If the x-coordinate is negative and the y-coordinate is positive, the point is in Quadrant II. If both coordinates are negative, the point is in Quadrant III. If the x-coordinate is positive and the y-coordinate is negative, the point is in Quadrant IV.

LESSON 4.5

Activity day (no answers for this lesson)

LESSON 4.6

EXERCISES

1. a. ii   **b.** iv   **c.** iii   **d.** i

2. a. $t \approx 0.18$ hr   **b.** $t \approx 0.47$ hr

    c. 24 represents the initial number of miles the driver is from his or her destination.

    d. 45 means that the driver is driving at a speed of 45 miles per hour.

3. a. $d \approx 38.3$ ft   **b.** $d \approx 25.42$ ft

    c. The walker started 4.7 feet away from the motion sensor.

    d. The walker was walking at a rate of 2.8 feet per second.

4. a. $x \approx 7.267$ **b.** $x = 11.2$

5. a. $-2L_1 + 10$; for the list given, both expressions give the result $\{17, 5, -12\}$.

    b. $4L_1 - 4L_2$; for the lists given, both expressions give the result $\{-2.8, -6.8, -40\}$.

6. a. The table shows that Louis burned 400 calories before beginning to run (400 is the Y_1-value for X-value 0). The difference in consecutive Y_1-values is 20.7, indicating that Louis burns 20.7 calories per minute while running. He wants to burn 700 calories.

    b. 400 ENTER , Ans + 20.7 ENTER , ENTER , . . .

    c. $y = 400 + 20.7x$

    d. 700 ENTER , Ans + 0 ENTER , ENTER , . . .

    e. $y = 700 + 0x$, or $y = 700$

    f. The y-intercept of Y_1, which is 400, is the number of calories burned after 0 minutes of running (that is, before Louis begins to run).

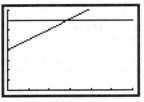

$[0, 30, 5, 0, 800, 100]$

    g. The approximate coordinates are (14.5, 700). This means that after 14.5 minutes of running Louis will have burned off 700 calories.

7. a. The -300 could represent a start-up cost of $300 for equipment and expenses, the 15 could represent the amount she earns per lawn, and N could represent the number of lawns.

    b. Possible questions and answers:

      How many lawns will Jo have to mow to break even? To answer this question, solve $-300 + 15N = 0$. Jo must mow 20 lawns.

      How much profit will Jo earn if she mows 40 lawns? To answer this question, substitute 40 for N. She would earn $-300 + 15(40)$ or $300.

    c. Subtracting 300 from $15N$ is the same as adding -300 to $15N$.

    d. The input variable is N for the number of lawns and the output variable is P for profit.

8. a. The speed at 0 seconds is 5 m/sec and the speed increases by 9.8 m/sec every second, so the equation is $s = 5 + 9.8t$, where t is the time in seconds and s is the speed in meters per second.

    b. $5 + 9.8(3) = 34.4$ m/sec

    c. Solve the equation $83.4 = 5 + 9.8t$. It would take 8 seconds for the object to reach a speed of 83.4 m/sec.

    d. Possible answer: It doesn't account for air resistance and terminal speed.

9. a. $y = 45 + 0.12 \cdot x$, where x represents the dollar amount his customers spend and y represents his daily income in dollars

    b.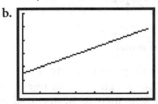

    $[0, 840, 120, 0, 180, 30]$

    c. $y = 45 + 0.12 \cdot 312 = \$82.44$

    d. Solving $45 + 0.12x = 105$ gives $x = 500$. Solving $45 + 0.12x = 120$ gives $x = 625$. So customers would have to spend between $500 and $625 in order for Manny to earn $105 to $120.

10. a. $y = 3.8x$, where x is the number of minutes spent cycling and y is the number of calories burned; $3.8(30) = 114$ calories

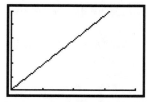

[0, 40, 10, 0, 120, 20]

b. $y = 114 + 6.9x$; $6.9(15)$ or 103.5 calories in Workout 2; 217.5 total calories

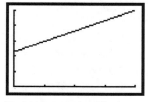

[0, 20, 5, 0, 250, 50]

c. $y = 217.5 + 7.3x$; $7.3(20)$ or 146 calories in Workout 3; 363.5 total calories

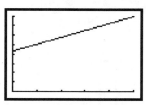

[0, 25, 5, 0, 400, 50]

d. Because Paula burns $30(3.2)$ or 96 calories walking, 96 would be added to the value of a in each equation. In the graphs, each y-intercept (and line) would be shifted up 96 units.

11. Possible answer: Write the percent as one ratio of a proportion. Put the part over the whole in the other ratio.

a. $\frac{8}{n} = \frac{15}{100}$, $n \approx 53.3$ **b.** $\frac{15}{100} = \frac{n}{18.95}$, $n \approx 2.8$

c. $\frac{p}{100} = \frac{326}{64}$, $p \approx 509.4$ **d.** $\frac{10}{100} = \frac{40}{n}$, $n = 400$

12. a. 22.4, 22.6, 22.1

b. About 22.4 miles per gallon

c. $\frac{22.4 \text{ miles}}{1 \text{ gallon}} \cdot 17.1 \text{ gallons} \approx 383$ miles

d. $\frac{1 \text{ gallon}}{22.4 \text{ miles}} \cdot 4230 \text{ miles} \approx 189$ gallons

13. Sample explanation: For each equation, I looked for the graph with a rate of change that matched the recursive rule. I also checked that the starting value of the routine was the y-intercept of the graph.

a. ii **b.** iv **c.** iii **d.** i

14. a. In 10 seconds, he cycled 140 meters, so he is riding at a rate of 14 meters per second.

b.

Time (sec)	Distance (m)
1	14
2	28
3	42
4	56
5	70
6	84
7	98
8	112
9	126
10	140

c. Possible routines:

0 [ENTER], Ans + 14 [ENTER], [ENTER], . . .

{0, 0} [ENTER],

{Ans(1) + 1, Ans(2) + 14} [ENTER], [ENTER], . . .

d. The points lie on a line.

e. $\frac{14 \text{ meters}}{1 \text{ second}} \cdot \frac{60 \text{ seconds}}{1 \text{ minute}} \cdot \frac{60 \text{ minutes}}{1 \text{ hour}}$ $= 50,400$ meters per hour. So Bjarne will ride 50,400 meters, or 50.4 kilometers, in 1 hour.

15. a. The value of the expression is -4 when $y = 5$.

5	
Ans − 8	−3
Ans · 4	−12
Ans/3	−4

b. Start with 8. Multiply by 3 to get 24. Divide by 4 to get 6. Add 8 to get 14. The solution is 14.

LESSON 4.7

EXERCISES

1. a.

Input	Output
20	100
−30	−25
16	90
15	87.5
−12.5	18.75

b.

L₁	L₂
0	−5.2
−8	74.8
24	−245.2
−35	344.8
−5.2	46.8

2. a. $w = -0.8°$ **b.** $w = -32.8°$

c. The wind chill temperature changes by 1.6° for each 1° change in actual temperature.

d. If the actual temperature is 0°, the wind chill temperature is $-52°$.

3. a. The rate is negative, so the line goes from the upper left to the lower right.

b. The rate is zero. The line is horizontal.

c. The rate is positive, so the line goes from the lower left to the upper right.

d. The rate for the speedier walker is greater than the rate for the person walking more slowly, so the graph for the speedier walker is steeper than the graph for the slower walker.

4. Possible answer:

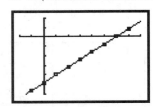

5. a. In each case, the rate of change can be calculated by dividing the difference of two output values by the difference of the corresponding input values.

 i. 3.5   **ii.** 8   **iii.** -1.4

b. The output value corresponding to an input value of 0 is the y-intercept.

 i. -6 **ii.** 1

 iii. 23; the output value for input -3 is 27.2. To get from input -3 to input 0, you add 3, so to get from output value 27.2 to the output value for 0, you must add $3 \cdot -1.4$: output $= 27.2 + 3(-1.4) = 23$.

c. **i.** $y = -6 + 3.5x$

 ii. $y = 1 + 8x$

 iii. $y = 23 - 1.4x$

6. a. The input variable x is the temperature in °F, and the output variable y is the wind chill temperature in °F. (The line is added in 6d.)

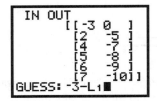

$[-10, 40, 5, -60, 20, 10]$

b. 1.6; for every 5°F increase in temperature, there is an 8°F increase in wind chill temperature, so the rate of change is $\frac{8}{5}$ or 1.6.

c. $y = -48 + 1.6x$

d. Both graphs show linear relationships with identical rates of change and identical y-intercepts. The graph of the points shows wind chill temperatures for temperatures of -5°F, 0°F, 5°F, 10°F, and so on. The graph of the equation shows wind chill temperatures for every temperature.

7. a. $35 + 0.8 \cdot 25 = 55$ miles

b. 50 minutes. One way to find this answer is to write the equation $75 = 35 + 0.8 \cdot x$ and then solve it by working backward, undoing the operations. Another way is to make a calculator graph and trace it to find the x-value corresponding to the y-value 75.

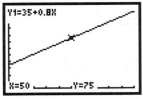

$[0, 100, 10, 0, 120, 10]$

8. Because length times width gives area, 7.3 and x represent the length and width. The number 200 represents the area of the rectangle in square units. The solution is about 27.4 units.

9. a. 990 square units

b. Possible answers:
$$33x = 990; \quad x = \frac{990}{33}; \quad x = \frac{1584 - 594}{33}$$

c. The height is $990 \div 33$, or 30 units.

10. Possible answer:

```
IN OUT
     [[-3  0  ]
      [2  -5 ]
      [4  -7 ]
      [5  -8 ]
      [6  -9 ]
      [7  -10]]
GUESS: -3-L₁■
```

11. a. Start with -15. Subtract -52 (that is, add 52) to get 37. Divide by 1.6 to get 23.125. The solution is 23.125. Check:
$-52 + 1.6(23.125) = -52 + 37 = -15$.

b. Start with 52. Subtract 7 to get 45. Divide by -3 to get -15. The solution is -15. Check:
$7 - 3(-15) = 7 - (-45) = 52$.

12. a.

Hours parked	ABC Parking	Cozy Car	The Corner Lot
1	5	3	15
2	7	6	15
3	9	9	15
4	11	12	15
5	13	15	15
6	15	18	15
7	17	21	15
8	19	24	15
9	21	27	15
10	23	30	15

Discovering Algebra Solutions Manual
©2002 Key Curriculum Press

Possible routines:

ABC Parking: {1, 5} ENTER,
{Ans(1) + 1, Ans(2) + 2} ENTER, ENTER, . . .

Cozy Car: {1, 3} ENTER,
{Ans(1) + 1, Ans(2) + 3} ENTER, ENTER, . . .

The Corner Lot: {1, 15} ENTER,
{Ans(1) + 1, Ans(2) + 0} ENTER, ENTER, . . .

b.

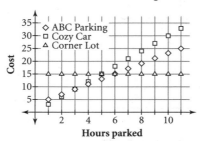

Downtown Parking

c. If you will be parking 3 hours or less, Cozy Car is the best deal. On the graph, its points are below the points for the other lots for "Hours parked" values of 3 or less. If you will be parked between 3 and 5 hours, ABC Parking is the best deal; its points are lowest for that section of the graph. If you plan to park more than 5 hours, The Corner Lot is the best deal.

d. No; because you have to pay for a whole hour for any fraction of the hour, the price of parking does not increase continuously.

13. a. 1 mile is 5280 feet or 1760 yards. 72 lengths is $72 \cdot 25 = 1800$ yards. So 72 lengths is not a mile. The actual number of lengths in a mile is $1760 \div 25$ or 70.4.

b. $\dfrac{1 \text{ mile}}{40 \text{ minutes}} \cdot \dfrac{5280 \text{ feet}}{1 \text{ mile}} \cdot \dfrac{1 \text{ minute}}{60 \text{ seconds}}$

$= 2.2$ feet per second

c. 1 kilometer ≈ 0.62 mile. There are 70.4 lengths in a mile, so there are $0.62 \cdot 70.4$ or about 43.65 lengths in a kilometer.

d. 40 lengths for a kilometer, 64 lengths for a mile

14. a. $y = 6 + 1.25x$

b.

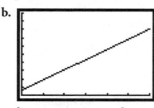

[0, 65, 10, 0, 100, 10]

c. Solve the equation $1.25x + 6 = 60$; $x = 43.2$, so Holly would have to rent 44 movies.

LESSON 4.8

EXERCISES

1. a. $2x = 6$ **b.** $x + 2 = 5$

   c. $2x - 1 = 3$ **d.** $2 = 2x - 3$

2. (*See table at bottom of page.*)

3. a. $0.1x + 12 - 12 = 2.2 - 12$

$$0.1x = -9.8$$

$$x = -98$$

b. $\dfrac{12 + 3.12x}{3} = -100$

$$12 + 3.12x = -300$$

$$12 + 3.12x - 12 = -300 - 12$$

$$3.12x = -312$$

$$x = 100$$

Lesson 4.8, Exercise 2.

Picture	Action taken	Equation
	Original equation.	$2x - 2 = 4$
	Add 2 to both sides.	$2x - 2 + 2 = 4 + 2$
	Remove 0 from left side.	$2x = 6$
	Divide both sides by 2.	$\dfrac{2x}{2} = \dfrac{6}{2}$
	Reduce.	$x = 3$

4. Possible answers:

  a. First multiply both sides by 10. Then subtract 120 from both sides.

  b. After multiplying both sides by 3, multiply both sides by 100. Then subtract 1200 from both sides. Then divide both sides by 312.

5. a.
$$144x = 12 \qquad \text{Original equation.}$$
$$\frac{144x}{144} = \frac{12}{144} \qquad \text{Divide both sides by 144.}$$
$$x = \frac{1}{12} \qquad \text{Divide.}$$

  b.
$$\tfrac{1}{6}x + 2 = 8 \qquad \text{Original equation.}$$
$$\tfrac{1}{6}x + 2 - 2 = 8 - 2 \qquad \text{Subtract 2 from both sides.}$$
$$\tfrac{1}{6}x = 6 \qquad \text{Remove the 0 and simplify.}$$
$$6 \cdot \tfrac{1}{6}x = 6 \cdot 6 \qquad \text{Multiply both sides by 6.}$$
$$x = 36 \qquad \text{Multiply.}$$

6. a. Add 10 to both sides. Divide both sides by 3.

  b. $(5, 5)$

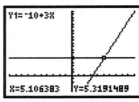

$$[-10, 10, 1, -5, 20, 1]$$

  c. $(5, 15)$

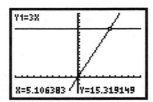

  d. $(5, 5)$

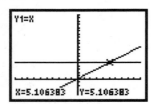

  e. The lines graphed are different in each case, but the x-coordinate of the intersection is the same: $x = 5$. This illustrates that transforming the equation by doing the same thing to both sides does not change the solution.

7. a.
$$4 - 1.2x = 12.4 \qquad \text{Original equation.}$$
$$4 - 4 - 1.2x = 12.4 - 4 \qquad \text{Subtract 4 from both sides.}$$
$$-1.2x = 8.4 \qquad \text{Simplify.}$$
$$\frac{-1.2x}{-1.2} = \frac{8.4}{-1.2} \qquad \text{Divide both sides by } -1.2.$$
$$x = -7 \qquad \text{Simplify.}$$

  b. Start with 12.4. Subtract 4 to get 8.4. Divide by -1.2 to get -7.

  c.

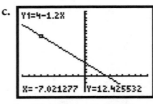

$$[-10, 10, 1, -5, 20, 1]$$

  d.

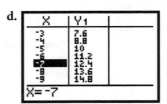

8. a. $x = 7$

Entry	Result
17 ENTER	17
Ans − 3 ENTER	14
Ans/2 ENTER	7

  b. $x = 197.6$

Entry	Result
101.0 ENTER	101.0
Ans − 2.2 ENTER	98.8
Ans/0.5 ENTER	197.6

  c. $x = -305.1$

Entry	Result
2.1 ENTER	2.1
Ans − 307.2 ENTER	−305.1

  d. $x = 0.75$

Entry	Result
7 ENTER	7
Ans/2 ENTER	3.5
Ans − 2 ENTER	1.5
Ans/2 ENTER	0.75

Discovering Algebra Solutions Manual
©2002 Key Curriculum Press

e. $x = 3444$

Entry	Result
0 ENTER	0
Ans + 6.2 ENTER	6.2
Ans * 6.2 ENTER	38.44
Ans − 4 ENTER	34.44
Ans/0.01 ENTER	34.44

9. a. $r = \dfrac{C}{2\pi}$

b. $A = \dfrac{1}{2}(hb)$ Original equation.

     $2A = hb$ Multiply both sides by 2.

     $\dfrac{2A}{b} = h$ Divide both sides by b.

c. $P = 2(l + w)$ Original equation.

     $\dfrac{P}{2} = l + w$ Divide both sides by 2.

     $\dfrac{P}{2} - w = l$ Subtract w from both sides.

d. $s = \dfrac{P}{4}$

e. $t = \dfrac{d}{r}$

f. $A = \dfrac{1}{2}h(a + b)$ Original equation.

     $2A = h(a + b)$ Multiply both sides by 2.

     $\dfrac{2A}{a + b} = h$ Divide both sides by $a + b$.

10. a. $\dfrac{1}{12}$ **b.** 6   **c.** 50   **d.** -2

11. a. $-\dfrac{1}{5}$ **b.** -17 **c.** 2.3   **d.** x

12. a. $y = \dfrac{1}{2}x + 1$. The output value is half the input value plus 1.

x	0	1	2	3	4
y	1	1.5	2	2.5	3

b. $y = -x$. The output value is the additive inverse (or negative) of the input value, or the sum of the input and the output value is 0.

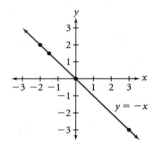

13. $\dfrac{\$90}{2.25} = \dfrac{x}{3}$, $x = \$120$

14. a. 350 ENTER , Ans + 120 ENTER , ENTER , . . .

     b. 38 months

     c. About \$203 per month for 22 months; one way to find this answer is to solve the equation $4800 = 350 + 22x$.

15. Sample calculator graph and equation:

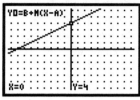

$[-9, 9, 1, -6, 6, 1]$

$y = 4 + \dfrac{1}{2}(x - 0)$

16. a.

Bagel Store		Grocery Store	
Bagels	**Cost ($)**	**Bagels**	**Cost ($)**
13	6.49	6	2.50
26	12.98	12	5.00
39	19.47	18	7.50
52	25.96	24	10.00
65	32.45	30	12.50
78	38.94	36	15.00
		42	17.50
		48	20.00
		54	22.50
		60	25.00

b. The line with the square markers represents the bagel store, and the line with the triangles represents the grocery store.

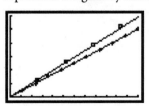

$[0, 2, 6, 0, 30, 5]$

c. Bagel store: $y = \dfrac{6.49}{13}x \approx 0.50x$, where x is the number of bagels and y is the cost

Grocery store: $y = \dfrac{2.50}{6}x \approx 0.42x$, where x is the number of bagels and y is the cost

d. Bagel store: about 50¢ per bagel

Grocery store: about 42¢ per bagel

These costs are the coefficients of x in the equations.

e. The grocery store, because its line is lower

f. Bernie's routine calculates each price by doubling the previous price. It works for the first two baker's dozens, because when you buy two baker's dozens, you are buying twice as much as when you buy one, so the price should double. However, if you buy three baker's dozens, the price should not be double the price for two. A correct routine would be 6.49 ENTER, Ans + 6.49 ENTER, ENTER, . . .

LESSON 4.9

IMPROVING YOUR REASONING SKILLS

Challenge students to explain the pattern. A locker is changed once for each factor of its number. For example, locker 24 is changed by students 1, 2, 3, 4, 6, 8, 12, and 24. So if a locker's number has an even number of factors, it is left closed. If a locker's number has an odd number of factors, it is left open. Those numbers with an odd number of factors are the perfect squares. The lockers left open at the end correspond to perfect squares—1, 4, 9, 16, 25, 36, 49, 64, 81, and 100. Ten lockers are left open.

Perfect squares have an odd number of factors because factors come in pairs: (1, 24), (2, 12), (3, 8), (4, 6). The square root of a perfect square (e.g., 36) is paired with itself: (1, 36), (2, 18), (3, 12), (4, 9), (6, 6). So the number of distinct factors is odd.

CHAPTER 4 Review

EXERCISES

1. a. $-x = 7$ Original equation.

     $x = -7$ Multiply both sides by -1.

b. $4.2 = -2x - 42.6$ Original equation.

     $46.8 = -2x$ Add 42.6 to both sides and remove the zero.

     $-23.4 = x$ Divide both sides by -2.

2. a. Rate: 1; rule: add 1; y-intercept: 3; equation: $y = 3 + x$

b. Rate: 0.01; rule: add 0.01; y-intercept: 0; equation: $y = 0.01x$

c. Rate: 2; rule: add 2; y-intercept: 5; equation: $y = 5 + 2x$

d. Rate: $-\frac{1}{2}$; rule: subtract $\frac{1}{2}$; y-intercept: 3; equation: $y = 3 - \frac{1}{2}x$

3. a. iii   **b.** i   **c.** ii

4. a. $y = -68.99$ **b.** $y = 4289.83$

c. $y = 0.14032$ **d.** $y = 238,723$

5. a. $y = x$ **b.** $y = -3 + x$

c. $y = -4.3 + 2.3x$ **d.** $y = 1$

6. a. 12 ENTER, Ans + 55 ENTER, ENTER, . . .

Possible assumptions: Tom's home is 12 miles closer to Detroit than is Traverse City. He traveled at a constant speed. We are measuring highway distance.

b.

Time (hr)	0	1	2	3	4	5
Distance from Traverse City (mi)	12	67	122	177	232	287

c. 55 miles per hour; Tom traveled 55 miles each additional hour.

7. a. The 0 represents no bookcases sold. The -850 represents a fixed cost, such as startup costs. Ans(1) represents the previously calculated number of bookcases sold. Ans(1) + 1 represents the current number of bookcases sold, one more than the previous number. Ans(2) represents the profit for the previous number of bookcases. Ans(2) + 70 represents the profit for the current number of bookcases—the company makes $70 more profit for each additional bookcase sold.

b. Use the x-axis to represent the number of bookcases sold and the y-axis to represent the profit. Then graph each data pair as a point, such as $(2, -710)$.

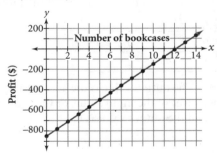

c. A profit is made at 13 bookcases; y becomes positive between 12 and 13 bookcases.

d. The -850, the company's profit if it sells 0 bookcases, is the y-intercept; 70, the amount of profit the company makes for each bookcase sold, is the rate of change; y goes up by $70 each time x goes up by 1 bookcase.

e. No; partial bookcases cannot be sold.

8. a. 3

b.

Sections	3	4	30	50
Logs	10	13	91	151

c. 4 $\boxed{\text{ENTER}}$, Ans + 3 $\boxed{\text{ENTER}}$, $\boxed{\text{ENTER}}$, . . .

d. 216 meters; one way to find this answer is to use the routine until you get a result of 217. The number of times you pressed $\boxed{\text{ENTER}}$, 72, is the number of fence sections. Because each section is 3 meters long, the length of the fence would be 72 · 3 or 216 meters.

9. a. 4 seconds

b. Away; the distance is increasing.

c. About 0.5 meter

d. $\frac{2.9 - 0.5}{4} = 0.6$ meter per second

e. $\frac{5.5 \text{ meters}}{0.6 \text{ meter/second}} = 9.1\overline{6}$ seconds; approximately 9 seconds

f. The graph is a straight line.

10. a. Let v represent the value in dollars and y represent the number of years: $v = 5400 - 525y$.

b. The rate of change is -525. In each additional year, the value of the computer system decreases by \$525.

c. The y-intercept is 5400. The original value of the computer system is \$5400.

d. By solving $5400 - 525y = 0$, you'll find that the x-intercept is about 10.3. This means that the computer system no longer has value after approximately 10.3 years.

11. a. $L_2 = -5.7 + 2.3 \cdot L_1$ **b.** $L_2 = -5 - 8 \cdot L_1$

c. $L_2 = 12 + 0.5 \cdot L_1$

12. a. $50 = 7.7t$; $t = \frac{50}{7.7} \approx 6.5$ seconds

b. $50 = 5 + 6.5t$; $t = \frac{50 - 5}{6.5} \approx 6.9$ seconds

c. Andrei wins. When Andrei finishes, his younger brother is $50 - (5 + 6.5(6.5)) \approx 2.8$ meters from the finish line.

13. a. $x = 3.5$. Possible methods:

You can undo the operations: Start with -5. Divide by 2 to get -2.5. Add 6 to get 3.5.

Or you can use the balance method:

$2(x - 6) = -5$	Original equation.
$x - 6 = -2.5$	Divide both sides by 2 and simplify.
$x = 3.5$	Add 6 to both sides and simplify.

b. $2(3.5 - 6) = 2(-2.5) = -5$

14. a. $x = 4.5$ **b.** $x = -4.1\overline{3}$ **c.** $x = 0.\overline{6}$

d. $x = 12.8$ **e.** $x = 6.\overline{3}$

15. a. $t \approx -1.2°$ **b.** $t \approx 38.1°$ **c.** $t \approx 10.9°$

d. $t \approx 27.4°$

TAKE ANOTHER LOOK

The distance between isometric lines tells the rate of change on the contour map. Closer lines indicate a greater rate of change. Rate of change in the graph sketch is the ratio $\frac{change\ in\ speed}{change\ in\ time}$. In the contour map, height is measured along the line or estimated between lines, and distance (projected on the earth "plane," not distance on the face of a slope) is true in all directions—but a scale-factor legend would be needed. On the graph sketch, because time is on the horizontal axis and speed is on the vertical axis, distance covered is the product of the coordinates. A scale on each axis would be needed. Here is a possible time-distance graph, with the time-speed graph shown for comparison.

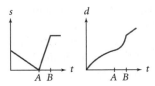

IMPROVING YOUR REASONING SKILLS

The plants are not growing at the same rate. Plant 1 is growing at a rate of 20 ÷ 6 or about 3.3 cm per day. Plant 2 is growing at a rate of 7 ÷ 6 or about 1.2 cm per day. Plant 3 is growing at a rate of 30 ÷ 6 or 5 cm per day.

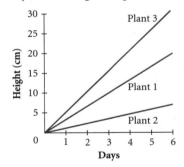

CHAPTER 5

LESSON 5.1

EXERCISES

1. The order of subtraction may vary.

a. $\frac{5 - 1}{3 - 1} = \frac{4}{2} = 2$ **b.** $\frac{5 - 3}{4 - 1} = \frac{2}{3}$

c. $\frac{6 - 2}{1 - 4} = \frac{4}{-3} = -\frac{4}{3}$

2. a. $Slope = \frac{change\ in\ y}{change\ in\ x} = \frac{7 - 4}{4 - 2} = \frac{3}{2} = 1.5$. To find another point on the line, start with a known point and add $change\ in\ x$ to the x-coordinate and $change\ in\ y$ to the y-coordinate. For example, if you start with $(4, 7)$, you get $(4 + $ *change in x*, $7 + $ *change in y*$) = (4 + 2, 7 + 3) = (6, 10)$. So, $(6, 10)$ is on the line.

b. *Slope* $= \frac{change\ in\ y}{change\ in\ x} = \frac{5 - (-1)}{2 - 6} = \frac{6}{-4} = \frac{3}{-2} = -1.5$. Starting with $(6, -1)$, another point on the line is $(6 + $ *change in x*$, -1 + $ *change in y*$)$ $= (6 + (-2), -1 + 3) = (4, 2)$.

c. *Slope* $= \frac{change\ in\ y}{change\ in\ x} = \frac{4 - 4}{8 - (-2)} = 0$. The line is a horizontal line through $y = 4$, so any point with a y-coordinate of 4 is on the line.

d. *Slope* $= \frac{12 - (-3)}{9 - 1} = \frac{15}{8} = 1.875$. Points will vary. One possible point is $(17, 27)$.

3. a. One way to find other points on the line is to start with $(0, 4)$ and repeatedly add 1 (the change in x) to the x-coordinate and 3 (the change in y) to the y-coordinate. Or, since $\frac{3}{1} = \frac{-3}{-1}$, you can add -1 to the x-coordinate and -3 to the y-coordinate. Two possible points are $(1, 7)$ and $(-1, 1)$.

b. One way to find other points on the line is to start with $(2, 8)$ and repeatedly add 1 to the x-coordinate and -5 to the y-coordinate. Or, because $-5 = \frac{5}{-1}$, you can also add -1 to the x-coordinate and 5 to the y-coordinate. Two possible points are $(3, 3)$ and $(1, 13)$.

c. Sample answer: $(12, 3), (4, 9)$

d. Sample answer: $(6, 7.2), (4, 6.8)$

4. Answers will vary.

5. a. **i.** The x-values don't change, so the slope is undefined.

ii. The y-values decrease as the x-values increase, so the slope is negative.

iii. The y-values don't change, so the slope is 0.

iv. The y-values increase as the x-values increase, so the slope is positive.

b. **i.** Using the points $(4, 0)$ and $(4, 3)$, we find the slope to be $\frac{3 - 0}{4 - 4} = \frac{3}{0}$. Because you can't divide by 0, the slope is undefined.

ii. Using the points $(1, 3)$ and $(4, -3)$, we find the slope to be $\frac{-3 - 3}{4 - 1} = \frac{-6}{3} = -2$.

iii. Using the points $(-4, -5)$ and $(-3, -5)$, we find the slope to be $\frac{-5 - (-5)}{-3 - (-4)} = \frac{-5 + 5}{-3 + 4} = \frac{0}{1} = 0$.

iv. Using the points $(0, -2)$ and $(4, 1)$, we find the slope to be $\frac{1 - (-2)}{4 - 0} = \frac{3}{4}$.

c. **i.** $x = 4$

ii. $y = 5 - 2x$

iii. $y = -5$

iv. $y = -2 + \frac{3}{4}x$.

6. a. The lines are parallel, so they have the same slope. The y-intercepts are different.

b. Line b matches the equation because it has a y-intercept of -3.

c. Line a has a y-intercept of 1 and a slope of $\frac{2}{5}$, so its equation is $y = 1 + \frac{2}{5}x$.

d. The slope, $\frac{2}{5}$, is the same in each equation. The y-intercepts, -3 and 1, are different.

7. a. Use the slope to move backward from $(4, 16.75)$: $(4 - 1, 16.75 - 2.95) = (3, 13.80)$, or $13.80 for 3 hours; $(3 - 1, 13.80 - 2.95) = (2, 10.85)$, or $10.85 for 2 hours

b. Continuing the process in 7a leads to $(0, 4.95)$, or 4.95 for 0 hours. This is the flat monthly rate for Hector's Internet service.

c. $y = 4.95 + 2.95x$, where x is time in hours and y is total fee in dollars.

d. Substitute 28 for x and solve for y: $y = 4.95 + 2.95(28) = 87.55$. The total fee for 28 hours is $87.55.

8. a. The slope between any two points is 30, so the points are on the same line.

b. m/min; the slope, 30, is the number of meters the balloon rises every minute.

c. The y-intercept (the height of the balloon at 0 minutes) is 14 and the slope is 30, so the equation is $y = 14 + 30x$.

d. Substitute 8 for x: $y = 14 + 30(8) = 14 + 240 = 254$. After 8 minutes, the balloon will be 254 meters high.

e. Solve $500 = 14 + 30x$ to find the time when the balloon reaches 500 meters:

$$500 = 14 + 30x$$
$$500 - 14 = 14 - 14 + 30x$$
$$486 = 30x$$
$$\frac{486}{30} = \frac{30x}{30}$$
$$16.2 = x$$

The balloon reaches 500 m in 16.2 minutes, so it is at a height of 500 m or less between 0 and 16.2 minutes.

9. Because the line decreases from left to right, the slope is $-\frac{a}{c}$. The y-intercept is e. So the equation is $y = e - \frac{a}{c}x$, $y = e + \frac{-a}{c}x$, or $y = e + \frac{a}{-c}x$.

10. a. Slope triangles will vary. Here is one example:

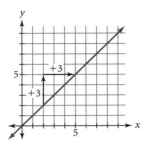

The change in y and the change in x are the same for any slope triangle.

b. Lines will vary. Here is one example:

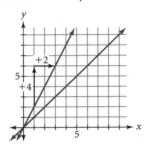

For a steeper line, the change in y is greater than the change in x. Numerically, the slope is greater than 1.

c. Lines will vary. Here is one example:

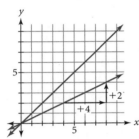

For a less steep line, the change in x is greater than the change in y. Numerically, the slope is between 0 and 1.

d. The line will decrease from left to right because the slope is negative. The line would be very steep because 15 is significantly greater than 1.

11. a. **i.** Line 2 is a better choice. A majority of points are closer to line 2 than to line 1.

ii. Either line 3 or line 4 is a reasonable fit.

b. **i.** Answers will vary but should show the general direction of the points and have about as many points above the line as below. Here is one possible line:

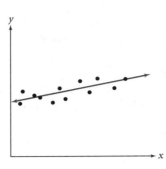

ii. The points show no linear pattern, so a line is not an appropriate model.

c. Answers will vary. The line should reflect the direction of the data, and about the same number of points should be above the line as below it.

12. a. $3x - 6$ **b.** $-4x + 20$ **c.** $-2x - 16$

13. Answers will vary. The sum of the ages must be 50, and the middle value must be 6. One possible set of ages is $\{3, 3, 6, 16, 22\}$.

14. a. $L_2 = 2.5(L_1 + 14)$; $\{27.5, 32.5, 40, 55, 60\}$

b. $L_2 = 2.5L_1 + 35$; yes, the results are the same.

c. $L_3 = \dfrac{(L_2 - 35)}{2.5}$ or $L_3 = \dfrac{L_2}{2.5} - 14$

15. a. 85%   **b.** 150%   **c.** 6.5%   **d.** 107%

LESSON 5.2

EXERCISES

1. a. No; although this line goes through four points, too many points are below the line.

b. No; although the slope of the line shows the general direction of the data, too many points are below the line.

c. Yes; about the same number of points is above the line as below the line, and the slope of the line shows the general direction of the data.

d. No; although the same number of points is above and below the line, the slope of the line doesn't show the direction of the data very well.

2. Vertical; $x = 2$

3. a. $y = -2 + \frac{2}{3}x$ **b.** $y = 2 - \frac{2}{3}x$

c. $y = -2 - 0.4x$ or $y = -2 - \frac{2}{5}x$

d. $y = 3$

4. a. There is a linear pattern.

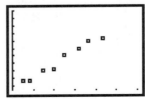

$[0, 36, 6, 120, 1200, 100]$

b. Answers will vary. Using the points (8, 376) and (19, 684), we find the slope to be 28.

c. The slope represents the number of quarters Penny saves per month.

d. $y = 28x$; the line needs to move up (the y-intercept needs to increase).

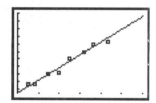

[0, 36, 6, 150, 1200, 50]

e. Answers will vary. A possible equation is $y = 152 + 28x$.

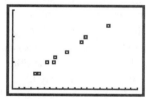

f. The y-intercept represents the number of quarters Penny's grandmother gave her.

g. Answers depend on the line students find. On her 18th birthday, Penny will have been saving for 36 months. Using the equation $y = 152 + 28x$, she will have $152 + 28(36)$ or 1160 quarters. The prediction may not be reliable because it extrapolates 10 months beyond the data.

5. a. The number of representatives depends on the population.

b. Let x represent the population in millions, and let y represent the number of representatives.

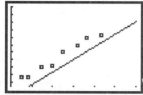

[0, 10, 0.5, 0, 15, 5]

c. Answers will vary. Two possible points are (3.3, 5) and (7.7, 12). The slope between these points is approximately 1.6. The equation $y = 1.6x$ appears to fit the data with a y-intercept of 0. The slope represents the number of representatives per 1 million people. The y-intercept means that a state with no population would have no representatives.

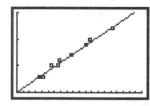

d. Answers depend on the equation students find in 10c. The equation $y = 1.6x$ gives $y = 1.6(33) \approx 52.8$ or 53 representatives. On July 19, 2000, California had 52 representatives.

e. Answers depend on the equation students find in 10c. Using $y = 1.6x$, estimate the population by solving $8 = 1.6x$. The solution is 5, so the estimated population of Minnesota is 5 million. According to census projections, the estimated population of Minnesota in July 1999 was 4.8 million.

f. A direct variation is a reasonable model because a state with no population would have no representatives, so the line should go through the origin.

6. a. No; each state has two senators regardless of its population.

b. $y = 2$, where x represents population in millions and y represents the number of senators

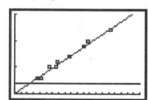

c. The graph is a horizontal line because there's no change in y, the number of senators, as x, the state population, changes.

7. a. Slope $= \dfrac{y_2 - y_1}{x_2 - x_1} = \dfrac{4.4 - 3.4}{4.5 - 2}$
$= 0.4$ meter per second

b. 2.6 meters. Possible explanation: As the time decreases by 1 second, the distance decreases by 0.4 meter. So after 1 second she is $3.4 - 0.4$ or 3 meters away, and after 0 seconds she is $3 - 0.4$ or 2.6 meters away.

c. $y = 2.6 + 0.4x$

8. a. The slope is negative because the distance decreases as the time increases.

b. The y-intercept represents the start distance for the walk. The x-intercept represents the elapsed time when the walker reaches the sensor.

c. Answers will vary. Quadrant II could indicate walking before you started timing. Quadrant IV could indicate that the walker walks past you (the distances behind you are considered negative).

9. a. Answers will vary. Sample answer: $y = -8 + 4x$

  b. Answers will vary. Sample answer: $y = -2x$

  c. $y = 6 + x$

  d. $y = 10$

10. a. All the lines have a slope of 3, so they are all parallel.

  b. All the lines cross the y-axis at 5; they radiate around the point $(0, 5)$.

  c. All the lines are parallel to the x-axis, or horizontal.

  d. All the lines are parallel to the y-axis, or vertical.

11. a. Neither; the x- and y-values do not have a constant product or a constant ratio.

  b. Inverse variation; the x- and y-values have a constant product. The equation is $y = \frac{100}{x}$.

  c. Direct variation; the x- and y-values have a constant ratio. The equation is $y = -2.5x$.

  d. Direct variation; the x- and y-values have a constant ratio. The equation is $y = \frac{1}{13}x$.

12. a. $8 - 12m = 17$ **b.** $2r + 7 = -24$

     $-12m = 9$ $2r = -31$

       $m = -0.75$ $r = -15.5$

  c. $-6 - 3w = 42$

     $-3w = 48$

       $w = -16$

13. a. Mean: $24.8\overline{6}$; median: 21

  b. Mean: 44.9; median: 40

  c. Mean: approximately 140.1; median: 145

  d. Mean: 85.75; median: 86.5

IMPROVING YOUR VISUAL THINKING SKILLS

The second abacus shows 84. The third shows 71,545. 27,059 would look like this:

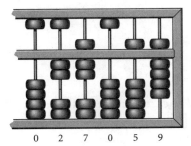

LESSON 5.3

EXERCISES

1. a. The equation $y = 3 + 4(x - 5)$ is in point-slope form $y = y_1 + m(x - x_1)$, where m is the slope and (x_1, y_1) is a point on the line. So the slope is 4, and $(5, 3)$ is a point on the line.

  b. Slope 2; point $(-3.1, 1.9)$

  c. Slope -3.47; point $(7, -2)$

  d. Slope -1.38; point $(2.5, 5)$

2. a. Point-slope form is $y = y_1 + m(x - x_1)$, where m is the slope and (x_1, y_1) is the point. Using slope 3 and point $(2, 5)$, we get the equation $y = 5 + 3(x - 2)$.

  b. $y = -4 - 5(x - 1)$

3. a. $\dfrac{13 - (-1)}{5 - (-2)} = \dfrac{14}{7} = 2$

  b. $y = -1 + 2(x + 2)$

  c. $y = 13 + 2(x - 5)$

  d. The graphs coincide, and the tables are identical.

4. a. Find the rate of change for any pair of data values. For example, if we use $(5, -31)$ and $(10, -24)$, the slope is $\dfrac{-24 - (-31)}{10 - 5} = \dfrac{7}{5} = 1.4$.

  b. Answers will vary. Using the point $(5, -31)$, we get the equation $y = -31 + 1.4(x - 5)$.

  c. Answers will vary. Using the point $(10, -24)$, we get the equation $y = -24 + 1.4(x - 10)$.

  d. The graphs coincide, and the tables are identical.

  e. To find the wind chill for a temperature of 0°F, you can substitute 0 into the equation. The wind chill is -38°F. This is the graph's y-intercept.

5. Answers will vary.

6. Segment a has slope 1. Two points on the segment are $(0, 0.5)$ and $(2, 2.5)$, so two possible equations are $y = 0.5 + 1(x - 0)$ and $y = 2.5 + 1(x - 2)$.

Segment b: $y = 2.5 - 0.75(x - 2)$ or $y = 1 - 0.75(x - 4)$

Segment c: $y = 1 + 1(x - 4)$ or $y = 3 + 1(x - 6)$

7. a. $\overline{AD}$: $y = 2 + 0.2(x + 1)$ or $y = 3 + 0.2(x - 4)$

     $\overline{BC}$: $y = -2 + 0.2(x + 3)$ or $y = -1 + 0.2(x - 2)$

     $\overline{AB}$: $y = 2 + 2(x + 1)$ or $y = -2 + 2(x + 3)$

     $\overline{DC}$: $y = 3 + 2(x - 4)$ or $y = -1 + 2(x - 2)$

  b. The slopes are the same; the coordinates of the points are different.

  c. Quadrilateral $ABCD$ appears to be a parallelogram. In 7b, we found that opposite sides have the same slope, which means they are parallel.

8. a. The data appear linear.

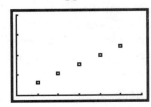

$[0, 6, 1, 0, 2, 0.5]$

b. The slope, $0.21 per ounce, is the cost for each additional ounce after the first.

c. Answers will vary; Using the point $(1, 0.34)$, we get the equation $y = 0.34 + 0.21(x - 1)$.

d. $y = 0.34 + 0.21(10 - 1) = 0.34 + 0.21(9)$ $= 0.34 + 1.89 = 2.23$. So the cost of mailing a 10-oz letter is $2.23.

e. The rates are given for weights not exceeding the given weights, so a package weighing 3.5 oz would cost the same as a 4-oz package, or $0.97. A package weighing 9.1 oz would cost the same as a 10-oz package, or $2.23.

f. No; a continuous line includes points whose x-values are not whole numbers and whose y-values are not possible rates.

9. a. The data fall in a linear pattern.

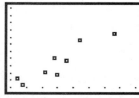

$[10, 50, 5, 250, 800, 50]$

b. Answers will vary. Using the points $(21, 360)$ and $(43, 620)$, we get the equation $y = 620 + 11.82(x - 43)$.

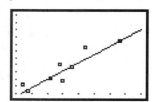

c. Answers will vary. The model $y = 620 + 11.82(x - 43)$ predicts that the sandwich will have 490 calories.

d. Answers will vary. Compared to the graph of $y = 620 + 11.82(x - 43)$, the point lies above the line. If a point lies above the line, then it has more calories than the model predicts.

e. Answers will vary. If we use $y = 620 + 11.82(x - 43)$ as a model, four points are above the line, two are on the line, and two are below the line.

f. Answers will vary.

g. Answers will vary. The equation $y = 620 + 11.82(x - 43)$ predicts that the sandwich will have 112 calories. This makes sense because not all calories in food come from fat, so fat-free foods do have calories.

10. a. $y = 152 + 2.4(x - 1980)$ or $y = 164 + 2.4(x - 1985)$

b. and **c.**

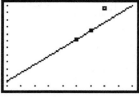

$[1955, 2000, 5, 85, 200, 10]$

The point $(1990, 196)$ is not very close to the line, so the line isn't a very good model for the data.

d.

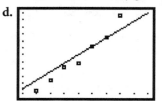

e. The data are generally linear, but the line doesn't fit it very well. A line with a steeper slope would be a better fit.

f. Answers will vary. The model $y = 152 + 3.4(x - 1980)$ gives a reasonable fit.

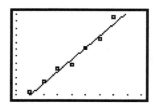

g. Answers will vary. The model $y = 152 + 3.4(x - 1980)$ predicts that 220 million tons of trash were produced in 2000.

11. a. Because volume and temperature are directly proportional, their ratio is constant. So $\frac{280}{3.5} = \frac{330}{x}$; $x = 4.125$, so the volume of gas is 4.125 liters.

b. 180 K; you can find this by solving the proportion $\frac{280}{3.5} = \frac{x}{2.25}$.

12. Possible answers:

a. $1(2 - 3)(4 - 5) = 1$

b. $1 - (2 - 3) - (4 - 5) = 3$

c. $(1 - 2)(3 - 4)5 = 5$

13. a. The slope is -1. The change in x from the given point $(3, 1)$ to $(5, \square)$ is 2. $\frac{Change\ in\ y}{Change\ in\ x} = -1$, so the change in y must be -2. The point is $(5, 1 - 2)$ or $(5, -1)$.

b. The slope is undefined. The line is vertical. So the x-coordinate of every point on the line is 2. The point is $(2, 3)$.

c. The slope is $-\frac{5}{2}$. The change in y from the given point $(-2, 2)$ to $(\square, -3)$ is -5, so the change in x must be 2. The point is $(-2 + 2, -3)$ or $(0, -3)$.

Discovering Algebra Solutions Manual
©2002 Key Curriculum Press

EXERCISES

1. a. Rewrite the first expression:
$3 - 3(x + 4) = 3 - 3x - 12 = -3x - 9$.
The expressions are not equivalent. The second
expression needs to be changed to $-3x - 9$.

  b. Rewrite the first expression:
  $5 + 2(x - 2) = 5 + 2x - 4 = 2x + 1$.
  The expressions are equivalent.

  c. Rewrite the second expression:
  $2 + 5(x - 1) = 2 + 5x - 5 = 5x - 3$.
  The expressions are equivalent.

  d. The second expression is equivalent to $-2x + 8$, so
  the expressions are not equivalent. You can change
  the second expression to $-2(x + 4)$ or $2(-x - 4)$.

2. a. $y = 14 + 3(x - 5)$ Original equation.

   $y = 14 + 3x - 15$ Distribute the 3.

   $y = -1 + 3x$ Add.

  b. $y = -5 - 2(x + 5)$ Original equation.

   $y = -5 - 2x - 10$ Distribute the -2.

   $y = -15 - 2x$ Subtract.

  c. $6x + 2y = 24$

   $6x - 6x + 2y = 24 - 6x$ Subtract $6x$ from both
   sides.

   $2y = 24 - 6x$ Subtract.

   $\dfrac{2y}{2} = \dfrac{24 - 6x}{2}$ Divide both sides by 2.

   $y = 12 - 3x$ Divide.

3. a. $3x = 12$ Original equation.

   $x = 4$ Division property.

  b. $-x - 45 = 47$ Original equation.

   $-x = 92$ Addition property.

   $x = -92$ Multiplication property.

  c. $x + 15 = 8$ Original equation.

   $x = -7$ Subtraction property.

  d. $\dfrac{x}{4} = 28$ Original equation.

   $x = 112$ Multiplication property.

4. a. $35 = 3(x + 8)$ Original equation.

   $35 = 3x + 24$ Distributive property.

   $11 = 3x$ Subtraction property.

   $3\frac{2}{3} = x$ Division property.

b. $\dfrac{15 - 3}{x - 4} = 10$ Original equation.

   $12 = 10(x - 4)$ Multiplication property.

   $12 = 10x - 40$ Distributive property.

   $52 = 10x$ Addition property.

   $5.2 = x$ Division property.

  c. $4(2x - 5) - 12 = 16$ Original equation.

   $8x - 20 - 12 = 16$ Distributive property.

   $8x - 32 = 16$ Subtract.

   $8x = 48$ Addition property.

   $x = 6$ Division property.

5. a. $(-5, 25)$

  b. Solve the equation $15 = 25 - 2(x + 5)$:

   $15 = 25 - 2(x + 5)$

   $-10 = -2(x + 5)$

   $-10 = -2x - 10$

   $0 = -2x$

   $0 = x$

6. a. $3(x - 4)$ **b.** $-5(x - 4)$ **c.** $4(8 + x)$
   d. $-7(x + 4)$

7. a. $y = 5(2 + x)$ **b.** $y = 5(x + 2)$

  c. The y_1-value is missing, which means it is zero;
  $y = 0 + 5(x + 2)$.

  d. $(-2, 0)$; this is the x-intercept.

8. a. Equations i and ii are equivalent. You can verify
  this by rewriting them in intercept form. Both
  equations are equivalent to $y = 24 - 2x$.

  b. Equations i and iii are equivalent. Both are
  equivalent to $y = -5 + 4x$.

  c. Equations ii and iii are equivalent. Both are
  equivalent to $y = 49 + 5x$.

  d. Equations i and iii are equivalent. Both are
  equivalent to $y = 14 + 6x$.

9. a. $x = 2$; the point $(2, 0)$ is the x-intercept.

  b. $y = 3$; the point $(0, 3)$ is the y-intercept.

  c.

d. The slope is $-\frac{3}{2}$. The equation is $y = 3 - \frac{3}{2}x$.

e.
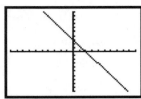

$[-10, 10, 1, -10, 10, 1]$

The two lines are the same, so the equations are equivalent.

f.

$3x + 2y = 6$	Original equation.
$2y = 6 - 3x$	Subtract $3x$ from both sides.
$y = 3 - \frac{3}{2}x$	Divide both sides by 2.

10. a. -4.4 **b.** $y = -4.4 - 4.2(x - 2)$

c. -0.5 **d.** $y = 6.1 - 4.2(x + 0.5)$

e. Answers will vary. You could rewrite each equation in slope-intercept form. Both are equivalent to $y = 4 - 4.2x$.

11. a. The slope is $\frac{17.75 - 15.20}{23 - 20} = 0.85$. Using the point $(20, 15.20)$, we get the equation $y = 15.20 + 0.85(x - 20)$.

b. $y = 15.20 + 0.85(25 - 20)$; $19.45

c. The equation is used to model the bill only when she is logged on for more than 15 hours. Substituting 15 for x gives the flat rate of $10.95 for all amounts of time less than 15 hours.

d. Solve $23.70 = 15.20 + 0.85(x - 20)$: $x = 30$. So Dorine was logged on for 30 hours.

12. a. Answers will vary depending on which point students use. Possible equations are $y = 568 + 4.6(x - 5)$, $y = 591 + 4.6(x - 10)$, $y = 614 + 4.6(x - 15)$, and $y = 637 + 4.6(x - 20)$.

b. $y = 545 + 4.6x$

c. The slope represents the number of calories burned per minute. The y-intercept represents the number of calories Avery burned from the time she went to sleep Friday night until she starting hiking.

d. Yes; it is equivalent to the slope-intercept equation $y = 545 + 4.6x$.

e. The point $(60, 821)$ tells you that if Avery hikes for 60 minutes, she will have burned a total of 821 calories since she went to sleep Friday night.

13. a. Answers will vary.

b. Germany had the largest increase ($25.91). Mexico had the smallest increase ($0.04).

c.
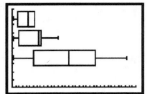

$[0, 35, 1, 0, 10, 1]$

From top to bottom, the plots represent 1975, 1985, and 1995. Students should notice that there is a much larger range in the data for 1995 than for 1975. The lowest compensation has not changed much, while the highest has increased considerably. The median compensation has increased.

14. a. This graph shows the slope triangles for 14a and 14b:

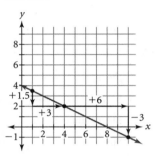

$$\frac{change\ in\ y}{change\ in\ x} = \frac{-1.5}{3} = -0.5$$

b. $\frac{change\ in\ y}{change\ in\ x} = \frac{-3}{6} = -0.5$

c. The slope triangles are similar, and the slopes are equal.

d. You would get a larger similar triangle and the same slope.

15. $z = \frac{3.8 + 5.4}{0.2} - 6.2$; $z = 39.8$

IMPROVING YOUR GEOMETRY SKILLS

1.

2. This is not possible; if the slope of one leg is negative, the slope of the other leg is the negative reciprocal, which must be positive.

3.
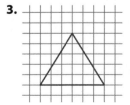

4.

5.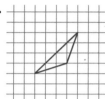

6.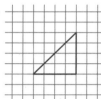

7. This is not possible; the sides would be parallel and therefore would never meet. The sides of a triangle must meet at a vertex.

LESSON 5.5

EXERCISES

1. a. $y = 1 + 2(x - 1)$ or $y = 5 + 2(x - 3)$

   b. $y = 3 + \frac{2}{3}(x - 1)$ or $y = 5 + \frac{2}{3}(x - 4)$

   c. $y = 6 - \frac{4}{3}(x - 1)$ or $y = 2 - \frac{4}{3}(x - 4)$

2. Estimates will vary. The answers show the equations in intercept form.

   a. $y = -1 + 2x$

   b. $y = \frac{7}{3} + \frac{2}{3}x$ or $y = 2.\overline{3} + 0.\overline{6}x$

   c. $y = \frac{22}{3} - \frac{4}{3}x$ or $y = 7.\overline{3} - 1.\overline{3}x$

3. a. 3   **b.** -4 **c.** 6

   The x-intercept of $y = b(x - x_2)$ is x_2.

4. a. Answers will vary. Using the points $(1982, 341)$ and $(1996, 362)$ gives the equation $y = 341 + 1.5(x - 1982)$, where x is the year and y is the concentration of CO_2 in ppm.

b. Answers will vary, but all graphs should look approximately like this:

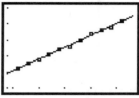

[1970, 2000, 5, 325, 375, 5]

c. Answers will vary. The equation $y = 341 + 1.5(x - 1982)$ gives 398 ppm.

d. Answers will vary. Using the equation in 4a gives an x-intercept of about 1755. It represents the year when the concentration of CO_2 would have been 0 ppm. This does not make sense because plants depend on CO_2, so there has been some concentration of CO_2 as long as there have been plants.

5. a.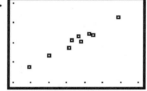

[10, 45, 5, 40, 120, 10]

b. Answers will vary. Using the points $(20, 67)$ and $(31.2, 88.6)$ gives a slope of approximately 1.9, and a possible equation is $y = 67 + 1.9(x - 20)$.

c. One possible answer:

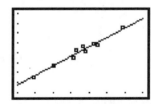

d. The slope is $\frac{212 - 32}{100 - 0}$ or 1.8. The possible equations are $y = 32 + 1.8(x - 0)$ and $y = 212 + 1.8(x - 100)$.

e. Answers will vary. The sample equation in 5b gives $y = 29 + 1.9x$. The equations in 5d both give $y = 32 + 1.8x$. The equations are not equivalent.

f. It is possible, but the difference could also be the result of measurement error or faulty procedures.

6. a.

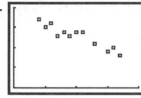

[0, 20, 5, 0, 20, 5]

b. Answers will vary. Using (13, 11) and (8, 14), we get the equation $y = 11 - 0.6(x - 13)$ or $y = 14 - 0.6(x - 8)$.

c. Answers will vary. Here is the graph of the equation in 6b:

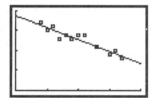

d. Answers will vary. Using $y = 11 - 0.6(x - 13)$ gives a concentration of dissolved oxygen of 17.6 ppm.

e. Answers will vary. Using $y = 11 - 0.6(x - 13)$ gives a temperature of 13°C.

7. a. $y = 3 + 2(x - 7)$ Original equation.

$y = 3 + 2x - 14$ Apply the distributive property.

$y = -11 + 2x$ Subtract.

b. $y = -11 + 41x + 28$ Original equation.

$y = 17 + 41x$ Add.

c. $y = 5 - 6(x - 9)$ Original equation.

$y = 5 - 6x + 54$ Apply the distributive property.

$y = 59 - 6x$ Add.

d. $y = 4(7 - x) - 19$ Original equation.

$y = 28 - 4x - 19$ Apply the distributive property.

$y = 9 - 4x$ Subtract.

8. a. 1, 7, 21, 45, 48

b. 30, 33, 40, 47, 74

c. 107, 120, 145, 153.5, 179

d. 75, 82, 86.5, 90.5, 94

9. a. The number of biscuits decreases by 3 each day, so the slope is -3.

b. Using the point (10, 106) and slope -3, we find the equation $y = 106 - 3(x - 10)$.

c. The box will be empty on the 46th day. You can find this by solving the equation

$y = 106 - 3(x - 10)$ or by reasoning that it will take 36 days to eat the 106 cookies that remain in the box. Because there were 106 cookies on the 10th day, it takes a total of $36 + 10$ or 46 days to finish the box.

d. The y-intercept, 136, is the number of cookies that were in the box when it was new.

10. a. Start with a number. Subtract 11. Divide by 9. Add 1. Multiply by 9. Add 2. The result will be your original number.

b. Check student work.

c. Dividing by 9 and multiplying by 9 undo each other. Adding 2 undoes the subtraction of 2 that results inside the parentheses from $-11 + 9(1)$.

LESSON 5.6

EXERCISES

1. a. 166, 405, 623, 1052, 1483

b. 204, 514, 756, 1194, 1991

c.

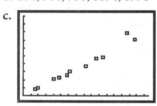

[0, 1650, 100, 0, 2500, 250]

d. The slope will be positive because as the flying distance increases so does the driving distance.

e. To make the rectangle, draw the vertical lines $x = 405$ and $x = 1052$, and the horizontal lines $y = 514$ and $y = 1194$. The Q-points are (405, 514) and (1052, 1194).

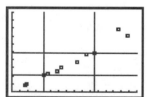

f. The slope is approximately 1.05. The equation is $y = 1194 + 1.05(x - 1052)$ or $y = 514 + 1.05(x - 405)$.

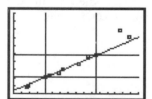

Discovering Algebra Solutions Manual
©2002 Key Curriculum Press

g. About 1054 miles; you can find this by substituting 919 for x in the equation or by tracing the graph.

h. About 535 miles; you can find this by substituting 651 for y in the equation and solving for x or by tracing the graph.

2. a. $y = 10 + 0.5(32 - 28)$; 12 grams of saturated fat

b. $15 = 10 + 0.5(x - 28)$

$5 = 0.5x - 14$

$19 = 0.5x$

$38 = x$; 38 grams of fat

3. For the data set in 3a, the slope will be positive, and you will choose the lower-left and upper-right corners of the rectangle for the Q-points. For the data set in 3b, the slope will be negative, and you will choose the upper-left and lower-right corners of the rectangle.

4. a. The five-number summary for *years* is 1952, 1962, 1974, 1986, 1996. The five-number summary for *time* is 43.5, 43.9, 44.5, 45, 46.7. The Q-points are (1962, 45) and (1986, 43.9). The slope of the line between these two points is approximately -0.056. The possible equations are
$y = 45 - 0.056(x - 1962)$ and
$y = 43.9 - 0.056(x - 1986)$.

b.

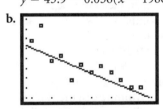

[1950, 2000, 8, 43, 47, 0.5]

c. The slope means that each time the year increases by 1, the winning time decreases by 0.056 second.

d. The prediction is 42.9 or 43.1 sec (depending on the equation the student uses). This value is about 1 second faster than his actual winning time.

e. Answers will vary. However, there is a physical limit to how fast a person can run. Eventually the times will have to level off.

5. Answers will vary. Q1 and Q3 for the x-values should be 4 and 12, respectively, and Q1 and Q3 for the y-values should be 28 and 47, respectively. If we create a data set with seven values, the quartiles will be the second and sixth values. The x-values can be 2, 4, 6, 8, 10, 12, 14. The y-values can be 22, 28, 30, 35, 42, 47, 53. Now we have to match up the x- and y-values so that one of the Q-points, say (12, 47), is in the data set and the other is not. One possible pairing is {(2, 22) (4, 30) (6, 28) (8, 35) (10, 42) (12, 47) (14, 53)}.

6. iv. Possible explanation: The y-values decrease as the x-values increase, so the slope of the line of fit must be negative, which narrows the choices to iii and iv. If you fit a line to the data using Q-points, the Q-points would be (11, 1.3) and (6, 2.2). The slope of the line through these points is -0.18. Equation iv is the equation of the line through these Q-points, so it is the best fit.

7. a. The Q-points for this data set are (4, 1.3) and (12, 6.3). The slope of the line through these points is 0.625, so the equation is $y = 1.3 + 0.625(x - 4)$ or $y = 6.3 + 0.625(x - 12)$.

b. The elevator is rising at a rate of 0.625 second per floor.

c. Substituting 60 for x gives a y-value of 36.3. So the elevator passes the 60th floor at 36.3 seconds after 2:00, or approximately 2:00:36.

d. Substituting 45 for y and solving gives an x-value of 73.92, so the elevator will be almost at the 74th floor.

8. a. The Q-points for this data set are (92, 1.3) and (84, 6.3). The slope of the line through these points is -0.625, so the equation is
$y = 1.3 - 0.625(x - 92)$ or
$y = 6.3 - 0.625(x - 84)$.

b. The elevator is moving down at a rate of 0.625 second per floor.

c. Substituting 10 for x gives a y-value of 52.55. So the elevator passes the 10th floor after 52.55 seconds, or at approximately 2:00:53.

d. Substituting 34 for y and solving gives an x-value of 39.68, so the elevator will be between the 39th and 40th floors.

9. a. Answers will vary.

b. At 28.8 sec, or at about 2:00:29, the elevators will pass at the 48th floor. One way to find this answer is to make a calculator table of both
$y = 1.3 + 0.625(x - 4)$ and
$y = 1.3 - 0.625(x - 92)$. When x is 48, the y-value for both equations is 28.8.

10. The size and cost are almost directly proportional. The 4-oz bottle costs $0.22 per oz, the 7.5-oz bottle costs $0.22 per oz, and the 18-oz bottle costs $0.2217 per oz. If you change the price of the 18-oz bottle to $3.96, then it also will cost exactly $0.22 per oz.

11. a. {0, 370} ENTER,
{Ans(1) + 1, Ans(2) − 54} ENTER, ENTER, . . .

Time (hr)	Distance from Mt. Rushmore (mi)
0	370
1	316
2	262
3	208
4	154
5	100
6	46

b.
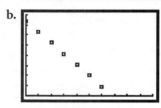
[0, 10, 1, 0, 400, 50]

c.
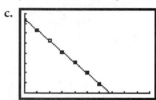

The line represents the distance from Mt. Rushmore at any time during the trip. The line lets you find the distance at any time; the points show the distance only at 1-hour intervals.

d. The slope is −54, which means that the distance from Mt. Rushmore decreases by 54 miles each hour.

e. The car will reach the Wall Drug Store after about 5.4 hours, or about 5 hours 24 minutes. You can find this by solving the equation $80 = 370 − 54x$ or by finding the x-value on the graph corresponding to the y-value 80.

f. The car will reach Mt. Rushmore in just under 7 hours. You can find this answer by solving the equation $0 = 370 − 54x$ or by finding the x-value on the graph corresponding to the y-value 0.

12. Answers will vary. Sample answer: To convert an equation from point-slope form to slope-intercept form, use the distributive property and then simplify. For example, to convert the equation $y = 4 + 2(x − 3)$ to slope-intercept form, use the distributive property to rewrite it as $y = 4 + 2x − 6$. Then simplify the equation and write it in the form $y = mx + b$. You get $y = 2x − 2$. You can check that

the equations are equivalent by making a graph or a table. If the equations are equivalent, the graphs will be identical and the values in the table will be equal.

LESSON 5.7

EXERCISES

1. a. $(6, 6)$ **b.** $(5, 9)$
   c. $y = 9 − 3(x − 5)$ **d.** $y = 24 − 3x$
   e. $(8, 0)$

2. a. $x = 10$ **b.** $x = −7.5$
   c. $x = 2.5$ **d.** $x = 41.5$

3. a.

$2x + 5y = 18$ Original equation.

$5y = 18 − 2x$ Subtract $2x$ from both sides.

$y = \dfrac{18 − 2x}{5}$ Divide both sides by 5.

or $y = 3.6 − 0.4x$

b.

$5x − 2y = −12$ Original equation.

$−2y = −12 − 5x$ Subtract $5x$ from both sides.

$y = \dfrac{−12 − 5x}{−2}$ Divide both sides by $−2$.

or $y = 6 + 2.5x$

4. a. Let x represent years, and let y represent distance in meters. The Q-points are $(1962, 60.09)$ and $(1990, 68.16)$. The slope of the line through these points is about 0.29, so the equation is $y = 60.09 + 0.29(x − 1962)$ or $y = 68.16 + 0.29(x − 1990)$. The slope, 0.29, means that the winning distance increases by 0.29 m each year. The y-intercept would be the distance for year 0, which is meaningless in this situation.

b. Using the equation $y = 60.09 + 0.29(x − 1962)$ gives a distance of 45.59 meters. This is 0.38 m more than the actual distance.

c. To find the year using the equation $y = 60.09 + 0.29(x − 1962)$, solve $80 = 60.09 + 0.29(x − 1962)$.

$80 = 60.09 + 0.29(x − 1962)$ Original equation.

$19.91 = 0.29(x − 1962)$ Subtract 60.09 from both sides.

$68.66 ≈ x − 1962$ Divide both sides by 0.29.

$2031 ≈ x$ Add 1962 to both sides and round off.

The solution is 2031, but because the Olympics are held only every 4 years, the answer is 2028 or 2032.

5. a. Let x represent the distance from Los Angeles in miles, and let y represent elapsed time in minutes. The Q-points are (411.5, 1385.5) and (1181.5, 240). The slope of the line through these points is about -1.49, so the equation is $y = 1385.5 - 1.49(x - 411.5)$ or $y = 240 - 1.49(x - 1181.5)$. The slope means that the elapsed time increases 1.49 minutes each time the distance decreases by 1 mile. To find the y-intercept, substitute 0 for x. The result is 1998.635. This means that when the train reaches Los Angeles (that is, when the distance from Los Angeles is 0), the elapsed time is about 2000 minutes. In other words, it takes 2000 minutes, or 33 hours 20 minutes, for the train to travel from Seattle to Los Angeles.

b. Approximately 1701 minutes, or 28 hours 21 minutes, by the first equation, or approximately 1702 minutes, or 28 hours 22 minutes, by the second equation.

c. You can find this by solving $600 = 1385.5 - 1.49(x - 411.5)$ or $600 = 240 - 1.49(x - 1181.5)$. The first equation gives about 939 miles, and the second gives about 940 miles. Here is the solution for the first equation:

$$600 = 1385.5 - 1.49(x - 411.5)$$
Original equation.

$$-785.5 = -1.49(x - 411.5)$$
Subtract 1385.5 from both sides.

$$527.2 \approx x - 411.5$$
Divide both sides by -1.49.

$$938.7 \approx x$$
Add 411.5 to both sides.

You are about 939 miles from Los Angeles.

6. a. Violin: $6(\$8.50) + 8(\$12.25) + 6(\$16.50) + 1(\$18.75) + 0(\$22.25) = \$266.75$

Viola: $0(\$8.50) + 4(\$12.25) + 8(\$16.50) + 3(\$18.75) + 1(\$22.25) = \$259.50$

Cello: $1(\$8.50) + 6(\$12.25) + 5(\$16.50) + 4(\$18.75) + 4(\$22.25) = \$320.00$

Bass: $1(\$8.50) + 1(\$12.25) + 2(\$16.50) + 2(\$18.75) + 0(\$22.25) = \$91.25$

b.
$$\begin{bmatrix} 266.75 \\ 259.50 \\ 320.00 \\ 91.25 \end{bmatrix}$$

c. Total Cost

$$\begin{matrix} \text{Violin} \\ \text{Viola} \\ \text{Cello} \\ \text{Bass} \end{matrix} \begin{bmatrix} 266.75 \\ 259.50 \\ 320.00 \\ 91.25 \end{bmatrix}$$

The entries tell you the total cost of the strings for each instrument.

d. No; you can't multiply matrix [B] by matrix [A], because the inside dimensions don't match.

7. $\dfrac{50 \text{ grains}}{3.24 \text{ grams}} = \dfrac{x \text{ grains}}{1 \text{ gram}}$; 15.4321 grains per gram

8. a. $5 : 9$

b. Purchase approximately 444 sets of ski equipment and 556 sets of snowboard equipment.

c. Sample answer: It would help to know who carried out the survey and what, if any, preferences they had. It would also be helpful to know the age and sex breakdown of the group surveyed and in what part of the country the visitors were from.

IMPROVING YOUR REASONING SKILLS

Here is a scatter plot of the data:

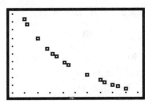

[20, 70, 5, 50, 150, 10]

This is the graph of an inverse variation, so the equation should be in the form $xy = k$ or $y = \frac{k}{x}$, where k is a constant. To find k, you can find the product of each pair of x- and y-values and calculate the mean. This gives $k = 3599.51 \approx 3600$, so the equation is $y = \frac{3600}{x}$. This equation fits the points very well.

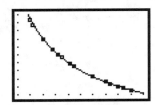

To predict the time a driver traveling 45 miles per hour would need for the trip, substitute 45 for x. The result is about 80 minutes. To find the travel speed required to complete the trip in 70 minutes, substitute 70 for y and solve for x. The result is about 51.4 miles per hour.

Activity day (no answers for this lesson)

CHAPTER 5 Review

EXERCISES

1. $$-3 = \frac{4 - 10}{x_2 - 2}$$

    $$-3(x_2 - 2) = -6$$

    $$x_2 - 2 = 2$$

    $$x_2 = 4$$

2. **a.** Slope: -3; y-intercept: -4

    b. Slope: 2; y-intercept: 7

    c. Slope: 3.8; y-intercept: -2.4

3. Line a has slope -1, y-intercept 1, and equation $y = 1 - x$.

    Line b has slope 2, y-intercept -2, and equation $y = -2 + 2x$.

4. **a.** $y = 13.6(x - 1902) + 158.2$ Original equation.

    $y = 13.6x - 25,867.2 + 158.2$ Distribute the 13.6.

    $y = 13.6x - 25,709$ Add.

    b. The y-coordinate of the point with x-coordinate 10 is -37. Using slope -5.2 and the point $(10, -37)$, we get the equation $y = -37 - 5.2(x - 10)$.

5. **a.** $(-4.5, -3.5)$ **b.** $y = 2x + 5.5$

    c. $y = 2(x + 2.75)$; the x-intercept is -2.75.

    d. The x-coordinate is 5.5. The equation is $y = 16.5 + 2(x - 5.5)$.

    e. Answers will vary. Possible methods are graphing, using a calculator table, and putting all equations in intercept form.

6. **a.** $4 + 2.8x = 51$ **b.** $38 - 0.35x = 27$

         $2.8x = 47$ $-0.35x = -11$

           $x \approx 16.8$ $x \approx 31.4$

    c. $11 + 3(x - 8) = 41$

         $3(x - 8) = 30$

           $x - 8 = 10$

              $x = 18$

    d. $220 - 12.5(x - 6) = 470$

        $-12.5(x - 6) = 250$

             $x - 6 = -20$

                $x = -14$

7. **a.** $y = 12,600 - 1,350x$

    b. The slope is $-1,350$; the car's value decreases by $1,350$ each year.

    c. The y-intercept is 12,600; Karl paid $12,600 for the car.

    d. The x-intercept is $9\frac{1}{3}$; in $9\frac{1}{3}$ years, the car will have no monetary value.

8. **a.** $43 = 30 + 0.375(x - 36)$

    b. $x \approx 71$ seconds

    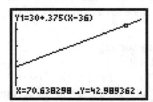

    $[0, 80, 10, 0, 50, 10]$

    c. $43 = 30 + 0.375(x - 36)$

         $13 = 0.375(x - 36)$

      $34.\overline{6} = x - 36$

      $70.\overline{6} = x$

9. **a.** Year: 1952, 1956, 1976, 1990, 2000
    Height: 1.67, 1.835, 1.93, 2.02, 2.05

    b. $(1962, 1.835)$ and $(1990, 2.020)$

    c. $y = 1.835 + 0.007(x - 1962)$ or $y = 2.020 + 0.007(x - 1990)$

    d. Answers will vary. There are more points below the line than above the line.

    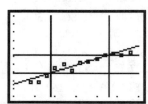

    $[1940, 2000, 10, 1.5, 2.5, 0.1]$

    e. Using $y = 1.835 + 0.007(x - 1962)$ gives the prediction 2.19 m.

10. **a.** $y = 2.25 + 0.13(x - 1976.5)$ or $y = 4.025 + 0.13(x - 1990.5)$

    b. The slope means that the minimum hourly wage increased about $0.13 per year.

c. Using $y = 2.25 + 0.13(x - 1976.5)$ gives the prediction $5.96.

d. Using $y = 2.25 + 0.13(x - 1976.5)$ gives the prediction 1967.

11. a. The equation is $y = a + bx$, where b is the slope and a is the y-intercept.

b. Use the points to find the slope. If the points are (x_1, y_1) and (x_2, y_2), then the slope is $\frac{y_2 - y_1}{x_2 - x_1} = b$. Then use the slope and one of the points to write the equation. Using the point (x_1, y_1) gives the equation $y = y_1 + b(x - x_1)$.

TAKE ANOTHER LOOK

The rate of change of a curve (other than a straight line) is not constant. In general you can't find the slope of a curve at a point by finding the slope of a line between two points on the curve, no matter how close together those points are. The average rate of change over the x-interval from 3 to 3.25 is not the same as from 3.25 to 3.5.

The average rate of change between the points $(8, 1.5)$ and $(8.5, 1.4)$ is -0.2. The average rate of change between $(3, 4)$ and $(3.5, 3.4)$ is -1.2. This tells us that the rate of change of the y-values is slower on the "wings" of the curve than at the portion of the graph nearest the origin.

The line through $(3, 4)$ with slope -1.2 is $y = 7.6 - 1.2x$.

CHAPTER 6

LESSON 6.1

EXERCISES

1. a. $(-15.6, 0.2)$ is a solution because $47 + 3(-15.6) = 0.2$ and $8 + 0.5(-15.6) = 0.2$.

b. $(-4, 23)$ is not a solution because $23 \neq 12 + (-4)$.

c. $(2, 12.3)$ is not a solution because $12.3 \neq 4.5 + 5(2)$. You can also tell that the ordered pair is not a solution because the equations represent parallel lines, which never intersect.

2. a. For one of the lines, the y-values increase as the x-values increase. For the other line, the y-values decrease as the x-values increase. Only table iv fits these conditions.

b. For both lines, the y-values increase as the x-values increase. Only table iii fits these conditions.

c. One of the lines is horizontal, so the y-values are constant. Only table i fits these conditions.

d. For both lines, the y-values decrease as the x-values increase. Only table ii fits these conditions.

3. a. $(8, 7)$. This is an exact solution because it satisfies both equations.

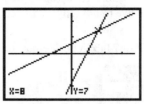

$[-18.8, 18.8, 5, -12.4, 12.4, 5]$

b. $(1.5, 0.5)$. This is an exact solution because it satisfies both equations.

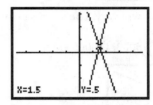

$[-4.7, 4.7, 1, -3.1, 3.1, 1]$

4. a. $(3.4, 15.5)$

X	Y₁	Y₂
3	14.5	17.9
3.1	14.75	17.3
3.2	15	16.7
3.3	15.25	16.1
3.4	15.5	15.5
3.5	15.75	14.9
3.6	16	14.3

X=3.4

b. $(7.3, -5.6)$

X	Y₁	Y₂
7	-5	-4.7
7.1	-5.2	-5
7.2	-5.4	-5.3
7.3	-5.6	-5.6
7.4	-5.8	-5.9
7.5	-6	-6.2
7.6	-6.2	-6.5

X=7.3

5. a. $y = 3 - 2x$. Substituting 1 for x gives $y = 3 - 2(1) = 1$. Substituting $(1, 1)$ into the original equation gives $4(1) + 2(1) = 6$. So, $(1, 1)$ satisfies both forms of the equation.

b. $y = -4 + 0.4x$. Substituting 1 for x gives $y = -4 + 0.4(1) = -3.6$. Substituting $(1, -3.6)$ into the original equation gives $2(1) - 5(-3.6) = 20$. So, $(1, -3.6)$ satisfies both forms of the equation.

6. a. Let P represent profit in dollars, and let N represent the number of "hits." Profit is income minus expenses. The income is the $2.50 per "hit," and the expenses are the $12,000 spent on setup and supplies. So, the equation for profit is $P = 2.5N - 12000$, or $P = -12000 + 2.5N$.

b. P represents profit in dollars, and N represents the number of "hits" to the web site. $5,000 is

Widget.kom's start-up cost, and $1.60 is the amount its advertisers pay per hit. Because Widget.kom spent less in start-up costs, its web site might be less attractive to advertisers, hence, the lower rate.

c. When $N = 7778$, $P \approx 7445$ in both equations.

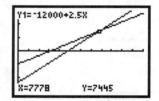

d. Graphing windows will vary. The graphs below are in the window
[0, 12000, 1000, −15000, 15000, 6000].

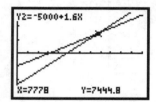

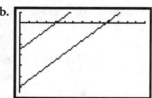

e. The intersection point is about (7778, 7445). This point can be found from the table or by tracing the graph. The point is fairly accurate. Substituting 7778 for N gives a P-value of 7445 in one equation and of 7444.8 in the other. These P-values are very close to each other.

f. The coordinates of the intersection point indicate that for 7778 hits, both companies make a profit of about $7,445.

7. a. $P = −5000 + 2.5N$

b.

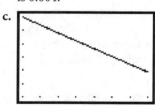

[0, 7000, 500, −13000, 2000, 2000]

c. The line for Sally's company (Gadget.kom) is parallel to and above the line for Gizmo.kom, indicating that Gadget.kom will always profit more than Gizmo.kom from the same number of hits.

d. Possible answer: The equations show that Sally pays $7000 less to start Gadget.kom, but she earns profits at the same rate as Gizmo.kom. So, her

profit will always be $7000 more for the same N-value.

8. a. The rate of change for University College is $30 per credit hour. The tuition for 1 credit is $55, so the fixed fees must be 55 − 30 or $25. So the equation for University College is $y = 25 + 30x$, where x is the number of credits and y is the tuition.

The rate of change for State College is $32 per credit hour. The tuition for 1 credit is $47, so the fixed fees must be 47 − 32 or $15. So, the equation for State College is $y = 15 + 32x$, where x is the number of credits and y is the tuition. The system is
$$\begin{cases} y = 25 + 30x \\ y = 15 + 32x \end{cases}$$

b. (5, 175). Check: 175 = 25 + 30(5), 175 = 15 + 32(5).

c. Answers will vary.

d. When a student takes 5 credit hours, the tuition at either college is $175.

e. For more than 5 credits, it is cheaper to attend University. For fewer than 5 credits, it is cheaper to attend State.

9. a. $$\begin{cases} d = 9 - t & \text{drill team member's distance from 0-yd mark} \\ d = 3 - 0.5t & \text{tuba player's distance from 0-yd mark} \end{cases}$$

b. (4, 5). After 4 seconds, the tuba player bumps into the drill team member at the 5-yard mark.

10. a. The equations give winning times of 44.46 seconds and 44.456 seconds. The difference is 0.004.

b. The equations give winning times of 42.948 seconds and 42.944 seconds. The difference is 0.004.

c.

[1950, 2020, 10, 40, 46, 1]

d. No. The graph in 10c appears to show one line. However, in 10a and b, the y-values for the same x-values are 0.004 apart. The lines are actually parallel but are so close they appear to be the same line on the graph. (Note: The two equations, which model the same data, are slightly different because the value of the slope was rounded to −0.054. The exact value of the slope is $\frac{-13}{240}$.)

11. a. To have exactly 1 solution, the lines need to have different slopes, so b can have any value except -5, and a can have any value.

    b. To have no solutions, the lines must be parallel—that is, they must have the same slope—but they must have different y-intercepts. So, b must be -5 and a can have any value but 2.

    c. To have infinitely many solutions, the lines must be identical, so $a = 2$ and $b = -5$.

12. a. *Miss B:* 5.769 minutes; *Club C:* 4.815 minutes

    b. *Miss B:* 24.81 gallons; *Club C:* 20.70 gallons

    c. *Miss B:* 21.67 miles; *Club C:* 25.96 miles

    d. *Miss B:* 0.504 mi/gal; *Club C:* 0.604 mi/gal

13. a. 85   **b.** -8.2 **c.** 3   **d.** 3.5

    e. 1.5

14. a. The N scale best matches this model. To calculate the table values easily, enter the denominators of the scales into list L₁. In list L₂, enter $= L_1 \cdot 4/5280$. In list L₃, enter $= L_1 \cdot 8/5280$.

Train gauge (name of scale)	Scale (model : actual)	Represented width (ft)	Represented width (mi)
Z	1 : 220	880	0.167
N	1 : 160	640	0.12
HO	1 : 87	348	0.066
S	1 : 64	256	0.048
O	1 : 48	192	0.036
Maxi	1 : 32	128	0.024
G	1 : 24	96	0.018

    b. The N scale best matches this model.

    c. 1 inch : 11 feet

15. a. $\begin{bmatrix} 1 & -11 \\ -6 & 8 \end{bmatrix}$ **b.** $\begin{bmatrix} 13 & -1 \\ 7 & 8 \end{bmatrix}$

16. a. $y = 5x - 2$ **b.** $y = 0.8 - 1.6x$

    c. $y = 1.5 + 3x$

LESSON 6.2

EXERCISES

1. Stage 3: Add $2.5t$ to both sides. Stage 5: Divide both sides by 4.

2. a. $(-2, 34)$ is not a solution because it satisfies only the first equation.

    b. $(4.25, 19.25)$ is a solution because $19.25 = 32 - 3(4.25)$ and $19.25 = 15 + 4.25$.

    c. $(2, 12.3)$ is not a solution because it satisfies only the first equation. You can also tell that the ordered pair is not a solution because the equations represent parallel lines, which never intersect.

3. Solution steps will vary. Sample solutions are given.

    a.
$14 + 2x = 4 - 3x$	Original equation.
$14 + 5x = 4$	Add $3x$ to both sides.
$5x = -10$	Subtract 14 from both sides.
$x = -2$	Divide both sides by 5.

    b.
$7 - 2y = -3 - y$	Original equation.
$7 - y = -3$	Add y to both sides.
$-y = -10$	Subtract 7 from both sides.
$y = 10$	Multiply both sides by -1.

    c.
$5d = 9 + 2d$	Original equation.
$3d = 9$	Subtract $2d$ from both sides.
$d = 3$	Divide both sides by 3.

    d.
$12 + t = 4t$	Original equation.
$12 = 3t$	Subtract t from both sides.
$4 = t$	Divide both sides by 3.

4. Solution steps will vary. A sample solution is given.

$y = 25 + 30x$	Original second equation.
$15 + 32x = 25 + 30x$	Substitute $15 + 32x$ (from the second equation) for y.
$15 + 2x = 25$	Subtract $30x$ from both sides.
$2x = 10$	Subtract 15 from both sides.
$x = 5$	Divide both sides by 5.

To find y, substitute 5 for x in either equation: $y = 25 + 30(5) = 175$. The solution is $(5, 175)$. Check: $175 = 25 + 30(5)$, $175 = 15 + 32(5)$.

5. a. $5x + 2(4 - 3x) = 5x + 8 - 6x = -x + 8$

    b. $7x - 2(4 - 3x) = 7x - 8 + 6x = 13x - 8$

6. Solution steps will vary. Sample solutions are given.

    a.
$y = 4 - 3x$	Original first equation.
$2x - 1 = 4 - 3x$	Substitute $2x - 1$ (from the second equation) for y.
$-1 = 4 - 5x$	Subtract $2x$ from both sides.
$-5 = -5x$	Subtract 4 from both sides.
$1 = x$	Divide both sides by -1.

To find y, substitute 1 for x in either equation: $y = 4 - 3(1) = 1$. The solution is $(1, 1)$. Check: $1 = 4 - 3(1)$, $1 = 2(1) - 1$.

b. Solve the second equation for x: $x = 1 - 3y$. Now substitute $1 - 3y$ for x in the first equation and solve for y.

$2x - 2y = 4$	Original first equation.
$2(1 - 3y) - 2y = 4$	Substitute $1 - 3y$ for x.
$2 - 6y - 2y = 4$	Apply the distributive property.
$2 - 8y = 4$	Combine $-6y$ and $-2y$.
$-8y = 2$	Subtract 2 from both sides.
$y = -\frac{1}{4}$	Divide both sides by -8.

To find x, substitute $-\frac{1}{4}$ for y in either equation:
$x + 3(-\frac{1}{4}) = 1$, so $x = 1 + \frac{3}{4} = \frac{7}{4}$. Check:
$2(1.75) - 2(-0.25) = 4$, $1.75 + 3(-0.25) = 1$.

7. a. Solution steps will vary. A sample solution is given.

$-12000 + 2.5N$ $= -5000 + 1.6N$	Set equations equal to each other.
$-12000 + 0.9N$ $= -5000$	Subtract $1.6N$ from both sides.
$0.9N = 7000$	Add 12000 to both sides.
$N = \frac{70000}{9} = 7777\frac{7}{9}$	Multiply both sides by 10 and then divide both sides by 9.

To find P, substitute $\frac{70000}{9}$ for N in either equation:

$$P = -12000 + 2.5\left(\frac{70000}{9}\right) = 7444\frac{4}{9}$$

b. The approximate solution, $N \approx 7778$ and $P \approx 7445$, is more meaningful because it is not possible to have a fractional number of web site hits.

8. a. There is no solution because the lines are parallel and slopes are equal.

b. Answers will vary. Possible explanation: $-5000 + 2.5N = -12000 + 2.5N$. Subtracting $2.5N$ from both sides gives $-5000 = -12000$, which is never true. So this system has no solutions.

9. a. $A + C = 200$ **b.** $8A + 4C = 1304$

c. The system is $\begin{cases} A + C = 200 \\ 8A + 4C = 1304 \end{cases}$. To solve this system, you could rewrite the first equation as $A = 200 - C$, and then substitute $200 - C$ for A in the second equation and solve for C. The solution to the system is $A = 126$ and $C = 74$. The theater sold 126 adult tickets and 74 child tickets.

10. a. The first walker starts at the 8.5-meter mark and walks toward the second walker at 0.5 m/sec. The second walker starts at the 2.5-meter mark and walks toward the first walker at 0.75 m/sec.

b. $d = 4.8$, $t = 6.1$

c. The two students passed each other at the 4.8-meter mark after 6.1 seconds.

11. a. $\begin{cases} d = 35 + 0.8t \\ d = 1.1t \end{cases}$; $t = 116\frac{2}{3}$, $d = 128\frac{1}{3}$. The pickup passes the sports car roughly 128 miles from Flint after approximately 117 minutes.

b. $\begin{cases} d = 220 - 1.2t \\ d = 1.1t \end{cases}$; $t \approx 95.7$, $d \approx 105.2$. The minivan meets the pickup truck about 105 miles from Flint after approximately 96 minutes.

c. $\begin{cases} d = 220 - 1.2t \\ d = 35 + 0.8t \end{cases}$; $t = 92.5$, $d = 109$. The minivan meets the sports car 109 miles from Flint after 92.5 minutes.

d. $220 - 1.2t = 2(35 + 0.8t)$; $t \approx 53.6$ minutes. The minivan is twice as far from Flint after about 53.6 minutes. At that time, the minivan is about 156 miles from Flint, and the sports car is about 78 miles from Flint.

e. Possible answer: The solutions found using substitution are exact, if not rounded off, whereas those found using recursive routines are approximations.

12. a. $y = 51.08 - 0.1215(x - 1972)$ or $y = 48.83 - 0.1215(x - 1992)$

b. $\begin{cases} y = 51.08 - 0.1215(x - 1972) \\ y = 45 - 0.054(x - 1962) \end{cases}$ or $\begin{cases} y = 48.65 - 0.1215(x - 1992) \\ y = 45 - 0.054(x - 1962) \end{cases}$

c. Answers will vary. The window shown is [1960, 2100, 4, 30, 55, 5].

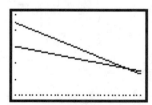

The approximate solution is (2070, 39).

d. Answers will vary. The solution for x is close to 2070, which is not an Olympic year. If the model is accurate, both the women's and men's times will be close to 39 seconds in the 2072 Olympics. The women's times will be faster than the men's times in Olympics after that. The equations also imply that eventually the winning times for both the women and the men will be 0 seconds, which is not reasonable.

13. a. $\dfrac{520 \text{ ft}}{43 \text{ sec}} = 12.1$ ft/sec

b. $605 \text{ ft} \cdot \dfrac{1 \text{ sec}}{12.1 \text{ ft}} = 50$ sec

c. The initial height of the elevator is 100 ft and the elevator travels at 12.1 ft/sec, so the equation for the height, y, after x seconds is $y = 100 + 12.1x$. To find the number of seconds it will take to get to the observation deck, solve the equation $520 = 100 + 12.1x$.

14. a. $2\dfrac{1}{6}$ **b.** $\dfrac{2}{3}$ **c.** $\dfrac{1}{6}$ **d.** $\dfrac{97}{60}$ or $1\dfrac{37}{60}$

15. a. i   **b.** iii   **c.** ii

LESSON 6.3

EXERCISES

1. a. $y = \dfrac{10 - 5x}{2}$ or $y = \dfrac{10}{2} - \dfrac{5}{2}x = 5 - \dfrac{5}{2}x$

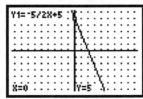

$[-9.4, 9.4, 1, -6.2, 6.2, 1]$

b. $y = \dfrac{30 - 15x}{6}$ or $y = \dfrac{30}{6} - \dfrac{15}{6}x = 5 - \dfrac{5}{2}x$

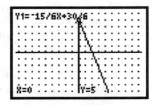

The graphs are the same because multiplying both sides of an equation by the same number results in an equivalent equation.

2. a. Substitute 6 for x and a for y and solve for a.

$5(6) - 2a = 10$

$30 - 2a = 10$

$-2a = -20$

$a = 10$

b. Substitute -4 for x and b for y and solve for b.

$5(-4) - 2b = 10$

$-20 - 2b = 10$

$-2b = 30$

$b = -15$

c. Substitute 25 for y and c for x and solve for c.

$5c - 2(25) = 10$

$5c - 50 = 10$

$5c = 60$

$c = 12$

d. Substitute -5 for y and d for x and solve for d.

$5d - 2(-5) = 10$

$5d + 10 = 10$

$5d = 0$

$d = 0$

3. a. Add the equations to eliminate x. You get $-5y = 5$, so $y = -1$. To find x, you can substitute -1 for y in either equation and solve for x. The result is $x = \dfrac{-15}{6}$ or -2.5. So, the solution is $(-2.5, -1)$.

b. You can eliminate y by multiplying the first equation by 2 and adding it to the second equation.

$$10x - 8y = 46$$
$$\underline{7x + 8y = 5}$$
$$17x = 51 \qquad \text{Add the equations.}$$
$$x = 3 \qquad \text{Divide by 17.}$$

So $x = 3$. To find y, substitute 3 for x in either equation and solve for y. The result is $y = -2$. So the solution is $(3, -2)$.

4. a. Multiply the first equation by -3 (or multiply the second equation by $\frac{1}{3}$).

b. $0 = 0$

c. The result is $y = -2.4 + 0.4x$ for both equations, so the equations represent the same line.

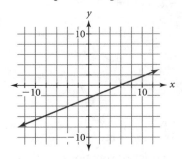

d. It does not change the graph.

5. a. Multiply the first equation by -5 and the second equation by 3, or multiply the first equation by 5 and the second equation by -3.

b. Multiply the first equation by -8 and the second equation by 7, or multiply the first equation by 8 and the second equation by -7.

6. (1) You can solve both equations for y in terms of x. Then graph the resulting equations in the same window and locate the point of intersection.

(2) You can solve both equations for y in terms of x. Then make a calculator table of both equations and zoom in to find the x-value for which the two y-values are the same.

(3) You can solve one equation for x in terms of y (or for y in terms of x) and then substitute the resulting expression for x (or for y) in the other equation.

(4) You can multiply both equations by numbers so that either the coefficients of x or the coefficients of y are opposites and then add the equations to eliminate a variable.

The solution is $(2, -2)$.

7. a. $(4, 2)$. Possible solution: Add the two equations to get $7x = 28$. Divide both sides by 7 to get $x = 4$. To find the value of y, substitute 4 for x in either equation. The result is $y = 2$.

b. $(3, -1)$. Possible solution: Subtract the second equation from the first to get $-2y = 2$. Divide both sides by -2 to get $y = -1$. To find the value of x, substitute -1 for y in either equation. The result is $x = 3$.

c. $(-3, -1)$. Possible solution: Subtract the second equation from the first to get $-3x = 9$. Divide both sides by -3 to get $x = -3$. To find the value of y, substitute -3 for x in either equation. The result is $y = -1$.

8.

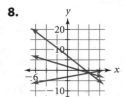

a. $y = -3 + 0.5x$ **b.** $y = 2 - 0.75x$

c. Adding the two original equations gives $4x + 2y = 14$. Solving for y gives $y = 7 - 2x$. The graph of this equation intersects the other two lines at their intersection point.

d. The solution of the system is also a solution of the sum of the equations.

9. a. $y = 163 - x$ and $y = -33 + x$

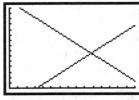

$[0, 150, 10, 0, 150, 10]$

b. Subtracting the second equation from the first gives $2y = 130$, so $y = 65$. The graph of this equation is shown as the horizontal line below.

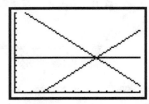

c. Adding the equations gives $2x = 196$, so $x = 98$. The graph of this equation is shown as the vertical line below.

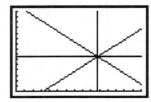

d. The four lines intersect at the same point, $(98, 65)$. The solution of the system is also a solution of the sum and difference of the equations.

10. Answers will vary. Substitute $(5, 2)$ for x and y in $4x + ay = b$ to get $20 + 2a = b$. Then find values of a and b that satisfy this equation. One possibility is $a = -3$ and $b = 14$, which gives the equation $4x - 3y = 14$.

11. a. Substitution

b. Her solution is not complete. Although she correctly found the value of x, she did not substitute it into one of the original equations to find the value of y.

12. a. $\begin{cases} w + p = 10 \\ 3.25w + 10.50p = 61.50 \end{cases}$

b. $w = 6, p = 4$. They bought 6 wallet-size pictures and 4 portrait-size pictures.

13. a. Let c represent gallons burned in the city and h represent gallons burned on the highway. Then the system is

$\begin{cases} c + h = 11 \\ 17c + 25h = 220 \end{cases}$

Discovering Algebra Solutions Manual
©2002 Key Curriculum Press

b. $c = 6.875$, $h = 4.125$. She used 6.875 gallons in the city and 4.125 gallons on the highway.

c. $\frac{17 \text{ mi}}{\text{gal}} \cdot 6.875 \text{ gal} = 116.875 \approx 117$ city mi;

$\frac{25 \text{ mi}}{\text{gal}} \cdot 4.125 \text{ gal} = 103.125 \approx 103$ hwy mi

d. Check: $\begin{cases} 6.875 + 4.125 = 11 \\ 17(6.875) + 25(4.125) = 220 \\ 116.875 + 103.125 = 220 \end{cases}$

14. a. Possible answer: $\frac{5}{8}$ **b.** Possible answer: $\frac{3}{4}$

c. Possible answer: $-\frac{9}{40}$ **d.** Possible answer: $\frac{2}{3}$

e. Possible strategy: Rewrite the fractions with a common denominator. Then, write another fraction with the same denominator and with a numerator between the two numerators.

15. a. The rest station temperature is 14 degrees lower than the temperature at the start. The temperature falls 4 degrees for every 1000 feet, so the elevation must be $\frac{14}{4} \cdot 1000$ or 3500 feet higher than the start point. So, the elevation at the rest station is $4300 + 3500$ or 7800 feet.

The highest point is 7600 feet higher than the start, so the temperature must be $\frac{7600}{1000} \cdot 4$ or 30.4 degrees colder than at the start. The temperature at the highest point must be $78 - 30.4$ or 47.6 degrees.

b. The slope is $\frac{-4 \text{ degrees}}{1000 \text{ feet}}$ or -0.004 deg/ft. Using this slope and the point $(4300, 78)$ gives the equation $T = 78 - 0.004(E - 4300)$. In slope-intercept form, this is $T = 95.2 - 0.004E$.

The slope is the rate of change in temperature for each increase of 1 foot in elevation. The y-intercept (or here the T-intercept) is the temperature at sea level (an elevation of 0 feet).

c. $95.2 - 0.004(20{,}320)$ or about 13.9°F

16. a. $y = -3 - 2(x - 5)$ **b.** $y = 7 + 2.5(x + 3)$

17. a. P (top) $= \frac{400}{769}$ or about 0.52

P (bottom) $= \frac{370}{769}$ or about 0.48

b. A trial is assigning a locker. An outcome is whether the locker is in the top row or the bottom row.

LESSON 6.4

EXERCISES

1. a. $\begin{cases} 2x + 1.5y = 12.75 \\ -3x + 4y = 9 \end{cases}$ **b.** $\begin{cases} \frac{1}{2}x = \frac{1}{2} \\ -x + 2y = 0 \end{cases}$

c. $\begin{cases} 2x + 3y = 1 \\ 2y = 0 \end{cases}$

2. a. $\begin{bmatrix} 1 & 4 & 3 \\ -1 & 2 & 9 \end{bmatrix}$ **b.** $\begin{bmatrix} 7 & -1 & 3 \\ 0.1 & -2.1 & 3 \end{bmatrix}$

c. $\begin{bmatrix} 1 & 1 & 3 \\ 1 & 1 & 6 \end{bmatrix}$

3. a. $(8.5, 2.8)$ **b.** $\left(\frac{1}{2}, \frac{13}{16}\right)$ **c.** $(0, 0)$

4. Divide row 1 by 4.2. $\begin{bmatrix} 1 & 0 & 3 \\ 0 & -1 & 5.25 \end{bmatrix}$

Multiply row 2 by -1. $\begin{bmatrix} 1 & 0 & 3 \\ 0 & 1 & -5.25 \end{bmatrix}$

The solution is $(3, -5.25)$.

5. a. $\begin{cases} 3x + y = 7 \\ 2x + y = 21 \end{cases}$ **b.** $\begin{bmatrix} 3 & 1 & 7 \\ 2 & 1 & 21 \end{bmatrix}$

6. a.

Description	Matrix
The matrix for $\begin{cases} 3x + 2y = 28.9 \\ 8x + 5y = 74.6 \end{cases}$	$\begin{bmatrix} 3 & 2 & 28.9 \\ 8 & 5 & 74.6 \end{bmatrix}$
Add 8 times row 1 to -3 times row 2 and put the result in row 2.	$\begin{bmatrix} 3 & 2 & 28.9 \\ 0 & 1 & 7.4 \end{bmatrix}$
Add -2 times row 2 to row 1 and put the result in row 1.	$\begin{bmatrix} 3 & 0 & 14.1 \\ 0 & 1 & 7.4 \end{bmatrix}$
Divide row 1 by 3.	$\begin{bmatrix} 1 & 0 & 4.7 \\ 0 & 1 & 7.4 \end{bmatrix}$

The solution is $(4.7, 7.4)$.

7. a.

	Adults	Children	Total (kg)
Monday	40	15	10.8
Tuesday	35	22	12.29

b. Let x represent the average weight of chips an adult eats and y represent the average weight of chips a child eats. The system is

$\begin{cases} 40x + 15y = 10.8 \\ 35x + 22y = 12.29 \end{cases}$

c. $\begin{bmatrix} 40 & 15 & 10.8 \\ 35 & 22 & 12.29 \end{bmatrix}$

d. Solution steps will vary.

Add -35 times row 1 to 40 times row 2.	$\begin{bmatrix} 40 & 15 & 10.8 \\ 0 & 355 & 113.6 \end{bmatrix}$
Divide row 2 by 355.	$\begin{bmatrix} 40 & 15 & 10.8 \\ 0 & 1 & 0.32 \end{bmatrix}$
Add -15 times row 2 to row 1.	$\begin{bmatrix} 40 & 0 & 6 \\ 0 & 1 & 0.32 \end{bmatrix}$
Divide row 1 by 40.	$\begin{bmatrix} 1 & 0 & 0.15 \\ 0 & 1 & 0.32 \end{bmatrix}$

e. Each adult ate an average of about 0.15 kg (150 g) of chips, and each child ate an average of 0.32 kg (320 g) of chips.

8.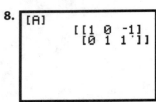

9. a. Let x represent the number of small trucks and y represent the number of large trucks. The system is $\begin{cases} 5x + 12y = 532 \\ 7x + 4y = 284 \end{cases}$.

b. $\begin{bmatrix} 5 & 12 & 532 \\ 7 & 4 & 284 \end{bmatrix}$

c. Solution steps will vary.

Add 7 times row 1 to -5 times row 2. $\begin{bmatrix} 5 & 12 & 532 \\ 0 & 64 & 2304 \end{bmatrix}$

Divide row 2 by 64. $\begin{bmatrix} 5 & 12 & 532 \\ 0 & 1 & 36 \end{bmatrix}$

Subtract 12 times row 2 from row 1. $\begin{bmatrix} 5 & 0 & 100 \\ 0 & 1 & 36 \end{bmatrix}$

Divide row 1 by 5. $\begin{bmatrix} 1 & 0 & 20 \\ 0 & 1 & 36 \end{bmatrix}$

d. Zoe should order 20 small trucks and 36 large trucks.

10. a. $\begin{cases} X + Y = 300 \\ 0.12X + 0.04Y = 30 \end{cases}$ **b.** $\begin{bmatrix} 1 & 1 & 300 \\ 0.12 & 0.04 & 30 \end{bmatrix}$

c. Solution steps will vary.

Add -0.12 times row 1 from row 2. $\begin{bmatrix} 1 & 1 & 300 \\ 0 & -0.08 & -6 \end{bmatrix}$

Divide row 2 by -0.08. $\begin{bmatrix} 1 & 1 & 300 \\ 0 & 1 & 75 \end{bmatrix}$

Subtract row 2 from row 1. $\begin{bmatrix} 1 & 0 & 225 \\ 0 & 1 & 75 \end{bmatrix}$

d. Will should mix 225 grams of flour X with 75 grams of flour Y.

11. a. $\begin{cases} m + t + w = 286 \\ m - t \quad\;\; = 7 \\ \quad\; t - w = 24 \end{cases}$

b. $\begin{bmatrix} 1 & 1 & 1 & 286 \\ 1 & -1 & 0 & 7 \\ 0 & 0 & -1 & 24 \end{bmatrix}$

The rows represent each equation. The columns represent the coefficients of each variable and the constants.

c. Solution steps will vary.

Subtract row 1 from row 2. $\begin{bmatrix} 1 & 1 & 1 & 286 \\ 0 & -2 & -1 & -279 \\ 0 & 1 & -1 & 24 \end{bmatrix}$

Divide row 2 by -2. $\begin{bmatrix} 1 & 1 & 1 & 286 \\ 0 & 1 & 0.5 & 139.5 \\ 0 & 1 & -1 & 24 \end{bmatrix}$

Subtract row 2 from row 3. $\begin{bmatrix} 1 & 1 & 1 & 286 \\ 0 & 1 & 0.5 & 139.5 \\ 0 & 0 & -1.5 & -115.5 \end{bmatrix}$

Divide row 3 by -1.5. $\begin{bmatrix} 1 & 1 & 1 & 286 \\ 0 & 1 & 0.5 & 139.5 \\ 0 & 0 & 1 & 77 \end{bmatrix}$

Subtract row 2 from row 1. $\begin{bmatrix} 1 & 0 & 0.5 & 146.5 \\ 0 & 1 & 0.5 & 139.5 \\ 0 & 0 & 1 & 77 \end{bmatrix}$

Add -0.5 times row 3 from row 1 and row 2. $\begin{bmatrix} 1 & 0 & 0 & 108 \\ 0 & 1 & 0 & 101 \\ 0 & 0 & 1 & 77 \end{bmatrix}$

d. They cycled 108 km on Monday, 101 km on Tuesday, and 77 km on Wednesday.

12. a. $\begin{bmatrix} 72 & 65 \\ 55 & 55 \\ 45 & 35 \end{bmatrix} - \begin{bmatrix} 31 & 28 \\ 26 & 24 \\ 21 & 16 \end{bmatrix} = \begin{bmatrix} 41 & 37 \\ 29 & 31 \\ 24 & 19 \end{bmatrix}$

b. If you are planning to be in the park for 3 days, then the 3-day ticket is a much better deal. The matrix showing the costs for three 1-day tickets is

$3 \cdot \begin{bmatrix} 31 & 28 \\ 26 & 24 \\ 21 & 16 \end{bmatrix} = \begin{bmatrix} 93 & 84 \\ 78 & 72 \\ 21 & 48 \end{bmatrix}$

c. The matrix showing the costs for two 1-day tickets is

$2 \cdot \begin{bmatrix} 31 & 28 \\ 26 & 24 \\ 21 & 16 \end{bmatrix} = \begin{bmatrix} 62 & 56 \\ 52 & 48 \\ 42 & 32 \end{bmatrix}$

These costs are less than the costs of the 3-day tickets, so if you are going for 2 days, you should buy two 1-day tickets.

13. a. 4 ENTER, Ans $-$ 0.5, ENTER, ENTER, . . .

b. -3 ENTER, Ans $+$ 2, ENTER, ENTER, . . .

c. 0.5 ENTER, Ans $-$ 1, ENTER, ENTER, . . .

d. 0 ENTER, Ans $+$ 1, ENTER, ENTER, . . .

14. a. The slope is 0.75, which is the cost per drink once you've bought the mug.

b. $y = 49.75 + 0.75(x - 33)$

c. $y = 25 + 0.75x$. The y-intercept is the cost of buying the mug.

15. Represent the system with a column matrix.

$$\begin{bmatrix} 1 & 3 \\ -2 & 1 \\ 3 & 23 \end{bmatrix}$$

Biancheng: Multiply the left column by 3 (the top number in the right column).

$$\begin{array}{ccc} 3(1) & \rightarrow & 3 \\ 3(-2) & \rightarrow & -6 \\ 3(3) & \rightarrow & 9 \end{array}$$

Zhichu: Subtract the right column from the left column once.

$$\begin{array}{ccc} 3 - 3 & \rightarrow & 0 \\ -6 - 1 & \rightarrow & -7 \\ 9 - 23 & \rightarrow & -14 \end{array}$$

Write a new equation and solve for y: $-7y = -14$ or $y = 2$.

Substitute and solve for x: $x - 2(2) = 3$ or $x = 7$.

LESSON 6.5

EXERCISES

1. a. Multiply by 4; $12 < 28$
   b. Multiply by -3; $-15 \geq -36$
   c. Add -10; $-14 \geq x - 10$
   d. Subtract 8; $b - 5 > 7$
   e. Divide by 3; $8d < 10\frac{2}{3}$
   f. Divide by -3; $-8x \geq -10\frac{2}{3}$

2. a. Answers will vary, but the values must be > 8.
   b. Answers will vary, but the values must be > -7.
   c. Answers will vary, but the values must be < 7.92.
   d. Answers will vary, but the values must be $< \frac{120}{13} = 9\frac{3}{13} \approx 9.2308$.

3. a. $x \leq -1$ **b.** $x > 0$ **c.** $x \geq -2$
   d. $-2 < x < 1$ **e.** $0 < x \leq 2$

4. a. $3 > x$ **b.** $y \geq -2$ **c.** $z \leq 12$ **d.** $n \leq 7$

5. a. $y = \dfrac{5.2 - 3x}{4} = 1.3 - 0.75x$
   b. $y = \dfrac{2x}{3} + 5$

6. Solution steps may vary.

a. $4.1 + 3.2x > 18$ Original inequality.
   $3.2x > 13.9$ Subtract 4.1 from both sides.
   $x > 4.34375 = \dfrac{139}{32}$ Divide both sides by 3.2.

b. $7.2 - 2.1b < 4.4$ Original inequality.
   $-2.1b < -2.8$ Subtract 7.2 from both sides.
   $b > 1.\overline{3}$ Divide both sides by -2.1 and reverse the inequality symbol.

c. $7 - 2(x - 3) \geq 25$ Original inequality.
   $7 - 2x + 6 \geq 25$ Apply the distributive property.
   $-2x + 13 \geq 25$ Add.
   $-2x \geq 12$ Subtract 13 from both sides.
   $x \leq -6$ Divide both sides by -2 and reverse the inequality symbol.

d. $11.5 + 4.5(x + 1.8) \leq x$ Original inequality.
   $11.5 + 4.5x + 8.1 \leq x$ Apply the distributive property.
   $19.6 + 4.5x \leq x$ Add.
   $19.6 \leq -3.5x$ Subtract $4.5x$ from both sides.
   $-5.6 \geq x$ or $x \leq -5.6$ Divide both sides by -3.5 and reverse the inequality symbol.

7. a. $3x - 2 \leq 7$ Original inequality.
   $3x \leq 9$ Add 2 to both sides.
   $x \leq 3$ Divide both sides by 3.

b. $4 - x > 6$ Original inequality.
   $-x > 2$ Subtract 4 from both sides.
   $x < -2$ Divide both sides by -1 and reverse the inequality symbol.

c. $3 + 2x \geq -3$ Original inequality.
   $2x \geq -6$ Subtract 3 from both sides.
   $x \geq -3$ Divide both sides by 2.

d. $10 \leq 2(5 - 3x)$ Original inequality.

    $10 \leq 10 - 6x$ Apply the distributive property.

    $0 \leq -6x$ Subtract 10 from both sides.

    $0 \geq x$ or $x \leq 0$ Divide both sides by -6 and reverse the inequality symbol.

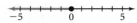

8. $50 + 7.5w > 120$; $w > 9.\overline{3}$. Ezra has been saving for at least 10 weeks.

9. a. Add 3 to both sides; $4 < 5$.

  b. Divide both sides by 2 (or multiply by 0.5); $3 > 1$.

  c. Multiply both sides by -3; $3 > -3$.

  d. Multiply both sides by 2; $0 < 6$.

10. a. $-9 < 9$ is true.   **b.** $21 \geq 51$ is false.

   c. $7 < 7$ is false.   **d.** $24 \geq 18$ is true.

11. a. $2x - 3 > 5x - 3x + 3$ Original inequality.

    $2x - 3 > 2x + 3$ Combine like terms.

      $-3 > 3$ Subtract $2x$ from both sides.

Because $-3 > 3$ is never true, the inequality has no solutions. You cannot graph this on a number line.

  b. $-2.2(5x + 3) \geq -11x - 15$ Original inequality.

    $-11x - 6.6 \geq -11x - 15$ Apply the distributive property.

        $-6.6 \geq -15$ Add $11x$ to both sides.

Because $-6.6 \geq -15$ is always true, every number is a solution.

12. a. $d \leq 30$, where d is the number of dollars spent on CDs

  b. $h \geq 48$, where h is the height of a rider

  c. $p \geq 3$, where p is the number of people in a carpool

  d. $a \geq 17$, where a is the age of a person who will be admitted

13. a. Multiply 12 by 3.2 to get 38.4. Subtract 38.4 from 72 to get 33.6.

  b. Square 5 to get 25. Subtract 25 from 3 to get -22. Multiply -22 by 1.5 to get -33. Add -33 to 2 to get -31.

  c. Divide 21 by 7 to get 3 and divide 6 by 2 to get 3. Subtract 3 from 3 to get 0.

14. a. 0.34 [ENTER], Ans + 0.21 [ENTER], [ENTER], . . .

Weight (oz)	Rate ($)
1	0.34
2	0.55
3	0.76
4	0.97
5	1.18
6	1.39
7	1.60
8	1.81
9	2.02
10	2.23
11	2.44

b.

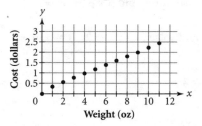

Postage Costs

c. A line would mean that the cost would pass through each amount between the different increments. For example, if a package weighed 0.5 ounce, you would pay $0.165. The line is not a useful way to show the costs because the cost increases discretely. Instead, you could draw segments for each whole ounce. Note the open and closed circles.

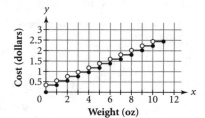

Postage Costs

d. $2.44

15. a. $-2x - 16$ **b.** $3 - 4y$ **c.** $-z + 5$

IMPROVING YOUR VISUAL THINKING SKILLS

- Three planes intersect in only one point if each pair of planes intersects in a line and the three lines intersect in one point. Such a system has one solution.

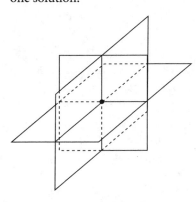

- If a system has an infinite number of solutions, the three equations might represent the same plane, but they might also represent planes that intersect in a line.

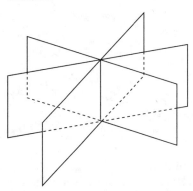

- If a system has no solutions, two of the planes may be parallel. Or two of the planes might intersect in a line and the third plane might be parallel to the line of intersection of the first two planes.

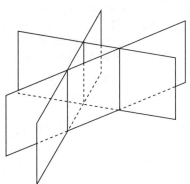

LESSON 6.6

EXERCISES

1. a. iii   **b.** ii   **c.** i   **d.** iv

2. a. $84x + 7y \geq 70$ Original inequality.

$7y \geq -84x + 70$ Add $-84x$ to both sides.

$y \geq -12x + 10$ Divide both sides by 7.

b. $4.8x - 0.12y < 7.2$ Original inequality.

$-0.12y < -4.8x + 7.2$ Add $-4.8x$ to both sides.

$y > 40x - 60$ Divide both sides by -0.12 and reverse the inequality symbol.

3. a.

b.

c.

d.

4. a.–c.

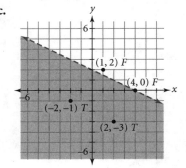

5. a.–c.

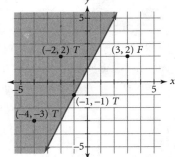

6. a. 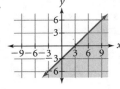   **b.**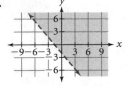

c.

7. a. $y \leq 1 - 2x$ **b.** $y < -2 + \frac{2}{3}x$

   c. $y > 1 - 0.5x$ **d.** $y \geq -2 + \frac{1}{3}x$

8.   **i.** *A, C, D, F, J*   **ii.** *B, C, D, F, I*

   iii. *B, C, D, F, G, I*   **iv.** *A, E, H, J*

    v. *A, E, G, H, J*   **vi.** *B, E, G, H, I*

  vii. *A, D, E, G, H, J*   **viii.** *B, C, F, I*

9. a. 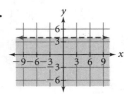   **b.**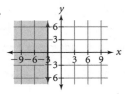

   c. 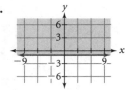   **d.**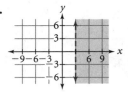

10. a. $F + 2S < 84$ **b.** $F + 2S = 84$

   c.

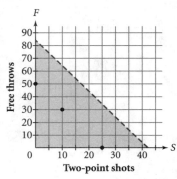

   d. Answers will vary. One possible answer, indicated by dots on the graph, is (0, 50), (10, 30), and (25, 0).

11.

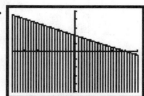

$[-5, 5, 1, -5, 5, 1]$

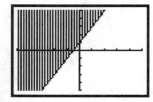

12. a.

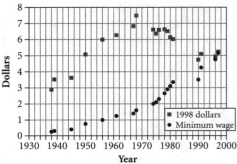

   b. The data for minimum wage is more linear than the data for equivalent dollars.

   c. Using the Q-points (1956, 1.00) and (1981, 3.35), the equation is
$y = 3.35 + 0.094(x - 1981)$
or $y = 1.00 + 0.094(x - 1956)$
or $y = -182.864 + 0.094x$.

   d.

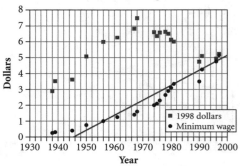

   e. The minimum wage has increased 9¢ every year on average. The actual dollar value has decreased since 1978 and was highest in 1968.

13. a. About 27 mph

   b. Possible explanation: Because $d = r \cdot t$, and the distance was the same for both Ellie and her grandmother, you can set the product of rate and time for Ellie equal to the product of rate and time for her grandmother. If you let r represent Ellie's grandmother's speed, then $2.5(65) = 6r$.

14. a. $y = \frac{7}{3}x - \frac{22}{3}$ **b.** $y = -\frac{5}{4}x - 3$

LESSON 6.7

EXERCISES

1. a. iii   **b.** i   **c.** ii

2. a. Yes. (1, 2) satisfies both inequalities.

b. No. $2 > 3$ is not true, so the first inequality is not satisfied.

c. No. $\frac{4}{3} > \frac{4}{3}$ is not true, so neither inequality is satisfied.

d. No. Because both $-3 > 5$ and $-3 > 2 - \frac{1}{2}(5)$ are false, neither inequality is satisfied.

3. a. $y \geq -x + 2;\ y \geq x - 2$

b.

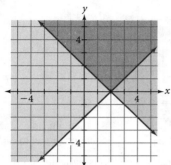

4. a.

b.

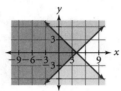

5. $\begin{cases} y > 2 - x \\ y < 2 \\ x < 3 \end{cases}$

6. a. The three inequalities are $y \geq -1250 + 0.40x$, $y \leq -1250 + 1.00x$, and $x \geq 0$.

b.

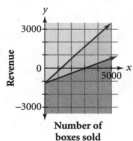

7. $\begin{cases} A \leq C \\ A + C \leq 75 \\ A \geq 0 \\ C \geq 0 \end{cases}$

b. All the points in the dark-shaded triangular region satisfy the system of inequalities. The point (50, 10) represents the situation in which 50 children escort 10 adults.

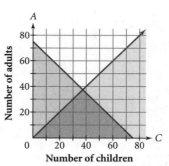

c. Answers will vary. It is possible to have all children and no adults at the restaurant. One possible additional constraint is that there must be at least one adult per five children, or $A \geq \frac{1}{5}C$. The solution for this set of constraints is shown below.

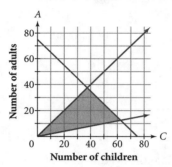

8. a. $r = 220 - a$, where a represents age in years and r represents the heart rate in beats per minute.

b. $\begin{cases} r \leq 0.90(220 - a) \\ r \geq 0.55(220 - a) \end{cases}$ or $\begin{cases} r \leq 198 - 0.09a \\ r \geq 121 - 0.55a \end{cases}$

c.

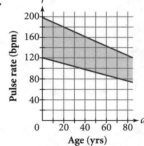

d. $a \geq 14$ and $a \leq 40$

e.

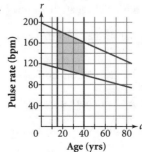

9. $x \geq 3$ and $y \geq -2 + \frac{1}{2}x$

10. $AB: y \leq \frac{2}{3}x + \frac{5}{3}$; $BC: y \leq -\frac{3}{5}x + \frac{59}{5}$;

$AC: y \geq \frac{1}{11}x + \frac{31}{11}$

11. The region is a pentagon.

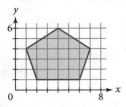

12. Region 1: $\begin{cases} y \geq 3 \\ y \geq x - 2 \\ y \leq \frac{1}{3}x + \frac{8}{3} \end{cases}$ Region 2: $\begin{cases} y \leq 3 \\ y \leq x - 2 \\ y \geq \frac{1}{3}x \end{cases}$

13. a. \$713.15   **b.** \$957.80

14. About 263 feet

15. a. 4   **b.** 10

c. $\dfrac{10((3x + 12) \div 5 - 1.4) - 10}{6}$

16. a. $x = 6, y = 21$ **b.** $x = -2, y = -1$

IMPROVING YOUR REASONING SKILLS

Crows	Cries
9	729
99	970,299
999	997,002,999
9,999	999,700,029,999
99,999	999,970,000,299,999

The TI-83 calculator begins rounding at 9,999 crows.

CHAPTER 6 Review

EXERCISES

1. Line a: $y = 1 - x$; line b: $y = 3 + \frac{5}{2}x$. To find the intersection point, you can solve the system using substitution:

$y = 3 + \frac{5}{2}x$	Original equation for line b.
$1 - x = 3 + \frac{5}{2}x$	Substitute $1 - x$ (from the line a equation) for y.
$-2 - x = \frac{5}{2}x$	Subtract 3 from both sides.
$-2 = \frac{7}{2}x$	Add x to both sides.
$-\frac{4}{7} = x$	Multiply both sides by $\frac{2}{7}$.

Using the equation for line a, $y = 1 - \left(-\frac{4}{7}\right) = \frac{11}{7}$. So, the point of intersection is $\left(-\frac{4}{7}, \frac{11}{7}\right)$.

2. One way to find the point of intersection is to solve the system by elimination. Adding the equations gives $4x = 16$, so $x = 4$. Substituting 4 for x in either equation gives $y = 1$. So, the point of intersection is $(4, 1)$. Check: $3(4) - 2(1) = 10$, $(4) + 2(1) = 6$.

3. The point of intersection is $(3.75, 4.625)$.

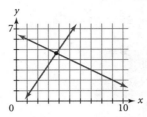

4. Solution steps may vary.

$16 + 4.3(x - 5)$ $= -7 + 4.2x$	Set the right sides of the equations equal to each other.
$16 + 4.3x - 21.5$ $= -7 + 4.2x$	Apply the distributive property.
$-5.5 + 4.3x$ $= -7 + 4.2x$	Subtract.
$0.1x = -1.5$	Add $-4.2x$ and 5.5 to both sides.
$x = -15$	Divide both sides by 0.1.
$y = -7 + 4.2(-15)$	Substitute -15 for x in the second equation and find y.
$y = -70$	Multiply and add.

The solution is $x = -15$ and $y = -70$.

5. a. The lines have the same slope but different y-intercepts (the lines are parallel).

b. The slopes are the same and the intercepts are the same (the equations represent the same line).

c. The lines have different slopes (the lines intersect in a single point).

6. a. $x > -1$ **b.** $x < 2$ **c.** $-2 \leq x < 1$

7. $x \leq -1$

8. $\begin{cases} y \leq x + 4 \\ y \leq -1.25x + 8.5 \\ y \geq 1 \end{cases}$

9. a. $\dfrac{15 \text{ m} \times 12 \text{ m}}{18 \text{ min}} = 10 \text{ m}^2/\text{min}$

b. $\dfrac{20 \text{ m} \times 14 \text{ m}}{40 \text{ min}} = 7 \text{ m}^2/\text{min}$

c. No. The area of Mr. Fleming's lawn is 396 m². Using his plan, Harold will cut only 10 m²/min · 10 min + 7 m²/min · 8 min, or 156 m².

d. $10h + 7l = 396$ **e.** $\frac{0.6l}{18 \text{ min}} = \frac{1}{30} \, l/\text{min}$

f. $\frac{0.6\, l}{40 \text{ min}} = \frac{3}{200} \, l/\text{min}$

g. Yes. He will use $\frac{1}{30} \, l/\text{min} \cdot 10 \text{ min} +$ $\frac{3}{200} \, l/\text{min} \cdot 8 \text{ min}$, or $\frac{34}{75}$ liter, and the tank holds 1.2 liters.

h. $\frac{h}{30} + \frac{3l}{200} = 1.2$

i. $l = 14.4 \text{ min}, h = 29.52 \text{ min}$

j. If he cuts for 29.52 minutes at the higher speed and 14.4 minutes at the lower speed, he will finish Mr. Fleming's lawn and use one full tank of gas.

10. $\begin{bmatrix} 1 & 0 & -3 \\ 0 & 1 & -8 \end{bmatrix}$

TAKE ANOTHER LOOK

If x is the number of scooters and y is the number of skateboards, then the following system describes the constraints:

$$\begin{cases} x \le 6000 \\ y \le 8000 \\ x + y \le 10{,}000 \\ x \ge 0 \\ y \ge 0 \end{cases}$$

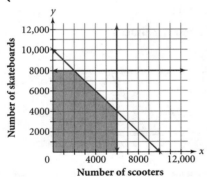

Profit: $15x + 10y$

Substituting the coordinates (6000, 4000) gives \$130,000, which is the greatest possible profit.

CHAPTER 7

LESSON 7.1

EXERCISES

1. a. Starting value: 16; multiplier: 1.25; 7th term: 61.035

b. Starting value: 27; multiplier: $\frac{2}{3}$ or $0.\overline{6}$; 7th term: $2.\overline{370}$ or $\frac{64}{27}$

2. $\{0, 100\}$ ENTER, $\{\text{Ans}(1) + 1, \text{Ans}(2) \cdot -1.6\}$ ENTER, ENTER, ... The first six terms are 100, −160, 256, −409.6, 655.36, −1048.576.

3. The constant multiplier is $(1 + 0.40)$ or 1.4, so the recursive routine is $\{0, 72\}$ ENTER, $\{\text{Ans}(1) + 1, \text{Ans}(2) \cdot (1 + 0.4)\}$ ENTER, ENTER, ... The first five terms are 72, 100.8, 141.12, 197.568, 276.5952.

4. a. $75(1 + 0.02)$ or $75(1.02)$

b. $1000(1 - 0.18)$ or $1000(0.82)$

c. $P(1 + r)$ **d.** $75 - 75 \cdot 0.02$

e. $80 - 80 \cdot 0.24$ **f.** $A - A \cdot r$

5. $\{0, 32\}$ ENTER, $\{\text{Ans}(1) + 1, \text{Ans}(2) \cdot 0.75\}$ ENTER, ENTER, ... Stage 2 has a shaded area of 18 square units.

6. a. $\{0, 20000\}$ ENTER, $\{\text{Ans}(1) + 1, \text{Ans}(2) \cdot (1 - 0.04)\}$ ENTER, ENTER, ...

b. The 5th term, \$16,986.93, represents the selling price of the car after four price reductions.

c. 17 weeks (the18th term of the sequence)

7. a. $\{0, 115\}$ ENTER, $\{\text{Ans}(1) + 1, \text{Ans}(2) \cdot (1 - 0.03)\}$ ENTER, ENTER, ...

b. 12 minutes

8. a. Increasing; starting value: 75; percent of increase: 2%

b. Decreasing; starting value: 1000; percent of decrease: 18%

c. Increasing; starting value: P; percent of increase: $(100 \cdot r)\%$

d. Decreasing; starting value: 75; percent of decrease: 2%

e. Decreasing; starting value: 80; percent of decrease: 24%

f. Decreasing; starting value A; percent of decrease: $(100 \cdot r)\%$

9. a. $\{0, 6.9\}$ ENTER, $\{\text{Ans}(1) + 1, \text{Ans}(2) \cdot (1 + 0.142)\}$ ENTER, ENTER, ...

b.

Year	Elapsed time (yrs), x	Spending (\$ billion), y
1970	0	6.9
1975	5	13.4
1980	10	26.0
1985	15	50.6
1990	20	98.2
1995	25	190.8
2000	30	370.5
2005	35	719.7

c.

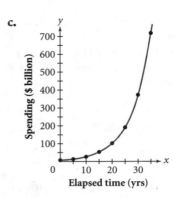

d. Answers will vary. The graph implies a smooth, ever-increasing amount of Medicare spending, which is probably not realistic.

10. a. $2 \text{ m} \cdot 0.85 = 1.7 \text{ m}$

b. $\{0, 2\}$ ENTER, $\{Ans(1) + 1, Ans(2) \cdot 0.85\}$ ENTER, ENTER, ...

c. Approximately 0.75 m

d. Approximately 1.97 feet. (Use the recursive routine $\{0, 10\}$ ENTER, $\{Ans(1) + 1, Ans(2) \cdot 0.85\}$ ENTER, ENTER, ...)

e. 19

f. Answers will vary. Sample answer: The mean of the rebound heights is 1.7 m, which is 85% of 2 m, and the median and mode are both 1.68 m, which is 84% of 2 m. However, only two of the balls tested met or exceeded 85% of the drop height, so I don't think the claim is fair.

11. a. *(See table at bottom of page.)*

b. *(See table at bottom of page.)*

c. The graph of the first plan is linear. The graph of the second is not; its slope increases between consecutive points.

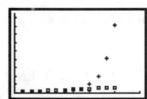

$[0, 15, 3, 0, 4750, 500]$

d. Possible answer: She should choose option 2 because the total donation is more than 12 times as much as with option 1.

12. $y = -1.2(x - 600)$; y-intercept: $(0, 720)$

13. a. i   **b.** iii   **c.** ii   **d.** iv

14. a. Let x represent the number of minutes of use, and let y represent the cost. $y = 12$

b. $y = 12 + 0.05(x - 60)$

c. $y = 10$ for 50 minutes or less of use; $y = 10 + 0.09(x - 50)$ for more than 50 minutes of use.

d. First plan: $16.50; second plan: $19.00. She should sign up for the first plan.

e. First plan: $12.00 (he pays only the flat rate of $12.00); second plan: $10.45. He should sign up for the second plan.

f. The solution of the system $\begin{cases} y = 12 + 0.05(x - 60) \\ y = 10 + 0.09(x - 50) \end{cases}$ is 87.5. So the plans cost the same for 87.5 minutes of use. The companies probably charge for whole minutes, so a person who thinks he or she will talk more than 87 minutes per month should choose the first plan. A person who thinks he or she will talk for less than 87 minutes per month should choose the second plan.

IMPROVING YOUR GEOMETRY SKILLS

Possible answers:

LESSON 7.2

EXERCISES

1. a. 7^8 **b.** $3^4 \cdot 5^5$ **c.** $(1 + 0.12)^4$

2. a. $450(1 + 0.2) = 540$ bacteria

b. $450(1 + 0.2)^7 \approx 1612$ bacteria

Exercise 11. a.

	Jan	Feb	Mar	Apr	May	June	July	Aug	Sep	Oct	Nov	Dec
Option 1	$50	$25	$25	$25	$25	$25	$25	$25	$25	$25	$25	$25
Option 2	$1	$2	$4	$8	$16	$32	$64	$128	$256	$512	$1,024	$2,048

Exercise 11. b.

	Jan	Feb	Mar	Apr	May	June	July	Aug	Sep	Oct	Nov	Dec
Option 1	$50	$75	$100	$125	$150	$175	$200	$225	$250	$275	$300	$325
Option 2	$1	$3	$7	$15	$31	$63	$127	$255	$511	$1,023	$2,047	$4,095

3. a. ii; $y = 4(2)^x$ has starting value 4 and constant multiplier 2. This matches table ii.

b. iii; $y = 4(0.5)^x$ has starting value 4 and constant multiplier 0.5. This matches table iii.

c. iv; $y = 2(4)^x$ has starting value 2 and constant multiplier 4. This matches table iv.

d. i; $y = 2(0.25)^x$ has starting value 2 and constant multiplier 0.25. This matches table i.

4. a. iv; the starting value is 1.05, and the constant multiplier is 0.95 or $(1 - 0.05)$. This matches equation iv.

b. ii; the starting value is 1.05, and the constant multiplier is $1 + 0.05$. This matches equation ii.

c. i; the starting value is 0.95, and the constant multiplier is $1 + 0.05$ or 1.05. This matches equation i.

d. iii; the starting value is 0.95, and the multiplier is $1 - 0.05$ or 0.95. This matches equation iii.

5. a. A is the starting value, or the value of y when $x = 0$. In this case, $A = 1.2$. r is the ratio of consecutive y-values (or the value each y-value is multiplied by to get the next, consecutive, y-value). For this table, $r = 2$. So, the equation is $y = 1.2 \cdot 2^x$.

b. The starting value (the value of y when $x = 0$) is 500. When $x = 2$, $y = 20$, and when $x = 3$, $y = 4$, which is $0.2 \cdot 20$. So, the value of r is 0.2. The equation is $y = 500 \cdot 0.2^x$.

c. The y-values for $x = 1, 2$, and 3 are 50, 20, and 8, respectively. Each y-value is 0.4 times the previous y-value, so the value of r is 0.4. To find the starting value, work backward: 50 (the y-value for $x = 1$) must be 0.4 times A (the y-value for $x = 0$), so $A = 50 \div 0.4 = 125$. The equation is $y = 125 \cdot 0.4^x$.

6. The number 500 represents an initial deposit of \$500. The multiplier $(1 + 0.04)$ means the account earns 4% interest each year. The variable x represents the number of years since the initial deposit. The variable y represents the balance after x years.

7. Students will self-check their work as they run the program.

8. The rate of growth is 4.5% per month, so the multiplier is $(1 + 0.045)$. An expression for the amount Stanley will owe after 4 months is $100(1 + 0.045)(1 + 0.045)(1 + 0.045)(1 + 0.045)$ or $100(1 + 0.045)^4$. Evaluating either expression gives about 119.25, so he will owe \$119.25.

9. a. The rate of decrease is 20% or 0.2, so the constant multiplier is $(1 - 0.2)$. After 1 year, the truck's value will be $11500(1 - 0.2)$ or \$9,200.

b. {0, 11500} ENTER,
{Ans(1) + 1, Ans(2) $\cdot$ (1 − 0.2)}
ENTER, ENTER, . . .

c.

Time elapsed (yrs)	Value (\$)
0	11,500
1	9,200
2	7,360
3	5,888
4	4,710.40

d. $y = 11{,}500(1 - 0.2)^x$

e.

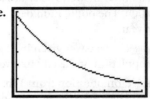

[0, 10, 1, 0, 12000, 2000]

10. a. 6 cm   **b.** 18 cm

c. The length of each segment is 3 times the length of the previous segment. The initial length is 2, so the length of the next segment is $2 \cdot 3 \cdot 3 \cdot 3$ or $2(3)^3$.

d. $2(3)^7 = 4{,}374$ and $2(3)^8 = 13{,}122$, so the longest segment that is less than 100 m (or 10,000 cm) has length $2(3)^7$.

11. Students will self-check their work as they run the program.

12. a. The number of layers doubles with each fold.

b. Estimates will vary.

c. Methods will vary. Eight folds gives 256 layers (512 pages), and nine folds gives 512 layers (1024 pages).

13. a. $y = 5000(1 + 0.05)^x$

b.

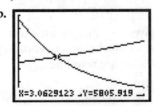

X=3.0629123 Y=5805.919

[0, 10, 1, 0, 12000, 2000]

The intersection point represents the time and the value of both cars when their value will be the same. By tracing the graph shown, students should see that both cars will be worth approximately \$5,806 after a little less than 3 years 1 month.

14. Answers will vary. Sample answer: The first equation could model a principal of \$400 to which \$20 is added each time period. The second equation could model a starting balance of \$400, with 5% interest added each time period. Both models have the same starting value, 400. In both models, $y = 420$ when $x = 1$. For x greater than 1, y increases much more quickly in the second model.

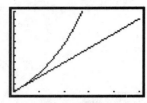

[0, 50, 10, 400, 1500, 100]

15. a. Answers will vary. Sample answer: A city has a population of 100,000. The population decreases by about 3.5% per year.

b. Sample problem based on answer given in 15a: What will be the population of the city in 7 years?

c. Sample solution based on question from 15b: $y = 100(1 - 0.035)^7 \approx 77.9$, so the population in 7 years will be about 77.9 thousand or 77,900.

16. a.

Number of steps, x	1	2	3	4
Perimeter (cm), y	4	8	12	16

b.

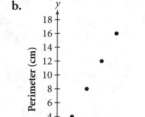

c. $y = 4x$, where y is the perimeter and x is the number of steps

d. 188 cm

e. Solving $74 = 4x$ gives $x = 18.5$. Because it is impossible to have a nonwhole number of steps, a perimeter of 74 cm is not possible.

LESSON 7.3

Exercises

1. a. $(5)(x)(x)(x)(x) = 5x^4$

b. $3x^4 \cdot 5x^6 = 3 \cdot 5 \cdot x^{4+6} = 15x^{10}$

c. $4x^7 \cdot 2x^3 = 4 \cdot 2 \cdot x^{7+3} = 8x^{10}$

d. $(-2x^2)(x^2 + x^4) = (-2x^2)(x^2) + (-2x^2)(x^4)$
$= -2x^{2+2} - 2x^{2+4} = -2x^4 - 2x^6$

2. a. $(3 \cdot 3 \cdot 3 \cdot 3 \cdot 3)(3 \cdot 3 \cdot 3 \cdot 3 \cdot 3 \cdot 3 \cdot 3 \cdot 3)$
$= 3^{13}$

b. $(7 \cdot 7 \cdot 7)(7 \cdot 7 \cdot 7 \cdot 7) = 7^7$

c. $(x \cdot x \cdot x \cdot x \cdot x \cdot x)(x \cdot x) = x^8$

d. $(y \cdot y \cdot y \cdot y \cdot y \cdot y \cdot y \cdot y)(y \cdot y \cdot y \cdot y \cdot y) = y^{13}$

e. $(x \cdot x \cdot y \cdot y \cdot y \cdot y)(x \cdot y \cdot y \cdot y)$
$= (x \cdot x \cdot x)(y \cdot y \cdot y \cdot y \cdot y \cdot y \cdot y) = x^3 y^7$

3. a. 3^{40} **b.** 7^{12} **c.** x^{12} **d.** y^{40}

4. a. $(rt)^2 = r^2 t^2$ **b.** $(x^2 y)^3 = x^{2 \cdot 3} y^3 = x^6 y^3$

c. $(4x)^5 = 1024x^5$

d. $(2x^4 y^2 z^5)^3 = 2^3 x^{4 \cdot 3} y^{2 \cdot 3} z^{5 \cdot 3} = 8x^{12} y^6 z^{15}$

5. Student 2 was correct. According to the order of operations, squaring should be done before multiplication.

6. a, d, and g; b and f; c and h; e has no match.

7. a, d, and g: 27,521.40084

b and f: 11,711.2344

c and h: 1060.32

e: 129,350.5839

8. a. $3x^2 \cdot 2x^4 = 3 \cdot 2 \cdot x^{2+4} = 6x^6$

b. $5x^2 y^3 \cdot 4x^4 y^5 = 5 \cdot 4 \cdot x^{2+4} \cdot y^{3+5} = 20x^6 y^8$

c. $2x^2 \cdot 3x^3 y^4 = 2 \cdot 3 \cdot x^{2+3} y^4 = 6x^5 y^4$

d. $x^3 \cdot 4x^4 = 4x^{3+4} = 4x^7$

9. Enclose the -5 in parentheses.

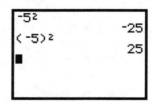

10. a. $2(3)^2 + 3(3) + 1 = 18 + 9 + 1 = 28$

b. $2(5)^2 + 3(5) + 1 = 50 + 15 + 1 = 66$

c. $2(-2)^2 + 3(-2) + 1 = 8 - 6 + 1 = 3$

d. $2(0)^2 + 3(0) + 1 = 0 + 0 + 1 = 1$

11. Possible answers:

a. $x^3 \cdot x^5 = x^8$ **b.** $(x^3)^5 = x^{15}$

c. $(3x)^5 = 3^5 x^5 = 243x^5$

d. Exponents are added when you multiply two exponential expressions with the same base. Exponents are multiplied when an exponential expression is raised to a power. An exponent is distributed when a product is raised to a power.

12. a. $500(1 + 0.015)^6$; $546.72

b. $46.72

c. $500(1 + 0.015)^{12}$; $597.81

d. $51.09

e. Answers will vary. The increase is greater between 6 and 12 months because the interest each month is a percent of a greater current balance.

13. a. $x(x^3 + x^4) = x \cdot x^3 + x \cdot x^4 = x^{1+3}x^{1+4} = x^4 + x^5$

b. $(-2x^2)(x^2 + x^4) = (-2x^2)(x^2) + (-2x^2)(x^4)$
$= -2x^{2+2} - 2x^{2+4} = -2x^4 - 2x^6$

c. $2.5x^{4.2}(6.8x^{3.3} + 3.4x^{4.2})$
$= (2.5x^{4.2})(6.8x^{3.3}) + (2.5x^{4.2})(3.4x^{4.2})$
$= 17x^{4.2+3.3} + 8.5x^{4.2+4.2} = 17x^{7.5} + 8.5x^{8.4}$

14. a. $3x \cdot 5x^3 = 15x^4$　　**b.** $x \cdot x^5 = x^6$

c. $2x^3 \cdot 2x^3 = 4x^6$

d. $3.5(x + 0.15)^4 \cdot (x + 0.15)^2$
$= 3(x + 0.15)^{4+2} = 3.5(x + 0.15)^6$

e. $(2x^3)^3 = 8x^9$

f. $(3(x + 0.05)^3)^2 = 3^2 \cdot (x + 0.05)^{3 \cdot 2}$
$= 9(x + 0.05)^6$

15. a. $4.5x - 47$

b. $4.5x - 47 > 0; x > 10.\overline{4}$. He must shovel 11 sidewalks to pay for his equipment.

c. $4.5x - 47 > 100, x > 32.\overline{6}$. He must shovel 33 sidewalks to pay for his expenses and buy a lawn mower.

16. $y \approx 8.81 - 1.87x$

17. a. $(5.3625, 0.70625)$

b. Approximately $(3.095, 0.762)$

LESSON 7.4

EXERCISES

1. a. $34,000,000,000 = 3.4 \times 10,000,000,000$
$= 3.4 \times 10^{10}$

b. $-2,100,000 = -2.1 \times 1,000,000 = -2.1 \times 10^6$

c. $10,060 = 1.006 \times 10,000 = 1.006 \times 10^4$

2. a. $7.4 \times 10^4 = 7.4 \times 10,000 = 74,000$

b. $-2.134 \times 10^6 = -2.134 \times 1,000,000$
$= -2,134,000$

c. $4.01 \times 10^3 = 4.01 \times 1000 = 4010$

3. a. $12x^6$　　**b.** $7y^{16}$

c. $2b^6 + b^5$　　**d.** $10x^4 - 6x^2$

4. a. $12x^5$　　**b.** $81y^{12}$

c. $50x^{11}$　　**d.** $27m^6n^9$

5. $3.5 \times 10^7 = 3.5 \cdot 10 \cdot 10 \cdot 10 \cdot 10 \cdot 10 \cdot 10 \cdot 10$
$= 35,000,000$;

$3.5^7 = 3.5 \cdot 3.5 \cdot 3.5 \cdot 3.5 \cdot 3.5 \cdot 3.5 \cdot 3.5$
$= 6433.9296875$

6. Because there are 3000 grams in 3 kilograms, multiply the number of atoms in 1 gram by 3000.

$3000 \times 5.58 \times 10^{21} = 3 \times 10^3 \times 5.58 \times 10^{21}$
$= (3 \cdot 5.58) \times 10^{3+21}$

$(3 \cdot 5.58) \times 10^{3+21} = 16.74 \times 10^{24}$
$= 1.674 \times 10 \times 10^{24}$
$= 1.674 \times 10^{25}$ atoms

7. a. $55.5 \times 6.02 \times 10^{23} = 334.11 \times 10^{23}$
$= 3.3411 \times 10^2 \times 10^{23} = 3.3411 \times 10^{25}$

b. $(6.02 \times 10^{23}) \times (6.02 \times 10^{23})$
$= 6.02^2 \times 10^{23+23}$
$= 36.2404 \times 10^{46}$
$= 3.62404 \times 10 \times 10^{46}$
$= 3.62404 \times 10^{47}$
$\approx 3.6 \times 10^{47}$

8. Answers will vary based on model of calculator used.

a. 2.5×10^2; 2.5E2　　**b.** 7.42×10^{12}; 7.42E12

c. -1.8×10^1; -1.8E1

9. a. Yes; both equal 51,800,000,000.

b. Al's answer

c. Possible answer: 518×10^8

d. Rewrite the number before the power of 10 in scientific notation. Then use the multiplication property of exponents to add the exponents on the 10's. For the example given, $4.325 \times 10^2 \times 10^3$
$= 4.325 \times 10^5$.

10. a. i. 6×10^{13}　　**ii.** 8.2×10^8

b. Regroup, multiply the numbers, and multiply the powers of 10 by adding the exponents. So, $(2 \times 10^5)(3 \times 10^8) = 2 \times 3 \times 10^5 \times 10^8$
$= 6 \times 10^{13}$.

c. $(4 \times 10^5)(6 \times 10^7) = 4 \times 6 \times 10^5 \times 10^7$
$= 24 \times 10^{12} = 2.4 \times 10^1 \times 10^{12} = 2.4 \times 10^{13}$

11. a. $2,000,000,000$; 2×10^9

b. $365 \times 2 \times 10^9 = 730 \times 10^9 = 7.3 \times 10^2 \times 10^9$
$= 7.3 \times 10^{11}$, so Americans make 7.3×10^{11} calls per year.

12. a. Because 60 minutes $= 1.5 \cdot 40$ minutes, a person sheds $1.5 \cdot 1,000,000$ or 1.5×10^6 cells per hour.

b. $365 \times 24 \times 1.5 \times 10^6$ or 1.314×10^{10} cells per year

13. a. 9.46×10^{12} km; 1.0×10^5 light-years

b. 9.46×10^{17} km

c. $\dfrac{(9.46 \times 10^{17})}{(1.27 \times 10^4)} \approx 7.45 \times 10^{13}$

14. a. 3.8 is the population (in millions) in 1900, 0.017 is the annual growth rate, t is the elapsed time in years since 1900, and P is the population (in millions) t years after 1900.

b. Answer depends on the current year. The interval is $0 \le t \le (current\ year - 1900)$.

c. Axes limits will vary depending on the current year. Here is a graph for the years from 0 through 2000.

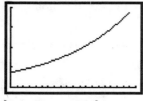

[0, 100, 5, 0, 20, 5]

d. Approximately 8.8 million

e. Answers will vary depending on the current year; $P = 3.8(1 + 0.017)^{50} \cdot (1 + 0.017)^{(\text{current year}-1950)}$

15.

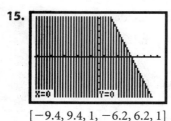

$[-9.4, 9.4, 1, -6.2, 6.2, 1]$

IMPROVING YOUR REASONING SKILLS

The answer is 27,682,574,402. The trick is finding a constant multiplier for the number of pairs of rats, not the number of individual rats. An exponential model is $2(7)^x$; 7 is the constant multiplier for pairs of rats (if each pair has 6 pairs of babies, then their number is increased 7 times); the 2 doubles the number of pairs, so the final answer is the number of individual rats. On a TI-83 Plus, the answer is shown in scientific notation as 2.76825744E10—the last two digits are not shown. If students subtract 27000000000, the result is 682574402 and the final two digits are revealed.

LESSON 7.5

EXERCISES

1. x^3y

2. a. $7^{12-4} = 7^8$
   b. $x^{11-5} = x^6$
   c. $\dfrac{12}{3}x^{5-2} = 4x^3$
   d. $\dfrac{7}{14}x^{6-3}y^{3-1} = 0.5x^3y^2$

3. Possible answer: $\dfrac{3^6}{3^2}$ means that there are 6 factors of 3 in the numerator and 2 factors of 3 in the denominator. That is, $\dfrac{3^6}{3^2} = \dfrac{3 \cdot 3 \cdot 3 \cdot 3 \cdot 3 \cdot 3}{3 \cdot 3}$. You can rewrite this as 2 factors of $\frac{3}{3}$, or 1, times 4 factors of 3. That is, $\frac{3}{3} \cdot \frac{3}{3} \cdot 3 \cdot 3 \cdot 3 \cdot 3 = \cdot 3 \cdot 3 \cdot 3 \cdot 3$. So $\dfrac{3^6}{3^2} = 3 \cdot 3 \cdot 3 \cdot 3 = 3^4$.

4. a. A
   b. y is the current value, which is 10,000; r is the rate of appreciation, which is 10% or 0.1; and x is the number of years the value has been appreciating, which is 20. So, the equation is $10,000 = A(1 + 0.1)^{20}$.

c.
$10,000 = A(1 + 0.1)^{20}$	Original equation.
$\dfrac{10,000}{(1 + 0.1)^{20}} = A$	Divide both sides by $(1 + 0.1)^{20}$.
$1486.43 \approx A$	Evaluate the exponential expression and divide.

The furniture was worth about $1,486 twenty years ago.

5. a. $(2x)^3 \cdot (3x^2)^4 = 8x^3 \cdot 81x^8 = 648x^{11}$
   b. $\dfrac{(5x)^7}{(5x)^5} = (5x)^{7-5} = (5x)^2 = 25x^2$
   c. $\dfrac{(2x)^5}{-8x^3} = \dfrac{32x^5}{-8x^3} = -4x^2$
   d. $(4x^2y^5) \cdot (-3xy^3)^3 = 4x^2y^5 \cdot (-3)^3x^3y^9$
      $= 4 \cdot -27 \cdot x^5y^{14} = -108x^5y^{14}$

6. $\dfrac{1.5 \times 10^{11}}{3 \times 10^3} = 0.5 \times 10^3 = 0.5 \times 1000 = 500$. So it takes 500 seconds, or about 8 minutes, for light to travel from the sun to the earth.

7. a. $\dfrac{1.0 \times 10^8}{7.6 \times 10^5} \approx 0.132 \times 10^3 = 0.132 \times 1000 = 132$. So the population density of Mexico was about 132 people per square mile.
   b. $\dfrac{1.3 \times 10^8}{1.5 \times 10^5} \approx 0.867 \times 10^3 = 0.867 \times 1000 = 867$. So the population density of Japan was about 867 people per square mile.
   c. The population density of Japan was about 6.6 times that of Mexico.

8. a. $5000(1 + 0.0025)^8 \approx 5100.88$. So they have $5,100.88.
   b. $5000(1 + 0.0025)^5 \approx 5062.81$. So they would have had $5,062.81.
   c. $5000(1 + 0.0025)^{10} \approx 5126.42$. So they will have $5,126.42.

9. Four days earlier. Possible solution methods:
   Method 1: Use a recursive routine.
   $\{0, 864\}$ ENTER,
   $\{\text{Ans}(1) + 1, \text{Ans}(2)/3\}$ ENTER, ENTER, . . .
   Method 2: Input the equation $y = 864\left(\frac{1}{3}\right)^x$ into a calculator. Then, look at the table to find the first x-value for which the corresponding y-value is less than 20.

10. $120,000(1 + 0.02)^{-5} \approx 108,688$. So 5 years ago the population was about 108,688.

11. a. $\dfrac{800,000,000}{25} = \dfrac{8 \times 10^8}{2.5 \times 10^1} = 3.2 \times 10^7$. So an elephant lives 3.2×10^7 minutes or about 61 years.
   b. $\dfrac{800,000,000}{1150} = \dfrac{8 \times 10^8}{1.15 \times 10^3} = 6.96 \times 10^5$. So a pygmy shrew lives 6.96×10^5 minutes or about 1.3 years.

c. $\frac{800,000,000}{60} = \frac{8 \times 10^8}{6 \times 10^1} \approx 1.33 \times 10^7$. So, you would expect a human to live 1.33×10^7 minutes or about 25.4 years.

12. First, convert 57,000 tons to pounds:

57,000 tons $\cdot \dfrac{2000 \text{ pounds}}{1 \text{ ton}} = 114,000,000$ pounds

$= 1.14 \times 10^8$ pounds

Use the fact that it takes 8 ounces, or 0.5 pound, of cotton to make a T-shirt to find the number of T-shirts that can be made with 1.14×10^8 pounds:

1.14×10^8 pounds $\cdot \dfrac{1 \text{ T-shirt}}{0.5 \text{ pound}}$

$= 2.28 \times 10^8$ T-shirts

Now, figure out how many T-shirts this is for each of the 275 million people in the United States:

$\dfrac{2.28 \times 10^8 \text{ T-shirts}}{2.75 \times 10^8 \text{ people}} \approx 0.83 \times 10^0$ T-shirts per person

$= 8.3 \times 10^{-1}$ T-shirts per person

13. Use dimensional analysis to find how many flowers it takes to make 1 ounce of honey.

$\dfrac{3 \times 10^{12} \text{ flowers}}{3.3 \times 10^3 \text{ tons}} \cdot \dfrac{1 \text{ ton}}{2 \times 10^3 \text{ pounds}} \cdot \dfrac{1 \text{ pound}}{16 \text{ ounces}}$

$\approx 2.84 \times 10^4$ flowers per ounce

So, to make 8 ounces of honey, it takes $8 \times 2.84 \times 10^4$ or about 2.272×10^5 flowers.

14. 14 years

15. a. (Answers recorded to tenths.) Mercury: 4.1 cm; Venus: 10 cm; Earth: 10.5 cm; Mars: 5.6 cm; Jupiter: 117.3 cm; Saturn: 94.7 cm; Uranus: 69.3 cm; Neptune: 41.3 cm; Pluto: 2 cm; Sun: 1152 cm. One way to find these answers is to set up and solve proportions of the form $\frac{planet's\ diameter}{Pluto's\ diameter} = \frac{x\ cm}{2\ cm}$, where x is the diameter of the planet in the model.

b. Possible answer: Halley should make her models much smaller because the model of Jupiter is 1 m in diameter and the model of the sun is greater than 11 m in diameter. It might be better to leave the sun out of her models altogether. If she makes Pluto with a diameter of 0.2 cm, Jupiter will be only about 12 cm in diameter.

LESSON 7.6

EXERCISES

1. a. $\dfrac{1}{2^3}$ **b.** $\dfrac{1}{5^2}$ **c.** $\dfrac{1.35}{10^4}$

2. a. $=$. Because $63.5 \times 10^4 = 6.35 \times 10 \times 10^4$ $= 6.35 \times 10^5$, the expressions are equal.

b. $<$. Because the powers of 10 are the same, you can just compare -5.24 to -5.2. Because $-5.24 < -5.2$, $-5.24 \times 10^{-7} < -5.2 \times 10^{-7}$.

c. $>$. Because $10^{-5} > 10^{-6}$, $2.674 \times 10^{-5} > 2.674 \times 10^{-6}$.

d. $>$. Because $10^{-4} < 10^{-3}$, $2.7 \times 10^{-4} < 2.8 \times 10^{-3}$, but then multiplying by -1 reverses the inequality symbol, so $-2.7 \times 10^{-4} > -2.8 \times 10^{-3}$.

3. a. -5; $0.0000412 = \dfrac{4.12}{100,000} = \dfrac{4.12}{10^5} = 4.12 \times 10^{-5}$

b. -4; $46 \times 10^{-5} = 4.6 \times 10^1 \times 10^{-5} = 4.6 \times 10^{-4}$

c. -4; $0.00046 = \dfrac{4.6}{10^4} = 4.6 \times 10^{-4}$

4. a. $45,647(1 + 0.028)^0$

b. The population 12 years ago

c. $45,647(1 + 0.028)^{-8} \approx 36,599$

d. $\dfrac{45,647}{(1 + 0.028)^{12}}$; $\dfrac{45,647}{(1 + 0.028)^8}$

5. Possible answer: A number raised to a negative power is equal to 1 over the number raised to the opposite power. So, $6^{-3} = \frac{1}{6^3} = \frac{1}{216}$. This is different from -6^3, which equals $-(6 \cdot 6 \cdot 6)$ or -216.

6. a. $(2x^3)^2(3x^4) = 12x^{10}$ **b.** $(5x^4)^2(2x^2) = 50x^{10}$

c. $3(2x)^3(3x)^{-2} = \dfrac{3(2x)^3}{(3x)^2} = \dfrac{3 \cdot 8x^3}{9x^2} = \dfrac{8x}{3}$

d. $\left(\dfrac{2x^4}{3x}\right)^3 = \dfrac{8x^{12}}{27x^3} = \dfrac{8x^9}{27}$

7. a. $3500(1 + 0.04)^{-4}$; approximately \$2,992

b. $250(1 + 0.04)^{-3}$; approximately \$222

c. $25(1 + 0.04)^{-5}$; approximately \$21

d. $126,800(1 + 0.04)^{-30}$; approximately \$39,095

8. a. $\dfrac{1.5 \times 10^5 \text{ square miles}}{1.3 \times 10^8 \text{ people}}$

$\approx 1.2 \times 10^{-3}$ square mile per person

b. $\dfrac{1.2 \times 10^{-3} \text{ square mile}}{1 \text{ person}} = \dfrac{27,878,400 \text{ square feet}}{1 \text{ square mile}}$

$\approx 3.35 \times 10^4$ square feet per person

9. a. True; $(2^3)^2 = 2^3 \cdot 2^3 = 2 \cdot 2 \cdot 2 \cdot 2 \cdot 2 \cdot 2 = 2^6$

b. False; $(3^3)^4 = 3^3 \cdot 3^3 \cdot 3^3 \cdot 3^3$ $= 3 \cdot 3 \cdot 3 \cdot 3 \cdot 3 \cdot 3 \cdot 3 \cdot 3 \cdot 3 \cdot 3 \cdot 3 \cdot 3 = 3^{12}$

c. False; $(10^{-2})^4 = \left(\dfrac{1}{10^2}\right)^4$

$= \left(\dfrac{1}{10 \cdot 10}\right)\left(\dfrac{1}{10 \cdot 10}\right)\left(\dfrac{1}{10 \cdot 10}\right)\left(\dfrac{1}{10 \cdot 10}\right)$

$= \dfrac{1}{10^8} = 10^{-8}$

d. True; $(5^{-3})^{-4} = \left(\dfrac{1}{5^3}\right)^{-4} = \dfrac{1}{\left(\dfrac{1}{5^3}\right)^4}$

$= \dfrac{1}{\left(\dfrac{1}{5 \cdot 5 \cdot 5}\right)\left(\dfrac{1}{5 \cdot 5 \cdot 5}\right)\left(\dfrac{1}{5 \cdot 5 \cdot 5}\right)\left(\dfrac{1}{5 \cdot 5 \cdot 5}\right)}$

$= \dfrac{1}{\dfrac{1}{5^{12}}} = \dfrac{1}{5^{-12}} = 5^{12}$

10. a. Original: 1×10^0; Abigail: 1×10^{-1}; Barbara: 1×10^{-2}; Cruz: 1×10^{-3}

b. 1×10^{-4} mile

c. Damien's string is only about 6.3 inches long, which is too short for a shoelace.

11. $36(1 + 0.5)^{(4-6)} = 36(1 + 0.5)^{-2}$

12. a. $1000(1 + 0.025)^2 \approx 1050.63$ and $1000(1 + 0.025)^4 \approx 1103.81$. So after 1 year she would have \$1,050.63, and after 2 years she would have \$1,103.81.

b. $1000(1 + 0.05)^1 = 1050$ and $1000(1 + 0.05)^2 = 1102.5$. So after 1 year she would have \$1,050, and after 2 years she would have \$1,102.50.

c. Possible answer: In the savings account, interest is added sooner, so the interest earns interest sooner.

13. 1×10^{-1} or $\frac{1}{10}$ of a chocolate bar per person

14. a. $x = \frac{28}{11} \approx 2.55$, $y = \frac{29}{11} \approx 2.64$

b. $x = -\frac{56}{13} \approx -4.31$, $y = -\frac{21}{13} \approx -1.62$

15. a. **i.** 4×10^5 **ii.** 3.1×10^{10}
  iii. 1.21×10^5 **iv.** 2×10^{-4}

b. Possible answer: Divide the coefficients of the powers of 10, and then divide the powers of 10 (subtract the exponents).

c. 0.6×10^5 or 6×10^4 in scientific notation

IMPROVING YOUR REASONING SKILLS

1. Possible definition: Factors of 10 are found so the exponent on 10 is a multiple of 3; the digits, a, before 10 can represent a decimal number $1 \leq a < 1000$.

2. a. 78×10^6 **b.** 9.45×10^3 **c.** 130×10^9
  d. 3.4×10^{-3} **e.** 310×10^{-3} **f.** 140×10^6

3. Answers will vary. Students should observe that engineering notation is related to the groups of three digits separated by commas in decimal numbers. That is, $n = 10^{-6}$, $\mu = 10^{-3}$, $k = 10^3$, $M = 10^6$, $G = 10^9$.

LESSON 7.7

EXERCISES

1. a. $1 + 0.15$; rate of increase: 15%

b. $1 + 0.08$; rate of increase: 8%

c. $1 - 0.24$; rate of decrease: 24%

d. $1 - 0.002$; rate of decrease: 0.2%

e. $1 + 1.5$; rate of increase: 150%

2. a. Decreasing   **b.** 12%   **c.** $y \approx 8.92$

d. The y-values approach 0.

3. $B = 250(1 + 0.0425)^t$

4. a. $108x^{18}$ **b.** $4x^5y^3$ **c.** 72   **d.** 1

e. $\dfrac{y^4}{x^3}$ **f.** $\dfrac{1}{8x^3}$ **g.** $\dfrac{2}{x^3}$ **h.** $\dfrac{54y^6}{x^4}$

5. a. The ratios are 0.957, 0.956, 0.965, 0.964, 0.963, 0.961, 0.959, 0.958, 0.971, and 0.955.

b. 0.9609, or about 0.96

c. $0.96 = 1 - 0.04$

d. $y = 47(1 - 0.04)^x$

e.

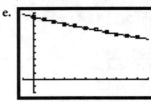

$[-1, 11, 1, -10, 50, 5]$

Adjustments to A or r are not necessary—the fit is good as is.

f. 55 minutes

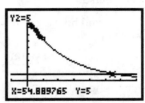

$[-10, 70, 10, -10, 50, 5]$

6. a. Possible answer: $y = 431(1 - 0.26)^x$, where 0.26 is derived from the mean ratio of about 0.74.

b. With each layer of plastic, the amount of light is reduced 26%.

c. With 9 layers, the reading would be below 30.

7. a. Possible answer: Let x represent years since 1990, and let y represent median price in dollars. An equation is $y = 85{,}000(1 + 0.06)^x$, where 0.06 is derived from the mean ratio of about 1.06.

b. Answers will vary depending on the current year. Students should substitute (*current year* $+ 5 - 1990$) for x.

c. Answers will vary depending on 7b. The answer should be the result of 7b multiplied by 0.10.

d. Answers will vary depending on 7c. The answer should be the result of 7c divided by 60.

8. Note 75 above middle C would be the highest audible note. Note -44 (44 notes below middle C) would be the lowest audible note.

9. $\dfrac{1 \text{ microsecond}}{1 \text{ nanosecond}} = \dfrac{1 \times 10^{-6} \text{ seconds}}{1 \times 10^{-9} \text{ seconds}} = 1 \times 10^3$. So there are 1000 nanoseconds in a microsecond.

10. a. 50%   **b.** $y = 32(1 + 0.5)^x$

c. 243 mosquitoes; 9,342 mosquitoes; 2,727,126 mosquitoes

d. Answers will vary. Possibilities include lack of resources and overcrowding.

11. a. $y = 2(1 + 0.5)^x$

    b. $y = 2(1 + 0.5)^{0.5} \approx 2.45$; approximately 2.45 liters

    c. Approximately 115 liters

    d. After about 30.4 minutes, or 30 minutes 24 seconds

12. a. y gets closer and closer to 0.

    b. No, because y can never equal 0. The number is just smaller than the calculator is able to represent.

    c. y approaches infinity.

13. $x = 3$ cm; $y = 7.2$ cm; $z = 9$ cm

14. $5(3 \times 10^8)^2 = 5(9 \times 10^{16}) = 45 \times 10^{16}$ or 4.5×10^{17} joules

LESSON 7.8

(No answers for this lesson)

CHAPTER 7 Review

EXERCISES

1. a. 3^4 **b.** 3^3 **c.** 3^2 **d.** 3^{-1}

    e. 3^{-2} **f.** 3^0

2. a. x^2 **b.** $\dfrac{2}{x}$ **c.** $1.23x^5$ **d.** $\dfrac{1}{3^x}$

    e. 3 **f.** $x^{7.7}$ **g.** 3^{4x} **h.** x^2

3. a. Answers will vary. Possible answer: A $300 microwave depreciates at a rate of 15% per year. In this situation, 300 is the original price of the microwave in dollars and 0.15 is the percent decrease expressed as a decimal.

    b. The years (x) for which the depreciating value of the microwave is at least $75.

    c. Answers will be $x \leq 8$ or $0 \leq x \leq 8$, depending on the situation described in 3a (negative integers may or may not make sense for the situation).

4. Answers will vary. Possible answer: $\dfrac{3^x}{3^x} = 3^{(x-x)} = 3^0$. Because any number divided by itself is 1, $3^0 = 1$.

5. a. $y = 200(1 + 0.4)^x$; missing value: 1505.9072

    b. $y = 850(1 - 0.15)^x$

x	y
-2	1176.4706
-1	1000.0000
4	443.7053

6. a. $-2,400,000$ **b.** 0.000325

    c. 3.714×10^{10} **d.** 8.011×10^{-8}

7. $72 \cdot 365 \cdot 9365 \cdot 0.15 = 36{,}916{,}830$, so the person will spend 36,916,830 seconds blinking. Now, convert this to years: $36{,}916{,}830 \div 60 \div 60 \div 24 \div 365 \approx 1.17$. In scientific notation, this is 1.17×10^0 years.

8. The equation $y = 0.75(1 + 0.03)^x$ represents the price of the soda x years after 1995. y first exceeds 2 when $x = 34$. So, the price will exceed $2 in 2029.

9. a. False; 3 to the power of 3 is not 9. The right side should be $27x^6$.

    b. False. You can't use the multiplication property of exponents if the bases are different. The right side should be $3^2 \cdot 2^3$ or 72.

    c. False. The exponent -2 applies only to the x. The right side should be $\dfrac{2}{x^2}$.

    d. False. The power property of exponents says to multiply the exponents. The right side should be $\dfrac{x^6}{y^9}$.

10. a. Possible answer: $y = 80(1 - 0.17)^x$, where x is the time elapsed in minutes and y is the maximum distance in centimeters. The multiplier $(1 - 0.17)$ is derived from the mean ratio of approximately 0.83.

    b. Approximately 15.0 cm

    c. 15 min

11. a. Let t be the number of T-shirts, and let s be the number of sweatshirts.

$$\begin{cases} t + s = 12 \\ 6t + 10s = 88 \end{cases}$$

    b. 8 T-shirts and 4 sweatshirts

12. a. Praying Mantis Length

1	7
2	1 2 6 6
3	4
4	8
5	3 3 3 4 6 6
6	2
7	
8	2
9	4 8
10	
11	
12	1

Key

1	7 means 1.7 cm

    b. 10.4 cm

    c. Mean: approximately 5.4 cm; median: 5.3 cm; mode: 5.3. Choice and explanations will vary.

13. a. 21 ENTER , Ans $-$ 4 ENTER , ENTER , ... ; 10th term $= -15$

    b. -5 ENTER , Ans $\cdot$ -3 ENTER , ENTER , ... ; 10th term $= 98{,}415$

    c. 2 ENTER , Ans $+$ 7 ENTER , ENTER , ... ; 10th term $= 65$

14. a.   **Plans for Ninth Graders**

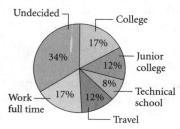

Plans for Twelfth Graders

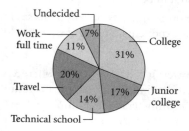

b. Approximately 68% increase

c. Approximately 41% decrease

d. Answers will vary. Possible answer: In Chad's school, 142 out of 698 12th graders, or about 20%, want to travel. So, for a class of 520, Marta might predict that $0.20 \cdot 520$ or 104 12th graders will travel after graduation.

15. a. $y = 1.6x$, where x is a measurement in miles and y is a measurement in kilometers.

b. 400 km   **c.** 3.2 km

d. Approximately 168 m

16. Right triangle

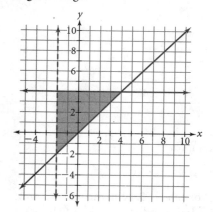

17. a. -4 **b.** 13   **c.** -12

18. a. Slope: $\frac{5}{2}$; y-intercept: $-\frac{11}{2}$

b. Slope: undefined; y-intercept: none

c. Slope: $-\frac{1}{2}$; y-intercept: $-\frac{5}{2}$

19. Answers will vary depending on the method used. The following possible answers used the Q-point method and a decimal approximation of the slope.

a. $y = 96 - 5.7(x - 5)$

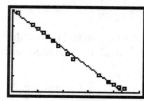

$[0, 25, 5, 0, 125, 25]$

b. $y = 124.5 - 5.7x$

c. Approximately 16 days

d. The y-intercept would become 200; $y = 200 - 5.7x$.

e. 86 grams

20. a. \$19,777   **b.** \$22,104

c. $23{,}039(1 + 0.0225)^{-8}(1 + 0.035)^{-2}$; approximately \$18,000

TAKE ANOTHER LOOK

By stating the order of 10, the scientist is including a range of values greater than or equal to 10,000,000 cells and less than 100,000,000 cells.

If a sample grows from several hundred cells to several thousand cells, it has increased roughly by a factor of 10.

If the sample grows from several thousand cells to several hundred thousand cells, it has increased by three orders of magnitude.

If the number of cells decreases by two orders of magnitude, $\frac{1}{100}$ of the cells remain.

1. The size of a cell is greater than or equal to 0.000001 meter and less than 0.00001 meter.

2. The length of a cow is greater than or equal to 1 meter and less than 10 meters.

3. This is incorrect because the units are not equivalent (meters vs. miles).

4. This is an increase by 26 orders of magnitude.

An increase of 100% does not represent an increase in order of magnitude; an increase of 100% implies the quantity increased by a factor of 2, whereas an order of magnitude implies that the quantity increased by a factor of 10.

CHAPTER 8

LESSON 8.1

EXERCISES

1. a. SBOHF   **b.** EPNBJO

  c. UBCMF   **d.** HSBQI

2. a. INPUT   **b.** OUTPUT

  c. RELATIONSHIP   **d.** RULE

3. a. A one letter-shift code shifts A to B, B to C, C to D, and so on. This is the code given in the table in Exercise 1. Using this table, the investigation title is decoded as SECRET CODES.

  b. The coding scheme is a letter-shift of $+1$. That is, each letter is shifted to the next letter in the alphabet, and the letter Z is shifted to A.

4. a. The possible inputs are the letters on the horizontal axis that have shaded squares above them: A, B, C, E, G, H, I, K, L, M, N, O, Q, U, V, Y, Z.

  b. The possible outputs are the letters on the vertical axis that have shaded squares to their right. The outputs are all 26 letters of the alphabet.

  c. No, the letters B, E, G, I, K, M, and Q each have more than one output.

5. a. The answer depends on whether students distinguish A.M. from P.M. If students *do not* make this distinction, there are 12 inputs: 1:00, 2:00, 3:00, 4:00, 5:00, 6:00, 7:00, 8:00, 9:00, 10:00, 11:00, 12:00. If students *do* distinguish A.M. from P.M., there are 24 inputs: 1:00 A.M., 1:00 P.M., 2:00 A.M., 2:00 P.M., and so on.

  b. Output: {0100, 0200, 0300, 0400, 0500, 0600, 0700, 0800, 0900, 1000, 1100, 1200, 1300, 1400, 1500, 1600, 1700, 1800, 1900, 2000, 2100, 2200, 2300, 2400}

  c. The answer depends on whether students distinguish A.M. from P.M. If students *do not* make this distinction, they should find that the relationship is *not* a function because each standard time corresponds to two military times. If students *do* make the distinction, they should find the relationship is a function because each standard time corresponds to a unique military time.

6. a. G   **b.** M   **c.** A   **d.** A

7. a. $L_1 = \{6, 21, 14, 3, 20, 9, 15, 14, 19\}$

    $L_2 = \{15, 30, 23, 12, 29, 18, 24, 23, 28\}$

  b. You have to subtract 26 from the numbers greater than 26. The new list L_2 is $\{15, 4, 23, 12, 3, 18, 24, 23, 2\}$.

  c. ODWLCRXWB

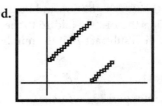

  d.

  $[-10, 37, 0, -5, 31, 0]$

  e. Avoid any multiple of 26, such as 0, -26, 26, -52, 52, and so on.

8. a. $L_1 = \{1, 2, \ldots, 26\}$

  b. $L_2 = \{2, 4, 6, 8, \ldots, 26, 2, 4, 6, 8, \ldots, 26\}$

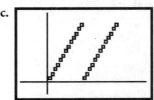

  c.

  d. Sylvana will have difficulty decoding because each coded letter has two possible inputs.

9. ALGEBRA

10. a. No, there are two coding choices for C and two decoding choices for B.

  b. If each input letter corresponded to only one output letter, coding would be easier.

  c. Change the grid so that each output letter on the vertical axis matches only one input letter on the horizontal axis.

11. a. Input: $\{0, 1, -1, 2, -2\}$, output: $\{0, 1, 2\}$. This is a function because each input has exactly one output.

  b. Input: $\{1, 4, 9\}$, output: $\{1, -1, 2, -2, 3, -3\}$. This is not a function because each input has two outputs.

12. a. Double the position of the letter and add 1. If the result is greater than 26, subtract 26 until the answer is not more than 26. This number is the position of the coded letter.

  b. GEIK

  c. You cannot decode SPY because the letter P is not in the range.

13. a. Possible rule: Subtract the input letter's position from 27 to get the output letter's position.

  b. Yes, each input corresponds to only one output.

  c. Answers will vary.

14. SHOFJEWHQFXO must decode to CRYPTOGRAPHY (the study of coding and decoding), so C codes to S, R codes to H, Y codes to O, P codes to F, and so on. If you use position numbers for the letters, 3 codes to 19, 18 codes to 8, 25 codes to 15, 16 codes to 6, and so on. So, the rule is subtract 10 from the letter's position and then add 26 if the number is less than 1. (Or, add 16 to the letter's position and then subtract 26 if the number is greater than 26.)

15. a. $28b^6$ **b.** $11a^3$ **c.** 1.75
   d. $1372d^3$ **e.** Not possible **f.** $4x^5$

16. $\dfrac{1 \text{ cal}}{4.1868 \text{ J}} = \dfrac{x \text{ cal}}{470 \text{ J}}; x = \dfrac{470}{4.1868} \approx 112$ calories

LESSON 8.2

EXERCISES

1. a. $\{1, 3.4, 5.4, 9.32, 11.4\}$
   b.

Domain x	Range y
-4	4.4
-1	2
2.4	-0.72
11	-7.6
14	-10

2.
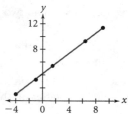

3.
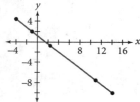

4. Both relationships are functions. Possible explanations: In the tables, every input value produces exactly one output value. Both graphs pass the vertical line test.

5. Sample answer: Start at the 2-m mark and stand still for 2 sec. Walk toward the 4-m mark at 2 m/sec for 1 sec. Stand still for another second. Walk toward the 8-m mark at 4 m/sec for 1 sec. Then stand still for 3 sec. Yes, the graph represents a function.

6. a. Yes; each input value has only one output value.
   b. No; many input values have two output values.

c. No; all the points on the vertical segment have the same input value but different output values.
   d. Yes; each input value has only one output value.

7. a. No; Los Angeles has more than one area code $(213, 310, \dots)$.
   b. Yes; each person has only one birth date.
   c. No; the same last name corresponds to many different first names. For example, if you look up the last name "Smith" in the phone book, you will see many different first names.
   d. Yes; each state has only one capital.

8. a. Graphs i, ii, iii, iv, and vi all pass the vertical line test, so they are functions.
   b. Graphs v and vii. Graph v represents a person walking at an infinite speed, which is not possible. Graph iv shows the person in two places at once, which is not possible.
   c. Sample conclusion: It is not possible to walk a graph that does not represent a function.

9. a. This is not a function because the input 3 has two different output values, 10 and 8.
   b. This is a function because each x-value corresponds to only one y-value.
   c. This is a function because each x-value corresponds to only one y-value.

10. Graphs must pass the vertical line test, pass through the points $(-2, 3)$ and $(3, -2)$, and have domain $-3 \le x \le 5$ and range $-4 \le y \le 4$. Sample graph:

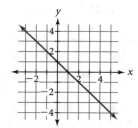

11. Graphs will not pass the vertical line test. They should include points $(-2, 3)$ and $(3, -2)$ and have the correct domain and range. Sample graph:

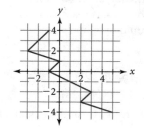

12. a. The graph is a line. This is a function because each x-value is paired with only one y-value.

x	y
2	-1
8	1
-4	-3
-1	-2
0	$-\frac{5}{3}$
5	0

b. This is a function because each x-value is paired with only one y-value.

x	y
-2	9
3	19
0	1
-3	19
-1	3
±2	9

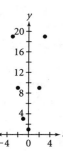

c. This is not a function because there are two y-values for many x-values.

x	y
-7	±3
1	1
-2	-2
-7	-3
-2	±2
2	0

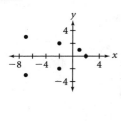

d. This is a function because each x-value is paired with only one y-value. Tables will vary. Sample table:

x	y
0	0
2	3
-2	-3
4	6
-4	-6
6	9

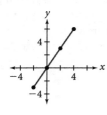

13. a. Domain: $\{-5, -4, -3, -2, -1, 0, 1, 2, 3, 4, 5\}$
Range: $\{0, 1, 2, 3, 4, 5\}$

b. Domain: $0 \leq x \leq 360$
Range: $-1 \leq y \leq 1$

c. Domain: all real numbers x
Range: $y > 0$

14. Answers will vary. In some typefaces, graphs of the letters V and W are functions because they pass the vertical line test. Most letters are not functions because they fail the vertical line test.

15. a. 23.125. Zoom in on the table by changing the start values and the table increments (Δ Tbl) until you find the x-value that corresponds to the y-value -15.

b. Use the trace function to find the point where the two graphs intersect.

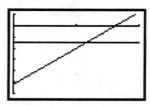

$[0, 40, 5, -60, 10, 10]$

16. a. $x = 24$
Equation $\frac{4(x-7)-8}{3} = 20$

Order	Undo	Work backward
x	20	24
$-(7)$	$+(7)$	17
$\cdot(4)$	$\div(4)$	68
$-(8)$	$+(8)$	60
$\div(3)$	$\cdot(3)$	20

b. $x = 9.75$
Equation $\frac{x-3}{4.5} = \frac{3}{2}$

Order	Undo	Work backward
x	$\frac{2}{3}$	9.75
$-(3)$	$+(3)$	6.75
$\div(4.5)$	$\cdot(4.5)$	$\frac{3}{2}$

LESSON 8.3

EXERCISES

1. a. The level of medication drops quickly at first and then decreases more slowly over time. After 10 hours, about 30 milligrams are still in the bloodstream.

b. The independent variable is time. The dependent variable is the amount of medication in the bloodstream.

c. The domain is the time in hours from 0 through 10. The range is the amount of medication in milligrams from about 30 through 500.

d. Answers will vary slightly. Assuming (1, 400) is a point on the curve, the equation is $y = 500(1 - 0.20)^x$.

2. Answers will vary.

a. Sample answer: The graph shows an inverse relationship that levels off. Once enough students are working, more will not help. A graph that shows a discrete function is also correct because students can be represented by whole numbers.

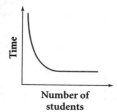

b. Sample answer: This graph shows an inverse relationship. Eventually the price will be so high that no one will buy a T-shirt.

c. Sample answer: Some product will be sold without any advertising. The product sold will increase as the advertising budget increases. Eventually the graph will level off because there is a limit to how much you can sell no matter how much you spend on advertising. This isn't shown on the graph.

3. a. The reading on the scale depends on the weight of the dog, so the dog's weight is the independent variable and the reading on the scale is the dependent variable.

b. The amount of time you spend in the plane depends on the distance you fly, so the distance between the cities is the independent variable and the amount of time in the plane is the dependent variable.

c. The wax sticks to the candlewick each time you dip it, so the number of dips is the independent variable and the diameter of the candle is the dependent variable.

4. a. The wind chill increases at a constant rate as the temperature increases, so Graph 2 is the best match.

b. A radioactive substance decays exponentially, so Graph 4 is the best match.

c. The height of the elevator increases at a constant rate as the floor number increases. Only whole-number values make sense for the floor number, so the graph should show individual points, rather than a line. Graph 1 is the best match.

d. Populations often grow exponentially, so Graph 3 would be the best choice.

e. Graph 5 is most likely.

5. x, y; independent, dependent; input, output; time, distance (or distance, time)

6. a. $0 \leq x \leq 8$ **b.** $2 \leq y \leq 8$

c. Before any time has elapsed, the distance is 2 meters.

d. $y = 4$; $y = 8$; $x = 2.5$

7. Answers will vary. A correct graph will consist of three line segments, each less steep than the one before it.

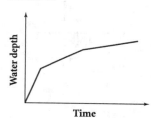

8. Graphs and descriptions will vary. Sample answers are given.

a. The independent variable is time. The dependent variable is the height of the grass. The line segments with positive slope indicate that the grass is growing. The sharply decreasing, almost vertical, segments indicate that the grass is being mowed.

b. The independent variable is the number of students. The dependent variable is the number of buses. As the number of students increases, the number of buses stays the same until a bus is filled, then the number of buses increases by 1. There are dots on the graph instead of lines because the numbers of buses and students must be integers.

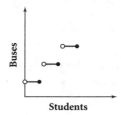

Students

c. The independent variable is time. The dependent variable is the height of the ball. The height of the ball increases until the ball reaches a maximum height, then the height decreases.

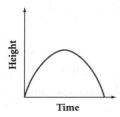

Time

d. The independent variable is the number of dice thrown, and the dependent variable is the probability of getting a 6. As the number of dice rolled increases, the probability of rolling a 6 increases. The graph will approach 1, but it will never reach 1 because you can never be absolutely certain to get a 6 no matter how many dice you roll. The graph is made up of individual points because the number of dice must be a whole number.

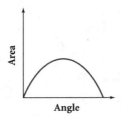

Number of dice

e. The independent variable is the angle size, and the dependent variable is the area inside the hanger. The area will increase to a maximum value and then decrease to 0.

Angle

9. a. Answers will vary. If the *x*-axis is labeled in days, a reasonable domain is from 0 to 120, with 0 representing May 1. A reasonable range might be from 0 to 8 inches.

b. Possible answer: A reasonable domain is the integers from 0 to 500. A reasonable range is the integers from 1 to 10.

c. Possible answer: A reasonable domain would be from 0 to 5 seconds. A reasonable range would be from 0 to 300 feet or 100 meters.

d. The domain is the set of non-negative integers. The range is $0 \leq x < 1$, where x is a real number. (If you throw no dice, the probability is 0. Even with a large number of dice you can't be sure of getting 1.)

e. Answers will vary. The domain is the angle measures from 0° to 180°. A reasonable range might be from 0 to 60 square inches.

10. a. Erica won in about 13.5 seconds.

b. Eileen was in the lead after 60 meters.

c. They were tied at approximately 3 seconds, 5.5 seconds, from 10.5 to 12 seconds, and just before the end of the race.

d. Eileen was in the lead from 0 to 3 seconds, from 5.5 to 10.5 seconds, and from 12 to about 13.2 seconds.

11. a. Sample answer: A ball is traveling toward the catcher; it is caught and held, then thrown back. A valid answer would also be that there is no scenario because velocity can't change instantaneously. The graph should be made up of at least three horizontal segments at heights of 0, 2, and −2.

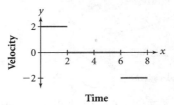

Time

b. Sample answer: As the school bus leaves a stop, its speed increases. It travels for a while at a constant speed. Then it slows down briefly and speeds up again to a faster speed than before. It travels at a constant speed for a while, then slows down and stops as it lets some students off. It speeds up again and levels off at a constant speed.

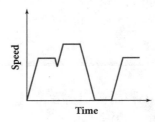

Time

c. Sample answer: The ball is shot from shoulder level. It rises to a maximum point, goes through the hoop, and then falls to the ground.

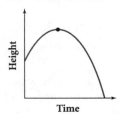

12. Graph depends on the answer to 11a. This graph corresponds to the sample graph in 11a. The slope of each segment corresponds to the speed in the graph in 11a. The object is traveling at a speed of 2 m/sec for 2 seconds, 0 m/sec for 4 seconds, and -2 m/sec for 2 seconds.

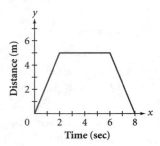

13. a. ... decreases. **b.** ... increases.

c. $h = \dfrac{1000}{\pi r^2}$

d.

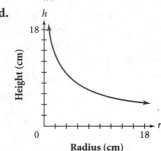

14. a. The slope is $\dfrac{10 - 8}{1 - 0} = 2$ and the y-intercept is 8, so the equation is $y = 8 + 2x$.

b. The ratio of consecutive y-values is $\dfrac{10}{8} = 1.25$ and the starting value is 8, so the equation is $y = 8(1 + 0.25)^x$.

15. a. -2.5 **b.** -4 **c.** $\dfrac{5}{3}$

16. a. $y = 5x$ **b.** $y = |x - 3| - 2$

c. $y = \dfrac{1}{4}x + 5$

LESSON 8.4

EXERCISES

1. a. $3(3) + 2 = 11, Y_1(3) = 11$

b. $3(-4) + 2 = -10, Y_2(3) = -10$

c. $(5)^2 - 1 = 24, Y_2(5) = 24$

d. $(-3)^2 - 1 = 8, Y_2(-3) = 8$

2. a. $-2(6) - 5 = -17$ **b.** $-2(0) - 5 = -5$

c. $3.75(2.5)^2 = 23.4375$ **d.** $3.75(2.5)^{-2} = 0.6$

3. a. 0 **b.** 4 **c.** 2 and 5

d. 0.5, 3, and 4.5

e. Three. You can see this by drawing the horizontal line $y = 0.5$. This line crosses the graph three times.

f. $x > 5$

g. Domain: $-1 \le x \le 7$; range: $0 \le y \le 6$

4. a. Dependent variable (y): temperature (°F); independent variable (x): time (hrs)

b. Domain: $0 \le x \le 24$; range: $5 \le y \le 35$

c. $f(10)$ **d.** $f(x) = 10$

5. a. $f(x) = 7x + 5$ **b.** $f(x) = 5 + 7(x - 1)$

6. a. The level of the lake on the 60th day of the year

b. At a certain time, the lake level was 3 inches below last year's mean.

c. On certain days, the lake level was the same as it was on day 150.

7. a. Amount of medication in milligrams

b. Time in hours

c. $0 \le x \le 10$; all real numbers x

d. $54 \le y \le 500, y > 0$

e. 500

f. About 4 hours

8. a. $f(x) = 650(1 - 0.085)^x$

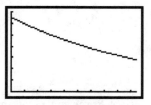

$[0, 9, 1, 0, 700, 100]$

b. The point of intersection is $(7.8, 325)$.

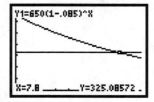

c. After 7.803 hours, there are 325 bacteria present.

9. Answers will vary.

a. Domain: all real numbers, lists of numbers, matrices of numbers. Range: non-negative numbers, lists and matrices of non-negative numbers. The command is a function because the same input always results in the same output.

b. Domain: all non-negative numbers or lists of non-negative numbers. Range: non-negative numbers or lists of non-negative numbers. The command is a function because the same input always results in the same output.

c. Domain: lists of any size of real numbers. Range: all real numbers. The command is a function because the same input always results in the same output.

d. Two answers are possible. (1) This command does not take an input, but it gives a different output, such as .471359732, each time. It is not a function. (2) This command takes any real number, the seed, as the input. It gives a real-number output that depends on the seed. Domain: All real numbers. Range: All real numbers. The command always gives the same output for the same seed, so it is a function.

10. a. $f(72) \approx 22.2°C$ **b.** $f(-10) \approx -23.3°C$
   c. $f(x) = 20; x = 68°F$ **d.** $f(x) = -5; x = 23°F$

11. a. $f(x)$: The independent variable x is time in seconds, and the dependent variable y is height in meters.

   $g(x)$: The independent variable x is time in seconds, and the dependent variable y is velocity in meters per second.

   b. $f(x)$: The domain is $0 \leq x \leq 3.2$. The range is $0 \leq y \leq 50$.

   $g(x)$: The domain is $0 \leq x \leq 3.2$. The range is $-31 \leq y \leq 0$.

   c. Answers will vary. For the graph of $f(x)$, the ball is dropped from an initial height of 50 meters. Its height decreases at a faster and faster rate until it hits the ground after about 3.2 seconds. For the graph of $g(x)$, the velocity starts at 0 m/sec and decreases at a constant rate, becoming more and more negative.

   d. In the 1st second, the ball falls about 5 m, from 50 m at $x = 0$ to about 45 m at $x = 1$.

   e. In the 2nd second, the ball falls about 15 m, from about 45 m at $x = 1$ to about 30 m at $x = 2$.

   f. The graph of $f(x)$ indicates that the ball hits the ground after about 3.2 seconds. The graph of $g(x)$ indicates that after 3.2 seconds, the velocity is about -31 m/sec. So, the ball hits the ground at a speed of 31 m/sec.

12. The ordered pairs could represent a function because each input has a unique output. The domain is $\{-2, 0, 1, 3\}$, and the range is $\{-2, 3\}$.

13. The ordered pairs do not represent a function because the input -2 has two different outputs, 3 and 0, and the input 3 has two different outputs, 1 and -2.

14. FUN DAYS AHEAD

15. a. $\dfrac{1}{2^9}$ **b.** 5^{10} **c.** $2^{12}3^6$ **d.** $\dfrac{1}{3^8 5^{12}}$

16. a. -1 **b.** $\dfrac{5}{11}$ **c.** 0

17. a. $x = -4$ **b.** $x = -0.75$
   c. $x = 4$

LESSON 8.5

EXERCISES

1. a.

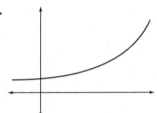
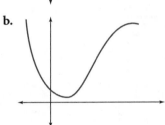

b.

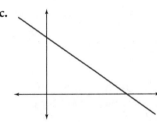

c.

d.

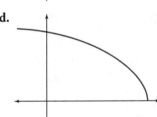

2. a. $0 \leq x < 4$ **b.** $4 \leq x < 6$ **c.** $4 \leq x < 10$
   d. $6 \leq x < 12$ **e.** $0 \leq x < 12$

3. a. Linear and increasing

   b. Nonlinear and increasing, fast rate of change, then slowing down

   c. Nonlinear and decreasing, fast rate of change, then slowing down

   d. Linear with a zero rate of change

4. a.

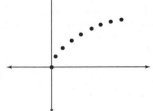

b.

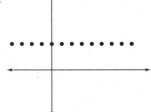

c.

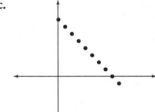

d.

5. Graph B is correct. The graph starts at 0, which represents the turtle's starting point at the pond. The first segment of the graph represents the turtle walking at a slow, steady pace. The graph then increases quickly, representing the dog running with the turtle. The flat part of the graph represents the dog stopping and dropping the turtle. The decreasing, linear segment represents the boy carrying the turtle back to the pond.

6. a. Moving away, speeding up

   b. Moving toward, speeding up

   c. Moving away, at a constant speed

   d. Moving toward, slowing down

   e. Moving toward, at a constant speed

   f. Moving away, slowing down

7. Answers will vary. The graph most likely would be decreasing, like b, d, and e. Graph d is probably the most realistic choice. As too many students get

involved, the amount of time won't change by much, and the amount of time will never be 0. In fact, some students may sketch a graph that begins to increase after too many students get involved.

8. a. Nonlinear and increasing with a faster and faster rate of change

   b. Nonlinear and decreasing with a faster and faster rate of change

   c. Linear and increasing with a constant rate of change

   d. Nonlinear and decreasing with a slower and slower rate of change

   e. Linear and decreasing with a constant rate of change

   f. Nonlinear and increasing with a slower and slower rate of change

9. a. About 11:00 A.M.

   b. Between 10:10 A.M. and 10:40 A.M.

   c. Between 9:00 and 9:45 A.M. and then again after 11:00 A.M.

10. The temperature dropped slowly from midnight until 6 A.M. and was fairly constant through the morning. At about 10 A.M., the temperature began a dramatic rise for 2 hours. Then the temperature continued to rise more slowly for another 7 hours until 7 P.M. The temperature dropped only slightly from 7 P.M. until midnight.

11. a. Independent variable: licks; dependent variable: mass

   b. Independent variable: scoops; dependent variable: cost

   c. Independent variable: amount of stretch; dependent variable: flight distance

   d. Independent variable: number of coins; dependent variable: number of heads

12. a. **i.** $4x + 2y = 16$
$$2y = 16 - 4x$$
$$y = \frac{16 - 4x}{2}$$
$$y = 8 - 2x$$

   ii. $4x - 2y = 16$
$$-2y = 16 - 4x$$
$$y = \frac{16 - 4x}{-2}$$
$$y = -8 + 2x$$

   b. **i.** $f(x) = 8 - 2x$ **ii.** $f(x) = -8 + 2x$

   c. **i.** $f(-1) = 10$ **ii.** $f(-1) = -10$

13. a. $y = -25.9 - 2.5x$

   b. Slope: -2.5, y-intercept: -25.9

Discovering Algebra Solutions Manual
©2002 Key Curriculum Press

14. Approximately 19.94. The exact answer, $\frac{1675}{84}$, makes the equation true.

15. 293, 307, 343.5, 431, 601

LESSON 8.6

EXERCISES

1. a. 7   **b.** 0.5

    c. $|-7 + 2| = |-5| = 5$ **d.** $|-7| + |2| = 7 + 2 = 9$

    e. -5 **f.** -5

    g. $|-4| \cdot |3| = 4 \cdot 3 = 12$ **h.** $\frac{|-6|}{|2|} = \frac{6}{2} = 3$

2. 10 and -10

3. a. $12 = 12$ **b.** $40 = 40$ **c.** $15 > 9$ **d.** $9 < 13$

    e. $4 = 4$ **f.** $16 > \frac{1}{16}$

4. a. $3(5) - 5 = 10$ **b.** $3(-2.5) - 5 = -12.5$

    c. $|-5 - 3| = |-8| = 8$ **d.** $|1 - 3| = |-2| = 2$

5.

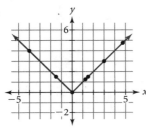

x	y
-4	4
-1.5	1.5
0	0
1.2	1.2
3	3
4.75	4.75

6.

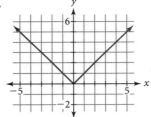

$y = |x|$, the absolute value function.

7. Because $y = 2.85$, substitute 2.85 for y in the first equation. This gives $2.85 = |x|$, so $x = 2.85$ or $x = -2.85$. The solutions are $(2.85, 2.85)$ and $(-2.85, 2.85)$. You could also solve the equation by graphing both equations and finding the intersection points.

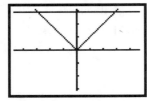

$[-4.7, 4.7, 1, -3.2, 3.2, 1]$

8. a. $x = -12$ or $x = 12$

b. $10 = |x| + 4$ Original equation.

   $6 = |x|$ Subtract 4 from both sides.

   $x = -6$ or   Find the values with an absolute value
   $x = 6$ of 6.

c. $10 = 2|x| + 6$ Original equation.

   $4 = 2|x|$ Subtract 6 from both sides.

   $2 = |x|$ Divide both sides by 2.

   $x = 2$ or   Find the values with an absolute value
   $x = -2$ of 2.

d. $4 = 2(|x| + 2)$ Original equation.

   $2 = |x| + 2$ Divide both sides by 2.

   $0 = |x|$ Subtract 2 from both sides.

   $x = 0$ Only 0 has an absolute value of 0.

9. The walker starts 5 meters from the motion sensor and walks toward the motion sensor at a rate of 1 meter per second for 4 seconds and then walks away from the motion sensor at the same rate for 4 seconds.

10. a. $Y_1 = 7$

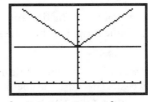

$[-8, 8, 1, -1, 14, 1]$

b. $Y_1 =$ any number less than 7; $Y_1 = 4$ is graphed below.

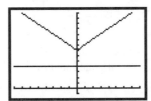

11. a. $g(x)$; $g(5) = |5| + 6 = 11$

b. $h(x)$; $h(1) = 18(1.5) = 27$

c. $g(x)$ or $h(x)$; $g(-2) = |-2| + 6 = 8$; $h(-2) = 18(1.5)^{-2} = 8$

d. $f(x)$; $f(3) = 7 + 4 \cdot 3 = 19$

12. a. When $x < 0$, $x + |x| = x + (-x) = 0$. When $x \geq 0$, $x + |x| = x + x + 2x$. So the graph looks like $y = 0$ for $x < 0$, and it looks like $y = 2x$ for $x \geq 0$.

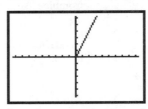

$[-9.4, 9.4, 1, -6.2, 6.2, 1]$

b. When $x < 0$, $\frac{x}{|x|} = \frac{x}{-x} = -1$. When $x > 0$, $\frac{x}{|x|} = \frac{x}{x} = 1$. When $x = 0$, $\frac{x}{|x|}$ is undefined. So the graph looks like $y = -1$ for $x < 0$, and it looks like $y = 1$ for $x > 0$. There is no point on the graph for $y = 0$.

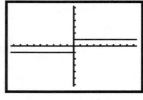

$[-9, 9, 1, -6, 6, 1]$

13. Spider Lake: The mean weight is 1.5 lb. If you find the absolute value of the deviation, $|\text{value} - \text{mean}|$, for each data value, you get 0.3, 0.6, 0.7, 0.1, 1.3, 0.5, 1.1, 0.9. The mean of these deviations is 0.675.

Doll Lake: The mean weight is 1.575. If you find the absolute value of the deviation, $|\text{value} - \text{mean}|$, for each data value, you get 0.675, 0.475, 0.025, 0.325, 0.525, 0.175, 0.175, 0.625. The mean of these deviations is 0.375.

The mean of the absolute values of the deviations is greater for Spider Lake, indicating that the values vary more from the mean.

14. a. $(-4.5, 1)$. Methods will vary. The elimination method is probably easiest because the coefficients of y are opposites, so adding the equations eliminates y.

b. $(3, -3)$. Methods will vary.

15. a. $-1\frac{2}{3} < x$ or $x > -1\frac{2}{3}$

b.

$3(2 - x) + 4 \geq 13$	Original equation.
$6 - 3x + 4 \geq 13$	Apply the distributive property.
$10 - 3x \geq 13$	Combine like terms.
$-3x \geq 3$	Subtract 10 from both sides.
$x \leq -1$	Divide both sides by -3 and reverse the inequality symbol.

c.

$-0.5 \geq -1.5x + 2(x - 4)$	Original equation.
$-0.5 \geq -1.5x + 2x - 8$	Apply the distributive property.
$-0.5 \geq 0.5x - 8$	Combine like terms.
$7.5 \geq 0.5x$	Add 8 to both sides.
$15 \geq x$	Divide both sides by 0.5.

IMPROVING YOUR REASONING SKILLS

To square a positive integer that ends in 5, take the part of the number before the 5 and multiply it by one more than itself. Then put 25 on the end of that product. For example, to square 115, find $11 \cdot 12$, which is 132, and then append 25 to get 13,225.

To find the square root of 7225, find two consecutive positive integers whose product is 72. Then put a 5 after the smaller of the integers. Because $8 \cdot 9 = 72$, $\sqrt{7225} = 85$. This procedure will be successful whenever the number preceding the 25 is the product of two consecutive integers.

LESSON 8.7

EXERCISES

1.

Side (cm)	Perimeter (cm)	Area (sq cm)
1	4	1
2	8	4
3	12	9
4	16	16
14	56	196
15	60	225
21	84	441
25.2	100.8	635.04
47	188	2209

2. Answers will vary. Possible answer: The rate of change from $x = 0$ to $x = 1$ is 1, but the rate of change from $x = 1$ to $x = 2$ is 3. Because the rate of change varies, the relationship is nonlinear.

3. a. $x = 6$ or $x = -6$ **b.** $x = 6$ or $x = -6$
c. $x = 3.8$ or $x = -3.8$ **d.** $x = 3.8$ or $x = -3.8$

4. a.

$4.7 = |x| - 2.8$	Original equation.
$7.5 = |x|$	Add 2.8 to both sides.
$x = 7.5$ or $x = -7.5$	Find the numbers with absolute value 7.5.

b.

$-41 = x^2 - 28$	Original equation.
$-13 = x^2$	Add 28 to both sides.

The square of a number must be greater than or equal to 0, so this equation has no real solutions.

c.

$11 = x^2 - 14$	Original equation.
$25 = x^2$	Add 14 to both sides.
$x = 5$ or $x = -5$	Find two numbers whose square is 25.

5. $-1 \le x \le 1$

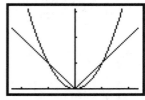

$[-2.35, 2.35, 1, 0, 3.1, 1]$

6. a. Because x^2 must be greater than or equal to 0, the equation $y = x^2$ has no solutions when $y < 0$.

   b. Because 0 is the only number with one square root, the equation $y = x^2$ has only one solution when $y = 0$.

   c. Because every positive number has two square roots, the equation $y = x^2$ has two solutions when $y > 0$.

7.

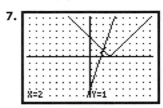

$[-9.4, 9.4, 1, -6.2, 6.2, 1]$

Possible answer: The solution is 2.

8. a. $5 = |x| - 3$ **b.** $-4 = x^2 - 8$
     $8 = |x|$ $4 = x^2$
     $x = 8$ or -8 $x = 2$ or -2

   c. $4 = 2|x| + 6$
          $-2 = 2|x|$
          $-1 = |x|$

   The absolute value of a number cannot be negative, so this equation has no real solutions.

9. a. $1 + 3 + 5 + 7 + 9 = 25$ or 5^2

   b. $1 + 3 + 5 + 7 + 9 + \cdots + 29 = 225$ or 15^2

   c. n^2

   d. Each large square in the pattern is created by adding a border of small squares to two sides of the previous square. The number of small squares added at each stage is the next odd number. So, the number of small squares in each large square is 1, then $1 + 3$, then $1 + 3 + 5$, and so on. That is, the number of squares in the nth large square is the sum of the first n odd integers. But, the number of small squares in each large square is also 1^2, then 2^2, then 3^2, and so on. So, the sum of the first n positive odd integers is n^2.

10. a. $y = 8 - 2x$ **b.** $y = x^2$

   c. $y = |x|$

11. a. There are sixteen 1-by-1 squares, nine 2-by-2 squares, four 3-by-3 squares, and one 4-by-4 square.

   b. A 3-by-3 grid has 14 squares (nine 1-by-1 squares, four 2-by-2 squares, and one 3-by-3 square). A 2-by-2 grid has 5 squares (four 1-by-1 squares and one 2-by-2 square). A 1-by-1 grid has 1 square.

   c. Answers will vary. Possible response: For an n-by-n grid, the number of 1-by-1 squares is n^2, the number of 2-by-2 squares is $(n - 1)^2$, the number of 3-by-3 squares is $(n - 2)^2$, and so on. So, a 5-by-5 grid would have $25 + 16 + 9 + 4 + 1$ or 55 squares.

12. Answers will vary. Possible answer: If x is a negative number, then x^2 is a negative times a negative, which is positive. If x is a positive number, then x^2 is a positive times a positive, which is also positive. If x is 0, then x^2 is 0 times 0, which is 0. So, x^2 must be greater than or equal to 0 no matter what x is.

13. a. To find the constant multiplier, divide the y-value for $x = 4$ by the y-value for $x = 3$. The result is $\frac{126.5625}{168.75}$ or 0.75. To find the starting value, you can start at 168.75, the y-value for $x = 3$, and divide by 0.75 three times. The result is 400. So, the equation is $y = 400(0.75)^x$.

   b.

x	y
0	400
4	126.5625
3	168.75
1	300
≈ -3.19	1000

14. a. $48x^9$ **b.** $30x^8$ **c.** $24x^9$ **d.** $62.5x^{14}$
   e. $-2.5x^3$ **f.** $-48x^{11}$ **g.** $\frac{6y^6}{x^6}$ **h.** $375x^3y^6$

IMPROVING YOUR VISUAL THINKING SKILLS

The numbers of cubes in the figures shown are $1^3 = 1$, $2^3 = 8$, and $3^3 = 27$. These are the volumes measured in cubic units. In general, if the side length of the cube is n, then the volume is $n \cdot n \cdot n$, which is n^3 or "n cubed."

The last two questions lead to a profound result, so let students play with them. If the length of one edge is doubled, the volume is multiplied by 8, which is 2^3. If the length of an edge is tripled, the volume is multiplied by 27, which is 3^3. In general, if the length is multiplied by k, the volume is multiplied by k^3. In even more generality, if all lengths in an n-dimensional figure are multiplied by k, the "size" (length, or area, or volume, or the equivalent for n dimensions) is multiplied by k^n.

EXERCISES

1. a. $-2 \le x \le 4$ **b.** $1 \le f(x) \le 3$ **c.** 1
   d. −1 and 3

2. a. This table represents a function because each
   x-value corresponds to only one y-value.

   b. This table does not represent a function because
   the input $x = 3$ has two different output values, 5
   and 7.

   c. This table represents a function because each
   x-value corresponds to only one y-value.

3. The graph shows that the object is moving at a
   constant velocity of 0.5 meter per second, so the
   graph of the velocity is a horizontal line segment at
   0.5 meter per second.

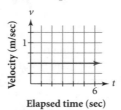

4. ARCHIMEDES (c. 287–212 B.C.E.), Greek
   philosopher and inventor, wrote about volumes, pi,
   and spirals.

   a. DESCARTES, René (1596–1650), French
   mathematician and philosopher, invented the
   coordinate system.

   b. HYPATIA (c. 370–415), woman Greek philosopher
   and mathematician.

   c. EUCLID (c. 300 B.C.E.), Greek geometer whose
   Elements was the chief source of geometric
   reasoning until the 19th century.

   d. This code shifts 20 spaces forward, or 6 spaces
   back, in the alphabet.

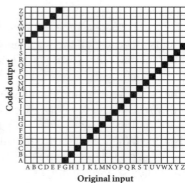

5. a. Possible answer: At the 20-minute mark, each girl
   is moving at the same velocity. Bea's velocity
   increases steadily in a linear fashion. Caitlin's
   velocity increases slowly at first and then at a faster
   and faster rate. Abby's velocity increases very
   quickly at first and then at a slower and slower rate.

   b. No. Until the 20-minute mark, Abby is moving
   faster than both Bea and Caitlin, so even when she
   slows down to their speed, she stays ahead.

6. a. $y = 4.25x + 1.00$
   b.

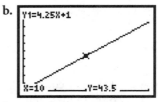

   [0, 20, 5, 0, 90, 10]

   c. It shifts the graph up 0.50 unit on the y-axis.
   d. $y = 4.25x + 1.50$

7. a. Answers will vary. The graph should pass the
   vertical line test. Sample graph:

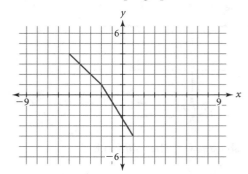

   b. Answers will vary. The graph will fail the vertical
   line test. Sample graph:

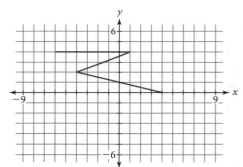

8.

A	B	C	D	E	F	G	H	I	J
1	2	3	4	5	6	7	8	9	10
2	4	6	8	10	12	14	15	18	20

K	L	M	N	O	P	Q	R
11	12	13	14	15	16	17	18
22	24	26	2	4	6	8	10

S	T	U	V	W	X	Y	Z
19	20	21	22	23	24	25	26
12	14	15	18	20	22	24	26

Discovering Algebra Solutions Manual
©2002 Key Curriculum Press

The code is a function because each input has only one output. The rule for decoding is not a function because each coded letter corresponds to two decoded letters. For example, the coded letter D corresponds to the decoded letters B and O.

9. a. $f(-3) = |-3| = 3$ **b.** $f(2) = |2| = 2$

c. 10 and -10

10. a.

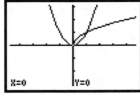

$[-4.7, 4.7, 1, -3.1, 3.1, 1]$

b. The graph of $y = \sqrt{x}$ looks like half of the graph of $y = x^2$ lying on its side.

c. The graph has one branch because the function is defined for $x \geq 0$ only. The $\sqrt{\ }$ symbol indicates only the positive root.

d. This equation does not represent a function because every input but 0 has two outputs. For example, if $x = 4$, $y = 2$ or $y = -2$.

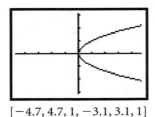

$[-4.7, 4.7, 1, -3.1, 3.1, 1]$

TAKE ANOTHER LOOK

The inverse of the equation that converts temperatures from degrees Celsius to degrees Fahrenheit is a function. Encourage exploration of several functions, both algebraically and with graphs. A function has an inverse that's a function if its graph passes the horizontal line test: no horizontal line crosses the graph at more than one point. Equivalently, some students may say that the graph "doesn't turn around." That is, it's either always increasing or always decreasing. Students should also realize that the inverse of a constant function or a step function will not be a function.

Often a function is restricted to a domain over which it's just increasing or decreasing in order to have an inverse function. For example, when $y = x^2$ is restricted to the domain of positive values for x, it has the inverse function $y = \sqrt{x}$.

CHAPTER 9

LESSON 9.1

EXERCISES

1. a. $(-2, 3), (4, 1), (2, -5)$

b. $(-5, 1), (3, 4), (6, -3), (-3, -5)$

2. a. A translation left 5 units

b. A translation right 1 unit and up 2 units

3. a. A translation up 4 units

b. The x-coordinates are unchanged.

c. The y-coordinates are increased by 4.

4. a.

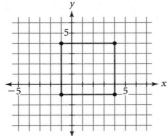

b. Translating the figure left 2 units decreases each x-coordinate by 2 (for example, $(1, 4)$ is translated to $(-1, 4)$). So, the image of the point (x, y) is $(x - 2, y)$.

5. a. The spider is translated right 10 units and down 8 units.

b. You need to add 10 to the original x-coordinates in list L1 to get the image x-coordinates in list L3. You also need to subtract 8 from the original y-coordinates in list L2 to get the image y-coordinates in list L4. So, L3 = L1 + 10 and L4 = L2 $-$ 8.

c. If the lower right spider were the original, the translation would be left 10 units (instead of right 10 units) and up 8 units (instead of down 8 units). So, the operations in the definitions from 5b would change to the inverse operations: L3 = L1 $-$ 10, L4 = L2 + 8.

6. a. Enter the x-coordinates into list L1. Enter the first x-coordinate again at the end of the list. Enter the y-coordinates (in the same order as the corresponding x-coordinates) into list L2. Enter the first y-coordinate again at the end of the list. So, L1 = {2, 5, 1, 2} and L2 = {-1, 0, 2, -1}. Then make a connected plot of L1 versus L2.

b. **i.** A translation up 4 units

ii. A translation left 5 units

iii. A translation right 3 units and down 2 units

7. a. This is a translation up 3 units. The coordinates of the image are $(2, 4)$, $(4, 6)$, and $(3, 3)$.

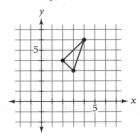

b. This is a translation left 2 units. The coordinates of the image are $(0, 1)$, $(2, 3)$, and $(1, 0)$.

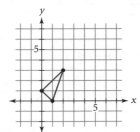

c. This is a translation right 3 units and down 1 unit. The coordinates of the image are $(5, 0)$, $(7, 2)$, and $(6, -1)$.

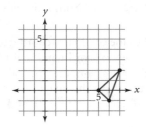

8. a. The original coordinates are $(1, 1)$, $(5, 1)$, and $(1, 6)$. A translation up 4 units adds 4 to each y-coordinate. The coordinates of vertices of the image are $(1, 5)$, $(5, 5)$, and $(1, 10)$.

b. The original coordinates are $(1, 1)$, $(5, 1)$, and $(1, 6)$. A translation left 7 units subtracts 7 from each x-coordinate. The coordinates of vertices of the image are $(-6, 1)$, $(-2, 1)$, and $(-6, 6)$.

9. a. A translation right 12 units and up 7 units

b. $(x + 12, y + 7)$

c. She should move each point $\frac{1}{20}$ of the total horizontal distance and $\frac{1}{20}$ of the total vertical distance with each frame. So, if (x, y) is a point on the figure in one frame, its image in the next frame would be $\left(x + \frac{12}{20}, y + \frac{7}{20}\right)$ or $(x + 0.6, y + 0.35)$.

10. a. In the 10th new frame, the image of point (x, y) is $(x - 10(0.25), y + 10(0.05))$. So, the new coordinates are $(4.5, 1.5)$, $(4.5, 2.5)$, $(5.5, 1.5)$, $(5.5, 2.5)$.

b. In the 25th new frame, the image of point (x, y) is $(x - 25(0.25), y + 25(0.05))$. So, the new coordinates are $(0.75, 2.25)$, $(0.75, 3.25)$, $(1.75, 2.25)$, $(1.75, 3.25)$.

c. In the 40th new frame, the image of point (x, y) is $(x - 40(0.25), y + 40(0.05))$. So, the new coordinates are $(-3, 3)$, $(-3, 4)$, $(-2, 3)$, $(-2, 4)$.

11. a. 17   **b.** -10

c. $f(x + 2) = 2 + 3(x + 2) = 2 + 3x + 6 = 8 + 3x$

d. $f(2x - 1) = 2 + 3(2x - 1) = 2 + 6x - 3$
$= -1 + 6x$

12. a. $x = 4$ **b.** $x = 3.\overline{3}$ **c.** $x = -4$

13. a. $y = -2 + x$ **b.** $y = 1 - 0.5(x - 1)$

c. $y = |x|$ **d.** $y = 1.5^x$

LESSON 9.2

EXERCISES

1. a. $2|5 + 4| + 1 = 2(9) + 1 = 18 + 1 = 19$

b. $2|-6 + 4| + 1 = 2|-2| + 1 = 2(2) + 1$
$= 4 + 1 = 5$

c. $(2|-2 + 4| + 1) + 3 = 2(2) + 1 + 3$
$= 4 + 1 + 3 = 8$

d. $2|(x + 2) + 4| + 1 = 2|x + 6| + 1$

2. a. $L_3 = L_1 + 8; L_4 = L_2 - 4$

b. A translation right 8 units and down 4 units

c.

$y = f(x)$	The original function.
$y = f(x - 8)$	Replace x with $x - 8$ to translate the graph right 8 units.
$y - (-4) = f(x - 8)$	Replace y with $y - (-4)$ to translate the graph down 4 units.
$y = f(x - 8) - 4$	Solve for y.

The equation for the image is $y = f(x - 8) - 4$.

3. a. $(1, -3)$ **b.** $(-5, -3)$

c. $(6, 4)$ **d.** $(-1, 0)$

4. a. A translation of $y = |x|$ right 1.5 units and down 2.5 units

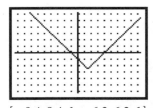

$[-9.4, 9.4, 1, -6.2, 6.2, 1]$

b. A translation of $y = x^2$ left 3 units

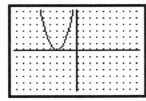

$[-9.4, 9.4, 1, -6.2, 6.2, 1]$

c. A translation of $y = |x|$ up 3.5 units

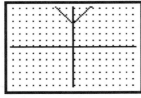

$[-9.4, 9.4, 1, -6.2, 6.2, 1]$

d. A translation of $y = 3^x$ left 1 unit and up 2 units

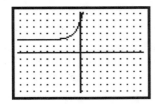

5. a. To translate down 2 units, replace y with $y - (-2)$ to get $y - (-2) = x^2$. Then, solve for y to get $y = x^3 - 2$.

   b. To translate the graph right 5 units, replace x with $x - 5$ to get $y = 4^{(x-5)}$.

   c. $y = |x|$ The original function.

   $y = |x + 4|$ Replace x with $x - (-4)$ to translate the graph left 4 units.

   $y - 1 = |x + 4|$ Replace y with $y - 1$ to translate the graph up 1 unit.

   $y = |x + 4| + 1$ Solve for y.

   The equation for the image is $y = |x + 4| + 1$.

6. a. A translation of $y = x^2$ right 1 unit and down 3 units; $y = (x - 1)^2 - 3$

   b. A translation of $y = |x|$ left 5 units and down 3 units; $y = |x + 5| - 3$

   c. A translation of $y = |x|$ right 6 units and up 4 units; $y = |x - 6| + 4$

   d. A translation of $y = x^2$ left 1 unit; $y = (x + 1)^2$

7. a. The input variable is t, time. The output variable is d, distance.

   b. Time is in seconds, and distance is in meters.

   c. Domain: $0 \le t \le 5$; range: $1 \le d \le 4$

   d. Possible answer: Beth starts 3 m from her teacher and walks toward the teacher at 1 m/sec for 2 sec. When she turns in her test, she is 1 m from the teacher. Beth then turns and walks away from the teacher at 1 m/sec for 3 sec.

   e. The graph is a translation of the graph of $d = |t|$ right 2 units and up 1 unit, so the function is $d = |t - 2| + 1$.

8. a. A translation down 4 units

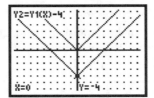

   b. A translation right 4 units

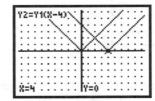

9. a. A translation right 3 units

   b. A translation left 2 units

   c. A translation down 2 units

   d. A translation up 3 units

10. a. Let x represent time in minutes, and let y represent temperature in degrees Celsius. The scatter plot suggests an exponential function.

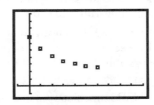

$[-1, 10, 1, -10, 100, 10]$

   b. Ratios to the nearest thousandth: 0.765, 0.788, 0.829, 0.882, 0.9, 0.926. The ratios are not approximately constant, so they do not appear to support the idea that this is an exponential function.

   c.

Time (min)	0	1	2	3	4	5	6
Temperature (°C)	47	31	20	13	9	6	4

The points have been translated down 21 units. The long-run value will now be 0°C.

d. Ratios to the nearest thousandth: 0.660, 0.645, 0.65, 0.692, 0.667, 0.667. The ratios are approximately constant. The mean of the ratios is approximately 0.66.

e. The starting value, A, is 47 and the rate of decrease, r, is $1 - 0.66$ or 0.34. So, the equation is $y = 47(1 - 0.34)^x$.

f. A translation up 21 units

g. To model the original data, translate the function $y = 47(1 - 0.34)^x$ up 21 units. This gives the equation $y = 47(1 - 0.34)^x + 21$.

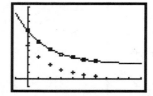

11. a. 20°C

b. Subtract the room temperature, 20°, from each temperature to get 221°C and 188°C.

c. The change in temperature is $221 - 188$ or 33°C per hour. The percent decrease is $\frac{33}{221}$ or about 15% per hour.

d. Because 221 is the initial value and 0.15 is the rate of decrease, the equation is $y = 221(1 - 0.15)^x$, where x is the time in hours and y is the temperature in degrees Celsius.

e. $y = 221(1 - 0.15)^x + 20$. The vertical translation is needed to make the long-run value 20°C.

f. $y = 221(1 - 0.15)^{(x-5)} + 20$. This horizontal translation is needed because the first temperature was measured 5 hours after the bowl left the kiln.

g. $f(0) = 221(1 - 0.15)^{(0-5)} + 20 \approx 518$. The temperature of the bowl immediately after it was removed from the kiln was approximately 518°C.

h. After 28 hours, the temperature is about 25.26°C. After 29 hours, the temperature is about 24.47°C. To make sure the temperature is 25°C or less, you should wait 29 hours.

12. a. The year is the input variable, x, and population in billions is the output variable, y.

b. Sketches will vary. The graph should be an increasing exponential function passing through the point (1999, 6.0).

c. (1999, 6.0)

d. If 6.0 billion were the population in year 0, the equation would be $y = 6.0(1 + 0.013)^x$. However, 6.0 billion is the population in 1999, so the function needs to be translated right 1999 units.

(This translates the point $(0, 6)$ to $(1999, 6)$.) So, the function is $y = 6.0(1 + 0.013)^{(x-1999)}$. An appropriate window might be [1990, 2010, 1, 5, 8, 1].

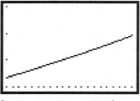

[1990, 2010, 1, 5, 8, 1]

e. 1990: 5.3 billion; 2010: 6.9 billion

13. a. The point $(0, 0)$ is translated to $(4, 8)$. So, $(4, 8)$ is one point on the new graph.

b. $y = b(x - 4) + 8$

c. The point $(0, 0)$ is translated to (H, V). So, (H, V) is one point on the new graph.

d. $y = b(x - H) + V$

14. a. 90.6%   **b.** Answers will vary.

c. $\frac{77 + 10}{85 + 10} = \frac{87}{95} \approx 0.916 \approx 91.6\%$

15. a. $(0.75, 6.5)$ **b.** $(-3.5, -24.5)$

c. $(3, 1)$

IMPROVING YOUR VISUAL THINKING SKILLS

The vertical shift divided by the horizontal shift is the same as the slope of Jose's line, so the line was in effect shifted along itself to lie on top of itself. You might ask what shift would have taken Tammy's line to itself. Students may be surprised to discover that any translation by the same amount horizontally and vertically will leave Tammy's line unchanged. A translation horizontally H units and vertically V units will leave a line with the slope $\frac{V}{H}$ unchanged. Ask if this could happen to figures other than lines, to help students appreciate the importance of lines' constant slope.

LESSON 9.3

EXERCISES

1. a. $0.5(5 - 3)^2 - 3 = 0.5 \cdot 4 - 3 = -1$

b. $0.5(-6 - 3)^2 - 3 = 0.5 \cdot 81 - 3 = 37.5$

c. $4[0.5(2 - 3)^2 - 3] = 4(0.5 \cdot 1 - 3)$
$= 4(-2.5) = -10$

d. $0.5(-x - 3)^2 - 3$

e. $-[0.5(x - 3)^2 - 3] = -0.5(x - 3)^2 + 3$

2. a. A translation of the graph of $y = x^2$ down 2 units; $y = x^2 - 2$

b. A translation of the graph of $y = |x|$ right 3 units; $y = |x - 3|$

Discovering Algebra Solutions Manual
©2002 Key Curriculum Press

c. A translation of the graph of $y = x^2$ left 2 units and down 1 unit; $y = (x + 2)^2 - 1$

d. A translation of the graph of $y = |x|$ right 1 unit and up 1 unit; $y = |x - 1| + 1$

3. a. A reflection across the x-axis

b. A translation right 6 units or a reflection across the y-axis

c. A translation left 2 units

d. A translation left 2 units and a reflection across the x-axis

4. a. Predictions will vary. This graph will be a reflection across the y-axis.

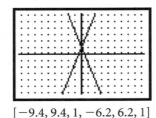

$[-9.4, 9.4, 1, -6.2, 6.2, 1]$

b. Predictions will vary. This graph will be a reflection across the x-axis.

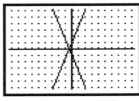

$[-9.4, 9.4, 1, -6.2, 6.2, 1]$

5. a. A reflection across the x-axis

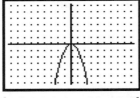

$[-9.4, 9.4, 1, -6.2, 6.2, 1]$

b. A translation left 3 units and a reflection across the x-axis

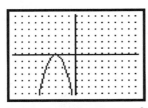

$[-9.4, 9.4, 1, -6.2, 6.2, 1]$

c. A reflection across the x-axis followed by a translation up 3 units

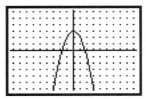

$[-9.4, 9.4, 1, -6.2, 6.2, 1]$

d. A reflection across the y-axis and a translation up 3 units (or just a translation up 3 units)

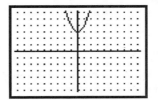

6. a. Possible answer: Enter the x-coordinates into list L1. Enter the first x-coordinate again at the end of the list. Enter the y-coordinates (in the same order as the corresponding x-coordinates) into list L2. Enter the first y-coordinate again at the end of the list. So, L1 = {2, 7, 7, 2} and L2 = {2, 2, 4, 2}. Then make a connected plot of L1 versus L2.

b. **i.** Let L3 = −L1 and L4 = L2, and make a connected plot of L3 versus L4.

ii. Let L3 = −L1 and L4 = −L2, and make a connected plot of L3 versus L4.

iii. Let L3 = L1 and L4 = −L2, and make a connected plot of L3 versus L4.

iv. Let L3 = L1 + 2 and L4 = −L2, and make a connected plot of L3 versus L4.

7. a. A reflection across the y-axis

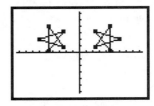

b. A translation left 8 units and a reflection across the x-axis

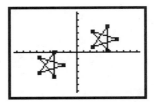

c. A translation right 2 units and down 4 units

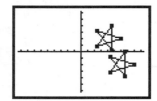

d. A reflection across the line $y = x$

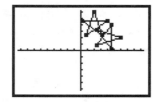

8. a. The graph looks like the graph of $y = |x|$ shifted right 4 units and up 1 unit, so the equation $y = |x - 4| + 1$ models the walk.

b. This graph shows Cheryl's walk.

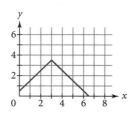

This is the graph of $y = |x|$ reflected across the x-axis and then shifted right 3 units and up 3.5 units. Its equation is $y = -|x - 3| + 3.5$.

c. Domain: $0 \leq x \leq 6$; range: $0.5 \leq y \leq 3.5$

9. To get to the star on the right, the star on the left is translated right 11 units and reflected across the x-axis. To accomplish this in 11 frames (with a top-to-bottom flip in each frame), each point must be translated right 1 unit and reflected across the x-axis in each frame. So, if a point has coordinates (x, y), the coordinates of its image in the next frame would be $(x + 1, -y)$.

10. a. A reflection across the x-axis followed by a translation right 3 units and up 6 units; $y = -(x - 3)^2 + 6$

b. A reflection across the x-axis and a reflection across the y-axis, followed by a translation left 2 units and down 4 units; $y = -f(-(x + 2)) - 4$

11. a. **i.** $y = -2$ **ii.** $y = 3.5$
  iii. $x = 3$ **iv.** $x = -4$ or $y = -4$

b. **i.** The transformation is the same as a reflection across the x-axis followed by a translation down 4 units, so the equation is $y = -x^2 - 4$.

ii. The transformation is the same as a reflection across the x-axis followed by a translation up 7 units, so the equation is $y = -|x| + 7$.

iii. The transformation is the same as a reflection across the y-axis followed by a translation right 6 units, so the equation is $y = 2^{-(x-6)}$.

iv. The transformation is the same as a reflection across the y-axis followed by a translation either down 16 units or left 8 units, or a reflection across the x-axis followed by a translation either down 8 units or left 4 units; the equation is equivalent to $y = -12 - 2x$.

c. A reflection across the horizontal line $y = b$ is the same as a reflection across the x-axis and a translation up or down $2b$ units, so the equation is $y = -f(x) + 2b$.

d. A reflection across the vertical line $x = a$ is the same as a reflection across the y-axis and a translation right or left $2a$ units, so the equation is $y = f(-x + 2a)$.

12. a. There is a 12% decrease per minute $(1 - 0.12 = 0.88)$.

b. As x gets larger and larger, y gets closer and closer to 0. So, the long-run value of y is 0 grams. This means that eventually all the reactant will be used.

c. As x gets larger and larger, y gets closer and closer to 100. So, the long-run value of y is 100 grams. This means that eventually only 100 grams will remain, and this 100 grams will never be consumed.

d. Both graphs are decreasing exponential graphs. The graph of $y = 500(0.88)^x$ shows a starting amount of 500 grams of reactant. The graph of $y = 500(0.88)^x + 100$ shows a starting amount of 600 grams of reactant. The second graph is a translation of the first graph up 100 units.

13. 47 tablespoons $\left(\frac{1 \text{ cup}}{16 \text{ tablespoons}}\right)\left(\frac{1 \text{ quart}}{4 \text{ cups}}\right) = \frac{47}{64}$ quart ≈ 0.734 quart

14. a. Possible answers using Q-points: $y = 36 + 3.6(x - 4)$ or $y = 72 + 3.6(x - 14)$

b. Approximately 22 minutes

IMPROVING YOUR REASONING SKILLS

Mayan numbers converted to base 10 numbers:

9	13	17	0	3
2	6	2	14	18
1	5	7	11	15
4	8	12	16	19

LESSON 9.4

EXERCISES

1. This is the graph of $y = |x|$ shifted right 5 units, so the equation is $y = |x - 5|$.

2. a.

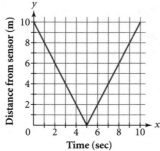

b. Each point on the graph in 2a is twice the distance from the x-axis as the corresponding point on $y = |x - 5|$. So, the graph is a vertical stretch of $y = |x - 5|$ by a factor of 2. The equation is $y = 2|x - 5|$.

3. a. On the graph of $y = |x - 5|$ in Exercise 1, if you start at the vertex and move right 5 units, you must move up 5 units to reach a point on the graph. On this graph, if you move right 5 units from the vertex, you must move *down* 6 units to reach a point on the graph, so the graph of $y = |x - 5|$ is flipped over the x-axis and stretched by a factor of $\frac{6}{5}$ or 1.2. It is also translated up 6 units. The equation is $y = -1.2|x - 5| + 6$.

b. Ted started at the motion sensor and walked away at 1.2 m/sec for 5 sec. When he was 6 m away, he turned and walked back toward the sensor at the same speed.

4. Answers will vary.

5. Answers will vary.

6. In a vertical stretch, all the y-coordinates are multiplied by a number. Because multiplying 0 by any number gives a result of 0, the point $(2, 0)$ will not be affected by a vertical stretch.

7. a. A vertical stretch of $y = x^2$ by a factor of 2

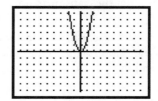

b. A vertical shrink of $y = |x|$ by a factor of 0.25, then a translation right 2 units and up 1 unit

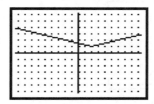

c. A reflection of $y = x^2$ across the x-axis, then a translation left 4 units and down 1 unit

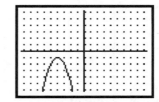

d. A vertical stretch of $y = |x|$ by a factor of 2 and a reflection across the x-axis, then a translation right 3 units and up 4 units

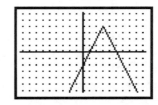

8. *(See table at bottom of page.)*

Lesson 9.4, Exercise 8.

Change	Equation	Transformation
Replace x with $x - 3$	$y = |x - 3|$	Translation right 3 units
Replace y with $y + 2$	$y = |x| - 2$	Translation down 2 units
Multiply the right side by -1	$y = -|x|$	**Reflection across the y-axis**
Replace y with $y - 2$	$y = |x| + 2$	**Translation up 2 units**
Multiply the right side by $\frac{1}{2}$	$y = \frac{1}{2}|x|$	Vertical shrink by a factor of $\frac{1}{2}$
Replace x with $x + 4$	$y = |x + 4|$	Translation left 4 units
Multiply the right side by 1.5	$y = 1.5|x|$	**Vertical stretch by a factor of 1.5**
Replace x with $x - 1$	$y = |x - 1|$	Translation right 1 unit
Multiply the right side by 3	$y = 3|x|$	**Vertical stretch by a factor of 3**

9. a. A reflection across the *x*-axis and a translation left 3 units. The order of the transformations does not matter.

  b. Possible answers: A vertical shrink by a factor of 0.5 followed by a translation right 2 units and up 1 unit. A translation right 2 units, followed by a vertical shrink by a factor of 0.5, followed by a translation up 1 unit.

10. a. A vertical stretch by a factor of 3

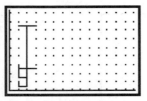

  [0, 28.2, 2, 0, 18.6, 2]

  b. A horizontal stretch by a factor of 3

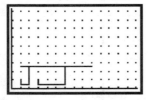

  c. A horizontal stretch by a factor of 3 and a vertical stretch by a factor of 3

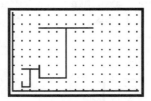

  d. A horizontal shrink by a factor of 0.5 and a vertical shrink by a factor of 0.5

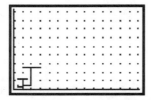

  e. A horizontal stretch by a factor of 2, a vertical stretch by a factor of 2, and a reflection across both the *x*- and *y*-axes

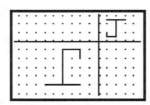

  [−18.8, 9.4, 2, −12.4, −6.2, 2]

  f. These transformations increase or decrease the overall size of the figure without changing its shape.

11. Predictions will vary.

  a. A vertical shrink by a factor of 0.5 and a reflection across the *x*-axis

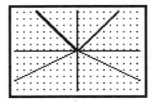

  b. A vertical stretch by a factor of 2 and a translation right 4 units

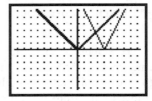

  c. A vertical stretch by a factor of 3 and a reflection across the *x*-axis, then a translation left 2 units and up 4 units (Note: The stretch, the reflection, and the translation left can be performed in any order, but the translation up must be done *after* the reflection and the stretch.)

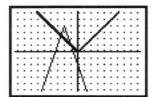

12. a. Answers will vary. The plot is shaped like an absolute value function. Students can experiment with transformations of $y = |x|$ until they find a good fit. Possible answer: $f(x) = -25|x - 3.2| + 80$

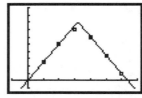

  b. Answers will vary. Using the equation in 12a, $f(2.5) = 62.5$. This means that the depth of the snow after 2.5 months (mid-December) was about 62.5 centimeters.

  c. Answers will vary. Using the equation in 12a, $x = 1.88$ or $x = 4.52$. This means that the depth of the snow was 47 cm after 1.88 months (end of November) and after 4.52 months (mid-February).

  d. Answers will vary. Using the answer in 12a, the snow was deepest after 3.2 months (early January). At that time, it was 80 cm deep.

13. The tree should move left 1 unit in each frame, and it should be shrunk vertically by a factor of 0.8. So, each move must transform the point (x, y) into the point $(x - 1, 0.8y)$.

14. a. Yes; when you substitute 1 for x, you get $y = a \cdot 1^2 = a$.

 b. Yes; when you substitute 1 for x, you get $y = a \cdot |1| = a$.

 c. No; unless $f(1) = 1$, a will not be the same as the y-value. For example, if $f(1) = 3$, then $y = a \cdot f(1) = a \cdot 3$. In this case, $a = \frac{y}{3}$.

15. a. $\frac{1}{2^9}$ **b.** 5^{10} **c.** $2^{12} \cdot 3^6$ **d.** $\frac{1}{3^8 \cdot x^{12}}$

16. a. x represents actual temperature, and y represents the wind chill temperature.

 b. Solve the equation $-15 = -52 + 1.6x$. The solution is $x = 23.125$, so if the wind chill temperature is $-15°F$ with a wind speed of 40 miles per hour, the actual temperature is approximately 23°F.

IMPROVING YOUR REASONING SKILLS

Possible equations for the horizontal stretch include $y = \left(\frac{x}{2}\right)^2$ and $y = (0.5x)^2$. Because these equations are equivalent to $y = 0.25x^2$, the horizontal stretch can also be considered a vertical shrink by a factor of 0.25. Just as a vertical dilation of $f(x)$ by a factor of a is given by $\frac{y}{a} = f(x)$, a horizontal stretch or shrink by a factor of b can be represented generically by $y = f\left(\frac{x}{b}\right)$. You may want to ask why the variable x is divided by the factor b. For a point (x, y) on the transformed equation, the point $\left(\frac{x}{b}, y\right)$ satisfies the original equation, so the new graph has the equation $y = f\left(\frac{x}{b}\right)$.

LESSON 9.5

There are no answers for this lesson.

LESSON 9.6

EXERCISES

1. a. Possible answer: A reflection of the graph of $y = x^2$ across the x-axis, then a translation up 2 units; $y = -x^2 + 2$

 b. A vertical shrink of the graph of $y = |x|$ by a factor of $\frac{1}{3}$ and a translation right 2 units; $y = \frac{1}{3}|x - 2|$

 c. Possible answer: A vertical shrink of the graph of $y = x^2$ by a factor of 0.5, then a translation right 1 unit and down 1 unit (Note: The translation right can be done before the shrink, but the translation down must be done *after* the shrink.); $y = 0.5(x - 1)^2 - 1$

 d. Possible answer: A vertical stretch of the graph of $y = |x|$ by a factor of 2 and a reflection across the x-axis, then a translation left 2 units and up 3 units (Note: The stretch, the reflection, and the translation right can be done in any order, but the translation down must be done *after* the reflection and the stretch.); $y = -2|x + 2| + 3$

2. Each y-value in the table is twice the corresponding y-value for $y = \frac{1}{x}$, so the equation is $y = \frac{2}{x}$.

3. The graph of $y = \frac{1}{x}$ contains the point $(-1, -1)$. The corresponding point on this graph is $(-1, 5)$. So, the graph is a vertical stretch of $y = \frac{1}{x}$ by a factor of 5 and a reflection across the x-axis. The equation is $y = -\frac{5}{x}$.

4. a. A vertical stretch by a factor of 4

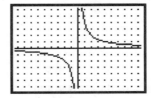

 b. A translation right 5 units and down 2 units

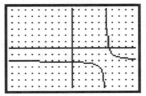

 c. A vertical shrink by a factor of 0.5, then a translation up 3 units

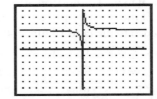

 d. A vertical stretch by a factor of 3, a reflection across the x-axis, and a translation left 3 units

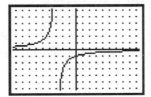

5. a. Decreasing; asymptotes at $x = 0$ and $y = 0$; domain: $x \neq 0$; range: $y \neq 0$

 b. Decreasing; asymptotes at $x = 5$ and $y = -2$; domain: $x \neq 5$; range: $y \neq -2$

 c. Decreasing; asymptotes at $x = 0$ and $y = 3$; domain: $x \neq 0$; range: $y \neq 3$

 d. Increasing; asymptotes at $x = -3$ and $y = 0$; domain: $x \neq -3$; range: $y \neq 0$

6. a. This is a graph of $y = \frac{1}{x}$ shifted right 3 units, so the equation is $y = \frac{1}{x-3}$.

b. This is a graph of $y = \frac{1}{x}$ shifted left 2 units, so the equation is $y = \frac{1}{x+2}$.

c. This is a graph of $y = \frac{1}{x}$ shifted right 1 unit and up 1 unit, so the equation is $y = \frac{1}{x-1} + 1$.

d. This is a graph of $y = \frac{1}{x}$ shifted right 1 unit and down 2 units, so the equation is $y = \frac{1}{x-1} - 2$.

7. a. $y = f(-x)$ or $y = \frac{1}{-x}$

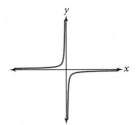

b. $y = -f(x)$ or $y = -\frac{1}{x}$ (See sketch above.)

c. The reflections produce the same graph because $\frac{1}{-x} = -\frac{1}{x}$.

8. a. $y = \frac{5}{x-10} - 100$

b. Possible answer: $y = \frac{-1}{x+3}$. For the graph to be decreasing, $y = \frac{1}{x}$ must be reflected across the x-axis. For the asymptote to be at $x = -3$, the graph must be shifted left 3 units.

c. Possible answer: $y = \frac{1}{(x-2)(x-3)(x+4)} + 2$. Vertical asymptotes occur at the x-values that make the denominator equal to 0 (but that do not make the numerator equal to 0). The horizontal asymptote occurs at the y-value equal to the constant that is added to the rational function.

d. $y = \frac{(x-1)}{x(x-1)}$. For the graph to look like $y = \frac{1}{x}$ but with a hole where $x = 1$, the function must have the same value as $y = \frac{1}{x}$ everywhere except where $x = 1$, and it must be undefined at $x = 1$.

9. Because 5% of the 0.5 liter of solution is salt, the solution contains 0.05(0.5) or 0.025 liter of salt. So, if x is the amount of water added in liters, and y is the concentration of salt, then the equation is $y = \frac{0.025}{0.5 + x}$. To find the amount of water that should be added to create a 1% solution, solve $\frac{0.025}{0.5 + x} = 0.01$. The solution is $x = 2$, so 2 liters need to be added.

10.

$-95 = \frac{5}{x-10} - 100$	Original equation.
$5 = \frac{5}{x-10}$	Add 100 to both sides.
$5(x-10) = 5$	Multiply both sides by $(x-10)$.
$x - 10 = 1$	Divide both sides by 5.
$x = 11$	Add 10 to both sides.

The checking methods will vary. This graph shows the solution as the intersection of $y = -95$ and $y = \frac{5}{x-10} - 100$.

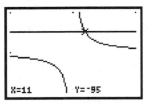

11. a. $700

b.

Additional businesses	0	5	10	15	20
Cost per business ($)	700.00	350.00	233.33	175.00	140.00

c. $y = \frac{3500}{5 + x}$, where x is the number of additional businesses that have signed up and y is the cost per business

d. $150 = \frac{3500}{5 + x}$; $x = 18.\overline{3}$; 19 additional businesses

12. a. $\frac{90}{16}$ or 5.625 lumens

b. Solve $20 = \frac{90}{d^2}$.

$20 = \frac{90}{d^2}$	Original equation.
$20d^2 = 90$	Multiply both sides by d^2.
$d^2 = 4.5$	Divide both sides by 20.
$d \approx 2.12$ or -2.12	

Only the positive solution, 2.12, makes sense in this situation. The distance from the bulb is about 2.12 meters.

13. a. $x < -2$ **b.** $x \geq -2$ **c.** $x \geq 4$

14. Vertex: $(3, 1)$; point to the left: $(2, 3)$; point to the right: $(4, 3)$. To create the graph of $y = 2(x-3)^2 + 1$, the graph of $y = x^2$ is translated right 3 units and up 1 unit, so the image of the vertex $(0, 0)$ is $(3, 1)$. To find the point to the left, substitute 2 for x. To find the point to the right, substitute 4 for x.

15. Vertex: $(-1, 2)$; point to the left: $(-2, -1)$; point to the right: $(0, -1)$.

IMPROVING YOUR VISUAL THINKING SKILLS

Fabric A has a 123123 ... pattern. You can interpret the pattern as a series of translations of (123) along the length of the fabric. The repeating unit must be as wide as the distance from stripe 1 to the next stripe 1. There are infinitely many units because you could measure from stripe 2 to the next stripe 2, or from the middle of stripe 3 to the middle of the next stripe 3, and so on.

Fabric B has a 123212321 ... pattern. You can interpret the pattern as a series of translations (1232) along the length of the fabric, or as a series of reflections across stripe 1 or stripe 3. The repeating unit will depend on the transformation chosen, but there will still be infinitely many units.

Fabric C has the same pattern along its length as Fabric B, and it has a 2121 . . . pattern across its width. You can interpret the pattern as generated by the same transformations noted for Fabric B; you can also interpret the pattern as a widthwise reflection across stripe 1 or stripe 2.

Fabric D has the same pattern along its length and across its width as Fabric A. You can interpret the pattern as a lengthwise or widthwise translation similar to Fabric A. There is no reflection.

Fabric D would result in the most expensive shirt. It's not possible to cut symmetrical pieces like sleeves or shirt fronts from a folded piece of fabric. Hence, there would be more fabric waste as pieces are individually positioned, and more time would be involved.

LESSON 9.7

EXERCISES

1. a. $(-2, 2), (1, 2), (-2, 6)$

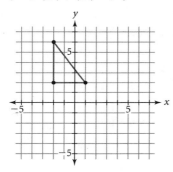

b. To shift down 3 units, you must add -3 to each y-coordinate, so you would need to add the matrix $\begin{bmatrix} 0 & 0 & 0 \\ -3 & -3 & -3 \end{bmatrix}$.

c. $\begin{bmatrix} -2 & 1 & -2 \\ 2 & 2 & 6 \end{bmatrix} + \begin{bmatrix} 0 & 0 & 0 \\ -3 & -3 & -3 \end{bmatrix}$

$= \begin{bmatrix} -2 & 1 & -2 \\ -1 & -1 & 3 \end{bmatrix}$

2. a. $\begin{bmatrix} -4 & -2 & -2 \\ 3 & 5 & 1 \end{bmatrix}$ (The order of the columns may vary.)

b. $\begin{bmatrix} -4 & -2 & -2 \\ 3 & 5 & 1 \end{bmatrix} + \begin{bmatrix} 9 & 9 & 9 \\ 0 & 0 & 0 \end{bmatrix} = \begin{bmatrix} 5 & 7 & 7 \\ 3 & 5 & 1 \end{bmatrix}$

c. $\begin{bmatrix} -4 & -2 & -2 \\ 3 & 5 & 1 \end{bmatrix} + \begin{bmatrix} -4 & -4 & -4 \\ -4 & -4 & -4 \end{bmatrix}$

$= \begin{bmatrix} -8 & -6 & -6 \\ -1 & 1 & -3 \end{bmatrix}$

3. a. $[6 \quad 15]$ **b.** $\begin{bmatrix} 6 \\ 15 \end{bmatrix}$

c. $[4 \cdot 2 + 7 \cdot 8] = [64]$

d. $\begin{bmatrix} 8 & 32 \\ 14 & 56 \end{bmatrix}$

4. a. $\begin{bmatrix} -1 & 0 \\ 0 & 1 \end{bmatrix}$ **b.** $\begin{bmatrix} 1 & -0 \\ 0 & 1 \end{bmatrix}$

5. a. A rectangle

b. Possible answer: For the x-coordinate, multiply row 1 of the transformation matrix by column 2 of the quadrilateral matrix: $[1 \quad 0] \cdot \begin{bmatrix} 2 \\ -1 \end{bmatrix} = 2$. This result goes in row 1, column 2, of the image matrix. For the y-coordinate, multiply row 2 of the transformation matrix by column 2 of the quadrilateral matrix: $[0 \quad 2] \cdot \begin{bmatrix} 2 \\ -1 \end{bmatrix} = -2$. This result goes in row 2, column 2, of the image matrix.

c. $\begin{bmatrix} -1 & 2 & 1 & -2 \\ 4 & -2 & -4 & 2 \end{bmatrix}$

d. A parallelogram

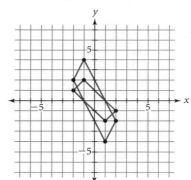

6. a. $[S] = \begin{bmatrix} 0 & 1 & 1 & 0 \\ 0 & 0 & 1 & 1 \end{bmatrix}$ (The order of the columns may vary.)

b. **i.** This matrix operation multiplies each y-coordinate by 3, resulting in a vertical stretch by a factor of 3.

  ii. This matrix operation multiplies each y-coordinate by -3, resulting in a vertical stretch by a factor of 3 and a reflection across the x-axis.

  iii. This matrix operation multiplies each x-coordinate by 4 and each y-coordinate by 2, resulting in a horizontal stretch by a factor of 4 and a vertical stretch by a factor of 2.

  iv. This matrix operation adds 4 to each x-coordinate and 2 to each y-coordinate, resulting in a translation right 4 units and up 2 units.

7. a. $[Q] = \begin{bmatrix} 2 & 3 & 6 & 7 \\ 2 & 4 & 5 & 1 \end{bmatrix}$ (The order of the columns may vary.)

b. $\begin{bmatrix} 1 & 0 \\ 0 & 0.5 \end{bmatrix} \cdot [Q] = \begin{bmatrix} 2 & 3 & 6 & 7 \\ 1 & 2 & 2.5 & 0.5 \end{bmatrix}$

c. $\begin{bmatrix} 0.5 & 0 \\ 0 & 0.5 \end{bmatrix} \cdot [Q] = \begin{bmatrix} 1 & 1.5 & 3 & 3.5 \\ 1 & 2 & 2.5 & 0.5 \end{bmatrix}$

d. $\begin{bmatrix} -1 & 0 \\ 0 & -1 \end{bmatrix}; \begin{bmatrix} -1 & 0 \\ 0 & -1 \end{bmatrix} \cdot [Q]$

$= \begin{bmatrix} -2 & -3 & -6 & -7 \\ -2 & -4 & -5 & -1 \end{bmatrix}$, which is a reflection across both the x- and y-axes. Multiplying by just $\begin{bmatrix} 1 & 0 \\ 0 & -1 \end{bmatrix}$ results in a reflection across the x-axis, and multiplying by just $\begin{bmatrix} -1 & 0 \\ 0 & 1 \end{bmatrix}$ results in a reflection across the y-axis.

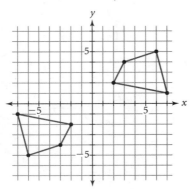

e. $\begin{bmatrix} -2 & -4 & -5 & -1 \\ 2 & 3 & 6 & 7 \end{bmatrix}$; a quarter-turn counterclockwise

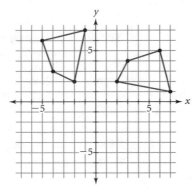

8. a. $y = x^2$

b. $[P] = \begin{bmatrix} -2 & -1 & 0 & 1 & 2 \\ 4 & 1 & 0 & 1 & 4 \end{bmatrix}$

c. $\begin{bmatrix} 1 & 2 & 3 & 4 & 5 \\ 6 & 3 & 2 & 3 & 6 \end{bmatrix}$. The matrix operation represents a translation right 3 units and up 2 units, so the equation is $y = (x - 3)^2 + 2$.

d. $\begin{bmatrix} 2 & 1 & 0 & -1 & -2 \\ 4 & 1 & 0 & 1 & 4 \end{bmatrix}$. The matrix operation represents a reflection across the y-axis, so the equation is $y = (-x)^2$ (or, because the graph is symmetric across the y-axis, just $y = x^2$).

9. a. Answers will vary. Sample answer:

$[R] = \begin{bmatrix} 0 & 3 & 4 \\ 0 & 2 & 0 \end{bmatrix}$

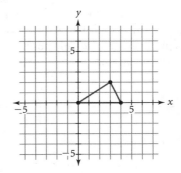

b. Answers will vary. Sample answer based on polygon in 9a:

$\begin{bmatrix} 0.5 & -0.866 \\ 0.866 & 0.5 \end{bmatrix} \cdot \begin{bmatrix} 0 & 3 & 4 \\ 0 & 2 & 0 \end{bmatrix}$

$= \begin{bmatrix} 0 & -0.232 & 2 \\ 0 & 3.598 & 3.464 \end{bmatrix}$

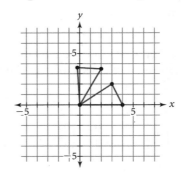

c. A rotation 60° counterclockwise about the origin, or the point $(0, 0)$

d. $\begin{bmatrix} -0.5 & -0.866 \\ 0.866 & -0.5 \end{bmatrix}$. Sample answer based on the polygon in 9a:

$\begin{bmatrix} -0.5 & -0.866 \\ 0.866 & -0.5 \end{bmatrix} \cdot \begin{bmatrix} 0 & 3 & 4 \\ 0 & 2 & 0 \end{bmatrix}$

$= \begin{bmatrix} 0 & -3.232 & -2 \\ 0 & 1.598 & 3.464 \end{bmatrix}$; a rotation 120° counterclockwise about the origin

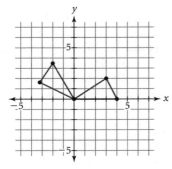

e. Possible answer: Multiply $\begin{bmatrix} 0.5 & -0.866 \\ 0.866 & 0.5 \end{bmatrix}$ by itself three times$(3 \cdot 60° = 180°)$. Then multiply the result by $[R]$.

f. Possible answer: Multiply $\begin{bmatrix} 0.5 & -0.866 \\ 0.866 & 0.5 \end{bmatrix}$ by itself six times $(6 \cdot 60° = 360°)$. Then multiply the result by $[R]$. Or just multiply $[R]$ by $\begin{bmatrix} 1 & 0 \\ 0 & 1 \end{bmatrix}$.

10. a.

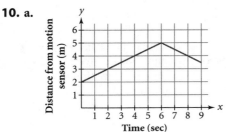

b. $y = 5 - 0.5|x - 6|$

11. a. Five-number summary (in millions): 114, 127, 159, 273, 1247

b. **Most Populated Countries, 1999**

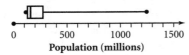

c. China and India

CHAPTER 9 Review

EXERCISES

1. a. A translation left 2 units and up 1 unit

   b. $(x - 2, y + 1)$

2. a. i. A vertical shrink by a factor of 0.5 and a translation left 6 units

   ii. Possible answers: A reflection across the x-axis, then a translation up 2 units; or a translation down 2 units, then a reflection across the x-axis.

   iii. Possible answer: A horizontal stretch by a factor of 2 and a reflection across the y-axis, then a translation right 5 units and down 3 units

(Note: The stretch, the reflection, and the translation down can be done in any order, but the translation right must be done *after* the stretch and the reflection.) Another answer: a translation left 3 units and down 3 units, followed by a reflection across the y-axis then left 1 unit.

   b. i. $L_3 = L_1 - 6$; $L_4 = 0.5 \cdot L_2$

   ii. Possible answer: $L_3 = L_1$; $L_4 = -L_2 + 2$

   iii. Possible answer: $L_3 = -2 \cdot L_1 + 5$; $L_4 = L_2 - 3$

3. Answers will vary. For these possible answers, list L_3 and list L_4 are used for the x- and y-coordinates, respectively, of the image.

   a. Let $L_3 = L_1$ and $L_4 = -L_2$, and make a connected plot of L_3 versus L_4.

   b. Let $L_3 = -L_1$ and $L_4 = L_2$, and make a connected plot of L_3 versus L_4.

   c. Let $L_3 = L_1 + 3$ and $L_4 = -L_2$, and make a connected plot of L_3 versus L_4.

4. a. A vertical stretch of the graph of $y = |x|$ by a factor of 2, then a translation up 1 unit

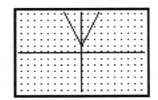

   b. A reflection of the graph of $y = |x|$ across the x-axis, then a translation left 2 units and up 2 units (Note: The left translation can be done before the reflection, but the up translation must be done *after* the reflection.)

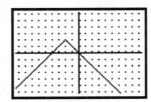

   c. A vertical shrink of the graph of $y = x^2$ by a factor of 0.5 and a reflection across the y-axis, then a translation down 1 unit (or, because the graph is symmetric across the y-axis, just a vertical shrink by a factor of 0.5, then a translation down 1 unit)

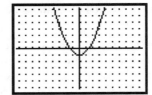

d. A reflection of the graph of $y = x^2$ across the *x*-axis, then a translation right 2 units and up 1 unit (Note: The right translation can be done before the reflection, but the up translation must be done *after* the reflection.)

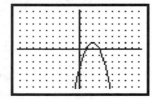

5. The graph of $g(x)$ is the image of the graph of $f(x)$ after a translation right 1 unit and up 2 units, so its equation is $g(x) = f(x - 1) + 2$.

6. a. $y = 3 - |x|$ **b.** $y = (x + 4)^2 - 2$
    c. $y = 0.5x^2 - 5$ **d.** $y = -2|x - 3| + 1$

7. a.

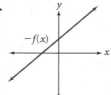

b. Answers will vary. A correct equation will have a negative slope and a negative *y*-intercept. Possible answer: $Y_1 = -x - 2$; $Y_2 = -Y_1$ reflects the graph across the *x*-axis (because $-Y_1 = -(-x - 2)$ $= x + 2$). This supports the answer to 7a.

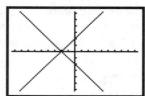

8. a. A translation right 3 units; asymptotes: $x = 3, y = 0$

b. A vertical stretch by a factor of 3 and a translation left 2 units; asymptotes: $x = -2, y = 0$

c. A translation right 5 units and down 2 units; asymptotes: $x = 5, y = -2$

9. a. A translation of $y = \frac{1}{x}$ right 3 units and down 2 units; $y = \frac{1}{x - 3} - 2$

b. A translation of $y = 2^x$ right 4 units and down 2 units; $y = 2^{(x-4)} - 2$

c. A reflection of $y = 2^x$ across the *x*-axis and across the *y*-axis, followed by a translation up 3 units (or a reflection of $y = 2^x$ across the *x*-axis, followed by a translation up 3 units, followed by a reflection across the *y*-axis); $y = -2^{(-x)} + 3$

d. A vertical stretch of $y = \frac{1}{x}$ by a factor of 4 and a reflection across the *x*-axis, followed by a translation up 1 unit and left 2 units (Note: The stretch, the reflection, and the translation left can be done in any order, but the translation up must be done *after* the stretch and the reflection.); $y = -\frac{4}{x + 2} + 1$

10. a. $[A] = \begin{bmatrix} -1 & 1 & 1 & -1 \\ 1 & 1 & -1 & -1 \end{bmatrix}$ (The order of the columns may vary.)

b. i. Nothing; the image is identical to the original square.

   ii. A reflection across the *x*-axis and across the *y*-axis, or a rotation of 180°

   iii. A vertical stretch by a factor of 3

   iv. A translation right 1 unit and up 1 unit

TAKE ANOTHER LOOK

The equation of the line of reflection is $y = x$. Students should find that the coordinates of each point are interchanged after the reflection. That is, the image of a point (x, y) is (y, x). For example, the image of $(2, 4)$ is $(4, 2)$. An example of a function whose inverse is also a function is $y = 2x$. An example of a function whose inverse is not a function is $y = x^2$.

CHAPTER 10

LESSON 10.1

EXERCISES

1. On a calculator, enter one side of the equation into Y_1 and the other into Y_2. Then find the number of intersection points.

a. Two solutions

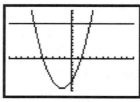

$[-10, 10, 1, -10, 15, 1]$

b. No solutions

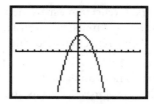

$[-10, 10, 1, -10, 10, 1]$

c. One solution

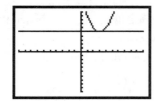

$[-10, 10, 1, -10, 10, 1]$

d. Two solutions

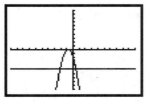

$[-10, 10, 1, -10, 10, 1]$

2. a. $x = -6$ and $x = 3$
b. There are no solutions.
c. $x = 3$
d. $x \approx -2.14$ and $x \approx 0.47$

3. a.

$x^2 = 18$	The original equation.
$\sqrt{x^2} = \sqrt{18}$	Take the square root of both sides.
$x = \pm\sqrt{18}$	The $\pm$ symbol shows the two numbers, $\sqrt{18}$ and $-\sqrt{18}$, whose square is 18.

b.

$x^2 + 3 = 52$	The original equation.
$x^2 = 49$	Subtract 3 from both sides.
$\sqrt{x^2} = \sqrt{49}$	Take the square root of both sides.
$x = \pm 7$	The $\pm$ symbol shows the two numbers, 7 and -7, whose square is 49.

c.

$(x - 2)^2 = 25$	The original equation.
$\sqrt{(x-2)^2} = \sqrt{25}$	Take the square root of both sides.
$x - 2 = \pm 5$	The $\pm$ symbol shows the two numbers, 5 and -5, whose square is 25.
$x = 2 \pm 5$	Add 2 to both sides.
$x = 7$ or	Evaluate.
$x = -3$	

d.

$2(x + 1)^2 - 4 = 10$	The original equation.
$2(x + 1)^2 = 14$	Add 4 to both sides.
$(x + 1)^2 = 7$	Divide both sides by 2.
$\sqrt{(x+1)^2} = \sqrt{7}$	Take the square root of both sides.
$x + 1 = \pm\sqrt{7}$	The $\pm$ symbol shows the two numbers, $\sqrt{7}$ and $-\sqrt{7}$, whose square is 7.
$x = -1 \pm \sqrt{7}$	Add -1 to both sides.

4. Sample answers:

a.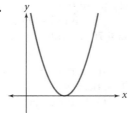

b.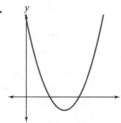

c.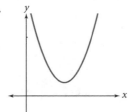

d.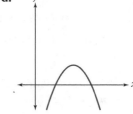

5. a. $h(0) = -4.9(0)^2 + 147 = 147$. This means that the ball was released from a height of 147 meters.

b.

$-4.9t^2 + 147 = 20$	The original equation.
$-4.9t^2 = -127$	Subtract 147 from both sides.
$t^2 = 25.92$	Divide both sides by -4.9.
$t = \pm 5.09$	Take the square root of both sides.

To find the solution graphically, graph $y = -4.9t^2 + 147$ and $y = 20$, and find the intersection points. The graph shows two solution points—$(5.09, 20)$ and $(-5.09, 20)$.

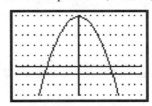

$[-10, 10, 1, -50, 150, 25]$

c. No, only the solution $(5.09, 20)$ makes sense because the time t must be positive.

d. The graph shows that the height is less than 20 meters when $t > 5.09$ seconds. (Note: $h(t)$ is also less than 20 when $t < -5.09$, but negative time values do not make sense in this situation.)

e. The ball hits the ground when $t \approx 5.48$ seconds because the positive x-intercept is near the point $(5.48, 0)$. (You could also find this answer by solving $-4.9t^2 + 147 = 0$ symbolically.)

6. a. Because the rocket is fired from the ground, the height is 0 meters when $t = 0$, so the graph goes through $(0, 0)$. The height is 108 meters when $t = 4.70$, so the graph goes through $(4.70, 108)$. Because the rocket hits the ground at 9.40 seconds, the height is 0 when $t = 9.40$, so the graph goes through $(9.40, 0)$.

b. Sample answer: $[-1, 10, 1, -10, 120, 10]$

c. The vertex is the highest point of the graph. The problem states that the rocket is at its highest point, 108 meters, after 4.70 seconds. So, the vertex is (4.7, 108).

d. The equation must be in the form $h(t) = a(t - 4.7)^2 + 108$. Because (0, 0) is on the graph, substitute it into the equation and solve for a:

$$0 = a(0 - 4.7)^2 + 108$$

$$0 = 22.09a + 108$$

$$-108 = 22.09a$$

$$-4.9 \approx a$$

So, the equation is $h(t) = -4.9(x - 4.7)^2 + 108$.

e. $h(3) = -4.9(3 - 4.7)^2 + 108$
$= -4.9(-1.7)^2 + 108 \approx 94$. The height at 3 seconds is about 94 meters.

f. Solve $-4.9(t - 4.7)^2 + 108 = 47$.

$-4.9(t - 4.7)^2 + 108 = 47$	The original equation.
$-4.9(t - 4.7)^2 = -61$	Subtract 108 from both sides.
$(t - 4.7)^2 = \dfrac{61}{4.9}$	Divide both sides by -4.9.
$t - 4.7 = \pm\sqrt{\dfrac{61}{4.9}}$	Take the square root of both sides.
$t = 4.7 \pm \sqrt{\dfrac{61}{4.9}}$	Add 4.7 to both sides.
$t \approx 1.17$ or	Evaluate.
$t \approx 8.23$	

At about 1.17 sec and 8.23 sec, the rocket will be 47 m above the ground.

7. a. $p(2) = -0.23(2 - 3.4)^2 + 4.2 \approx 3.75$. After the ball has gone 2 m horizontally, it will be approximately 3.75 m above the ground.

b. Solve $-0.23(x - 3.4)^2 + 4.2 = 2$.

$-0.23(x - 3.4)^2 + 4.2 = 2$	The original equation.
$-0.23(x - 3.4)^2 = -2.2$	Subtract 4.2 from both sides.
$(x - 3.4)^2 = \dfrac{2.2}{0.23}$	Divide both sides by -0.23.
$x - 3.4 = \pm\sqrt{\dfrac{2.2}{0.23}}$	Take the square root of both sides.
$x = 3.4 \pm \sqrt{\dfrac{2.2}{0.23}}$	Add 3.4 to both sides
$x \approx 0.31$ or	Evaluate.
$x \approx 6.49$	

The ball will be 2 m above the ground when it has gone 0.31 m horizontally and again when it has gone 6.49 m horizontally. Exact solutions to the equation are $3.4 \pm \sqrt{\dfrac{220}{23}}$.

c. When the ball is released, the horizontal distance x is 0, so find $p(x)$ when $x = 0$: $p(0) = -0.23(0 - 3.4)^2 + 4.2 = 1.5412$. So, the ball's height is 1.5412 meters when it is released.

d. When the ball hits the ground, $p(x) = 0$, so solve $-0.23(x - 3.4)^2 + 4.2 = 0$.

$-0.23(x - 3.4)^2 + 4.2 = 0$	The original equation.
$-0.23(x - 3.4)^2 = -4.2$	Subtract 4.2 from both sides.
$(x - 3.4)^2 = \dfrac{4.2}{0.23}$	Divide both sides by -0.23.
$x - 3.4 = \pm\sqrt{\dfrac{4.2}{0.23}}$	Take the square root of both sides.
$x = 3.4$ $\pm\sqrt{\dfrac{4.2}{0.23}}$	Add 3.4 to both sides.
$x \approx -0.87$ or	Evaluate.
$x \approx 7.67$	

Only the positive solution makes sense in this situation. The ball hits the ground when it has traveled about 7.67 m horizontally. The exact solutions to the equation are $3.4 \pm \sqrt{\dfrac{420}{23}}$.

8. a. The graph shows that only one solution exists at the intersection of $y = 4$ and $y = -2(x - 3)^2 + 4$. Tracing the graph shows the intersection point is (3, 4), so the solution is $x = 3$.

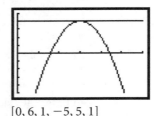

$[0, 6, 1, -5, 5, 1]$

b. The table shows the solution is $x = 3$.

X	Y₁	Y₂
0	-14	4
1	-4	4
2	2	4
3	4	4
4	2	4
5	-4	4
6	-14	4

X=3

c.

$4 = -2(x - 3)^2 + 4$	The original equation.
$0 = -2(x - 3)^2$	Subtract 4 from both sides.
$0 = (x - 3)^2$	Divide both sides by -2.
$0 = x - 3$	Take the square root of both sides.
$3 = x$	Subtract 3 from both sides.

Discovering Algebra Solutions Manual
©2002 Key Curriculum Press

9. a. The x-intercepts indicate when the projectile is at ground level.

b. 2.74 seconds and 7.26 seconds

c. The x-coordinate of the vertex is halfway between the x-coordinates of the x-intercepts. So, to find the x-coordinate of the vertex, find the average of 2.74 and 7.26, which is 5. To find the y-coordinate of the vertex, evaluate $h(t)$ for $t = 5$: $h(5) = 25$. So, the vertex is $(5, 25)$.

d. The projectile is at its maximum height of 25 meters after 5 seconds.

e. $h(3.2) = 9.124$. The height at 3.2 seconds is 9.124 meters.

f. Answers will vary. The horizontal line $y = 12.5$ intersects the parabola twice—when $x \approx 3.4$ seconds and when $x \approx 6.6$ seconds.

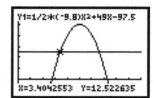

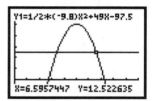

10. $-3x + 4 > 16$ The given inequality.

$\quad -3x > 12$ Subtract 4 from both sides.

$\quad\quad x < -4$ Divide both sides by -3 and reverse inequality symbol.

11. The slope of the line is $\frac{1-6}{6-0} = \frac{-5}{6}$ and the y-intercept is 6, so the equation for the line is $y = 6 - \frac{5}{6}x$. Because the line is solid and the area above it is shaded, the inequality is $y \geq 6 - \frac{5}{6}x$.

LESSON 10.2

EXERCISES

1. The x-coordinate of the vertex is halfway between the roots, 3 and -2, so to find the x-coordinate of the vertex, average the roots: $\frac{3 + (-2)}{2} = 0.5$.

2. Substitute 0.5 for x to obtain $y = 0.4(0.5)^2 - 0.4(0.5) - 2.4 = -2.5$, or use a table.

3.
$$0 = (x + 1.5)^2 - 7.25$$
$$7.25 = (x + 1.5)^2$$
$$\pm\sqrt{7.25} = x + 1.5$$
$$-1.5 \pm \sqrt{7.25} = x$$
$$x \approx 1.192582404 \text{ or}$$
$$x \approx -4.192582404$$

The solutions are very close to the approximations in Examples A and B.

4. a. $x \approx -2.732, 0.732$ **b.** $x \approx -1.869, 0.535$

5. a.
$$(x + 3)^2 = 7$$
$$(x + 3) = \pm\sqrt{7}$$
$$x = -3 \pm \sqrt{7}$$
$$x \approx -5.646, -0.354$$

b.
$$(x - 2)^2 - 8 = 13$$
$$(x - 2)^2 = 21$$
$$x - 2 = \pm\sqrt{21}$$
$$x = 2 \pm \sqrt{21}$$
$$x \approx -2.583, 6.583$$

6. Answers will vary. The solutions, -5.646 and -0.354, are the x-intercepts of the intersection points of the graphs.

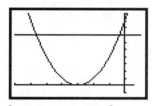

$[-7, 1, 1, -1, 10, 1]$

7. a. The ball is on the ground when $h = 0$. So, to find the times when the ball is on the ground, solve $-16t^2 + 48t = 0$. The solutions are $t = 0$ and $t = 3$, so the ball is on the ground at 0 seconds and at 3 seconds.

b. The ball is at its highest point when $t = 1.5$ seconds, halfway through its flight.

c. $h = 36$ when $t = 1.5$, so the ball goes 36 feet high.

8. a. The ball hits the ground between 3.67 seconds when the height is still positive and 3.68 seconds when the height is negative.

b. Starting the table at 3.67 and setting ΔTbl equal to 0.001 gives an answer of 3.676 seconds.

c. According to the table, the maximum height occurs between 1.81 and 1.82 seconds after Taylor hits the ball. Zooming in on a calculator table, the ball is at its highest point at about 1.81 seconds. At this time, it is 55.5624 feet high.

9. a. Possible answer: The ball is thrown from an initial height of about 5 meters. It reaches a maximum height of about 25 meters in 2 seconds and hits the ground at about 4.3 seconds. The graph shows negative heights, so the ball might have been thrown from the edge of a cliff or from a balcony.

b. Possible answer: The ball is thrown upward with a velocity of 20 meters per second and slows down at a constant rate. At 2 seconds, it is not moving. Then it starts falling. It is moving downward at a speed of 22 meters per second when it hits the ground.

c. The ball is at its maximum velocity when it is released. From that point, the velocity decreases until it reaches 0. As the ball falls, its speed increases, but because the ball is moving in a negative direction (toward the ground), the velocity decreases, becoming more negative. So, because the velocity of the ball decreases as time increases, the slope of the graph is negative.

d. This is when the ball is at its maximum height and not moving. Its velocity is zero.

e. From the second graph, the velocity is 15 meters per second when $t = \frac{1}{2}$ second and -15 meters per second when $t = 3\frac{1}{2}$ seconds. From the first graph, you can see that these are the two times when the ball is about 13 meters high.

f. The domain for both graphs is $0 \leq t \leq 4.3$. The range for the height graph is $0 \leq h(t) \leq 26$. The range for the velocity graph is $-23 \leq v(t) \leq 20$.

10. a. Bo's ball reaches its highest point 0.5(3.4), or 1.7, seconds after it is hit. Gale's ball reaches its highest point 0.5(4.7), or 2.35, seconds after it is hit.

b. You can't tell whose ball goes farther or higher. Gale's ball is in the air longer, but we don't know whether this is because she hit it farther or because she hit it higher.

11. a.

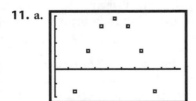

$[0, 9.4, 1, -10, 20, 5]$

b. It is the vertical line $x = 4.5$.

c. (4.5, 19)

d. Figure out how the graph of $y = x^2$ is transformed to get this graph. The graph of $y = x^2$ increases by 1 as you move left or right 1 unit from the vertex. This graph decreases by 3 as you move left or right 1 unit from the vertex. So, the graph of $y = x^2$ is reflected over the x-axis and stretched vertically by a factor of 3. The vertex of $y = x^2$ is

(0, 0) and the vertex of this graph is (4.5, 19), so $y = x^2$ is also translated right 4.5 units and up 19 units. The equation for this graph must be $y = -3(x - 4.5)^2 + 19$.

12. a. $y = 2 + \frac{1}{3}x$ **b.** $y = 3.5 - \frac{1}{4}x$

IMPROVING YOUR VISUAL THINKING SKILLS

A plane perpendicular to the axis will form a circle. To form an ellipse, the plane should be tilted, but not to the extent that it becomes parallel to the edge, when it forms a parabola. Any greater tilt of the plane, including parallel to the cone's axis, will intersect both pieces of the cone and form a hyperbola.

Circular section

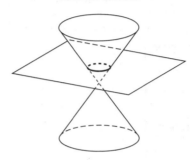

Elliptical section

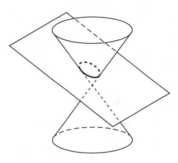

Hyperbolic section

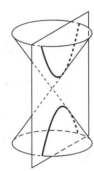

A plane through the cone's vertex might intersect the cone in a point, a single line (if the plane is tangent to the cone), or a pair of lines (if the plane contains the axis). These figures are called *degenerate conics*.

LESSON 10.3

EXERCISES

1. a. Yes; three terms (trinomial)

b. Yes; two terms (binomial)

c. No. The first term has a negative exponent.

d. No. The expression is equivalent to $3x^{-2} - 5x + 2$, which has a negative exponent.

e. Yes; one term (monomial)

f. Yes; three terms (trinomial)

g. Yes; two terms (binomial)

h. Not a polynomial as written, but it is equivalent to $3x - 6$, so there are two terms (binomial).

Discovering Algebra Solutions Manual
©2002 Key Curriculum Press

2. a. This diagram shows that
$(x + 5)^2 = x^2 + 5x + 5x + 25 = x^2 + 10x + 25.$

	x	5
x	x^2	$5x$
5	$5x$	25

b. This diagram shows that
$(x - 7)^2 = x^2 - 7x - 7x + 49 = x^2 - 14x + 49.$

	x	-7
x	x^2	$-7x$
-7	$-7x$	49

c. First, expand $(x - 2)^2$. The diagram shows that
$(x - 2)^2 = x^2 - 4x + 4$. Then, multiply by 3:
$3(x - 2)^2 = 3(x^2 - 4x + 4) = 3x^2 - 12x + 12.$

	x	-2
x	x^2	$-2x$
-2	$-2x$	4

3. a.

	x	2
x	x^2	$2x$
2	$2x$	4

$(x + 2)^2 = x^2 + 4x + 4$

b.

	x	12
x	x^2	$12x$
12	$12x$	144

$(x + 12)^2 = x^2 + 24x + 144$

c.

	x	-7
x	x^2	$-7x$
-7	$-7x$	49

$(x - 7)^2 = x^2 - 14x + 49$

4. a. $(x + 5)^2 + 4 = x^2 + 10x + 25 + 4$
$= x^2 + 10x + 29$

b. $2(x - 7)^2 - 8 = 2(x^2 - 14x + 49) - 8$
$= 2x^2 - 28x + 98 - 8$
$= 2x^2 - 28x + 90$

c. $-3(x + 4)^2 + 1 = -3(x^2 + 8x + 16) + 1$
$= -3x^2 - 24x - 48 + 1$
$= -3x^2 - 24x - 47$

d. $0.5(x - 3)^2 - 4.5 = 0.5(x^2 - 6x + 9) - 4.5$
$= 0.5x^2 - 3x + 4.5 - 4.5$
$= 0.5x^2 - 3x$

5. a.

	x	2
x	x^2	$2x$
4	$4x$	8

$+$

$(x + 2)(x + 4) = x^2 + 6x + 8$

b.

	x	3
x	x^2	$3x$
5	$5x$	15

$+$

$(x + 3)(x + 5) = x^2 + 8x + 15$

c.

	x	2
x	x^2	$2x$
-5	$-5x$	-10

$+$

$(x - 5)(x + 2) = x^2 - 3x - 10$

d.

	x	0
x	x^2	$0x$
-3	$-3x$	0

$+$

$(x - 0)(x - 3) = x^2 - 3x$

6. a. The coordinates of the vertex are $(2, 3)$.

b. $y = (x - 2)^2 + 3$

c. $y = (x - 2)^2 + 3$
$= x^2 - 4x + 4 + 3$
$= x^2 - 4x + 7$

7. No. Possible explanation: By squaring the values inside the parentheses, Heather is accounting for only two of the four rectangles in a squaring diagram. She needs to add the two rectangles that sum to the middle term.

8. a. 70 meters

b. To find the speed, solve $50 = 0.0056x^2 + 0.14x$ by tracing a graph or zooming in on a table. The speed is about 83 kph.

9. a. The vertex is at $(0.4, 2.5)$, so the ball reaches a maximum height of 2.5 meters.

b. $h(t) = -4.9(t - 0.4)^2 + 2.5$
$= -4.9(t^2 - 0.8t + 0.16) + 2.5$
$= -4.9t^2 + 3.92t - 0.784 + 2.5$
$= -4.9t^2 + 3.92t + 1.716$

c. The pitcher released the ball at a height of 1.716 meters.

10. a. Yes

   b. No. The right side should be $2x^2 - 18.8x + 46.98$.

   c. No. The right side should be $-3.5x^2 - 11.2x - 11$.

   d. Yes

11. a. Meaningful domain: $0 \le x \le 6.5$; meaningful range: $0 \le y \le 897.81$

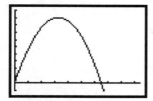

[0, 9.4, 1, −100, 1000, 100]

   b. Answers will vary. Possible answer: Average the two x-intercepts to find the x-coordinate of the vertex. Then substitute this value into the equation to find the y-coordinate of the vertex. The vertex is (3.25, 897.8125).

   c. A price of $3.25 gives the maximum income, $897.81.

   d. If the price of a yo-yo is $0 or $6.50, there will be no income.

   e. If $x = 5$, then $y = -85(5)^2 + 552.5(5) = 637.5$. This means that if the Warehouse charges $5 per yo-yo, the income will be $637.50.

12. a.

	x	y	3
x	x^2	xy	$3x$
y	xy	y^2	$3y$
3	$3x$	$3y$	9

$x^2 + y^2 + 2xy + 6x + 6y + 9$

   b.

	$2x$	$-y$	5
$2x$	$4x^2$	$-2xy$	$10x$
$-y$	$-2xy$	y^2	$-5y$
5	$10x$	$-5y$	25

$4x^2 + y^2 - 4xy + 20x - 10y + 25$

13. $x^2 + 8x + 16$. Answers will vary.

14. No, it doesn't pass a vertical line test.

15. The message is POLYNOMIALS.

   a. 16; P **b.** 15; O **c.** 12; L **d.** 25; Y
   e. 14; N **f.** 15; O **g.** 13; M **h.** 9; I
   i. 1; A   **j.** 12; L **k.** 19; S

LESSON 10.4

EXERCISES

1. a. $x + 4 = 0$ or $x + 3.5 = 0$, so $x = -4$ or $x = -3.5$.

   b. $x - 2 = 0$ or $x - 6 = 0$, so $x = 2$ or $x = 6$.

   c. $x + 3 = 0$ or $x - 7 = 0$ or $x + 8 = 0$, so $x = -3$ or $x = 7$ or $x = -8$.

   d. $x = 0$ or $x - 9 = 0$ or $x + 3 = 0$, so $x = 0$ or $x = 9$ or $x = -3$.

2. a.

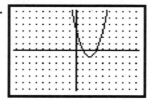

[−9.4, 9.4, 1, −6.2, 6.2, 1]

The x-intercepts are 1 and 3, so the factored form is $y = (x - 3)(x - 1)$.

   b.

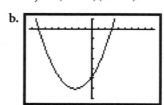

[−9.4, 9.4, 1, −35, 5, 5]

$y = (x + 8)(x - 3)$

   c.

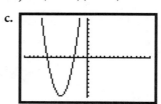

[−14.1, 14.1, 1, −9.3, 9.3, 1]

$y = (x + 3)(x + 9)$

   d.

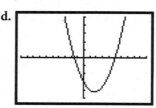

[−20, 20, 2, −50, 50, 10]

$y = (x - 10)(x + 3)$

3. a. The x-intercepts are 7 and −2.

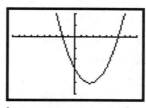

[−10, 10, 1, −25, 10, 5]

b. The x-intercepts are -1 and -8.

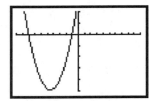

$[-10, 10, 1, -25, 10, 5]$

c. The x-intercepts are 11 and -7.

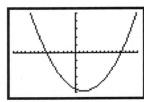

$[-15, 15, 1, -250, 250, 50]$

d. The x-intercepts are -5 and 9.

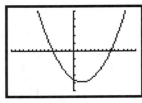

$[-15, 15, 1, -25, 25, 5]$

4. a. $y = (x - 2.5)(x + 1)$

b. $y = (x + 4)(x + 4)$ or $y = (x + 4)^2$

c. $y = (x + 2)(x - 2)$

d. $y = (x - r_1)(x - r_2)$

5. a. The graph has two x-intercepts, -1 and 3.

b. The x-coordinate of the vertex is 1, the average of the x-intercepts. To find the y-coordinate, substitute 1 for x in the equation, $y = (1 + 1)(1 - 3) = 2(-2) = -4$. So, the vertex is $(1, -4)$.

c. $y = (x - 1)^2 - 4$; a translation of $y = x^2$ left 1 unit and down 4 units

6. a. Yes

b. No; change to $(x - 6)(x - 5)$.

c. No; change to $2(x - 3.5)(x + 1)$ or $(2x - 7)(x + 1)$ or $(x - 3.5)(2x + 2)$.

d. No; change to $4(x + 1)^2$.

e. Yes

f. No; change to $(x + 6)(x - 6)$.

7. a. *(See table at bottom of page.)*

b. The sum of the roots needs to be -2, and the product needs to be -8. The numbers 2 and -4 satisfy this requirement.

8. a. Answers may vary. Most students will answer $y = (x - 3)(x - 7)$, but any equation of the form $y = a(x - 3)(x - 7)$ is correct.

b. Answers depend on the equation in 8a. The equation $y = (x - 3)(x - 7)$ has vertex $(5, -4)$.

c. Answers depend on the equation in 8a, but for any correct equation, the x-intercepts are 3 and 7, and the x-coordinate of the vertex is 5. Answer based on equation in 8a: $y = -(x - 3)(x - 7)$; x-intercepts: $x = 3$ and $x = 7$; vertex: $(5, 4)$.

d. Answers depend on the equation in 8a, but for any correct equation, the x-intercepts are 3 and 7, and the x-coordinate of the vertex is 5. Answer based on equation in 8a: $y = 2(x - 3)(x - 7)$; x-intercepts: $x = 3$ and $x = 7$; vertex: $(5, -8)$.

e. Possible answer: There are infinitely many quadratic equations with x-intercepts 3 and 7. Each is created by substituting a different value of a into $y = a(x - 3)(x - 7)$. Hence, all are vertical stretches or shrinks and/or reflections of $y = (x - 3)(x - 7)$ across the x-axis. The x-coordinate of the vertex is always 5, but the y-coordinate depends on the value of a.

9. The equation must be in the form $y = a(x + 3)(x - 9)$. To find the value of a, substitute the coordinates of the vertex $(3, -9)$ into the equation:

$$-9 = a(3 + 3)(3 - 9)$$

$$-9 = a \cdot 6(-6)$$

$$-9 = -36a$$

$$0.25 = a$$

The equation is $y = 0.25(x + 3)(x - 9)$.

10. a. If the width is 30 feet, the length is $200 - 2(30)$ or 140 feet. The area is then $30 \cdot 140$ or 4200 square feet.

b. $l = 200 - 2w$

Lesson 10.4, Exercise 7. a.

Factored form	Roots	Sum of roots	Product of roots	General form
$y = (x + 3)(x - 4)$	-3 and 4	$-3 + 4 = 1$	$(-3)(4) = -12$	$y = x^2 - 1x - 12$
$y = (x - 5)(x + 2)$	5 and -2	$5 - 2 = 3$	$5(-2) = -10$	$y = x^2 - 3x - 10$
$y = (x + 2)(x + 3)$	-2 and -3	-5	6	$y = x^2 + 5x + 6$
$y = (x - 5)(x + 5)$	-5 and 5	0	-25	$y = x^2 - 25$

c. $A = w \cdot l = w(200 - 2w)$. If the width is 30 feet, then $A = 30(200 - 2 \cdot 30) = 30(140) = 4200$, which matches the answer from 10a.

d. Solve $w(200 - 2w) = 0$. The solutions are $w = 0$ and $w = 100$, so widths of 0 ft and 100 ft give an area of 0.

e. The maximum area corresponds to the vertex of the graph, which is (50, 5000). So, a width of 50 ft gives the maximum area, 5000 sq ft.

11. a. x-intercepts: $x = 3$ and $x = -3$

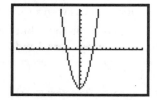

$[-14.1, 14.1, 1, -9.3, 9.3, 1]$

b. $y = (x - 3)(x + 3)$

c. The x-intercepts are the positive and negative square roots of the number subtracted from x^2.

d. **i.** $y = (x + 7)(x - 7)$

ii. $y = (4 + x)(4 - x)$

iii. $y = (x + \sqrt{47})(x - \sqrt{47})$

iv. $y = (x + \sqrt{28})(x - \sqrt{28})$

e. There are no x-intercepts. The graph is above the x-axis.

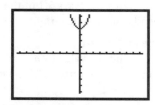

$[-14.1, 14.1, 1, -9.3, 9.3, 1]$

f. Because there are no x-intercepts, there is no factored form of the equation.

12. Answers will vary. Possible answer: Derek is correct because substituting 4 or -4 for x gives $0 = 16 + 16$, or 32, not 0; the roots should satisfy the equation.

13. Possible answer:

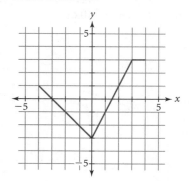

14. Possible answer:

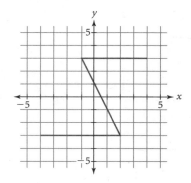

LESSON 10.5

There are no answers for this lesson.

LESSON 10.6

EXERCISES

1. a.

$2(x + 3)^2 - 4 = 0$	The original equation.
$2(x + 3)^2 = 4$	Add 4 to both sides.
$(x + 3)^2 = 2$	Divide both sides by 2.
$x + 3 = \pm\sqrt{2}$	Take the square root of both sides.
$x = -3 \pm \sqrt{2}$	Add -3 to both sides.

b. $x = 5 \pm \sqrt{2}$

c. $x = -8 \pm \sqrt{\dfrac{7}{3}}$

d. $x = -6 \pm \sqrt{\dfrac{7}{5}}$

2. a. $x - 5 = 0$ or $x + 3 = 0$, so $x = 5$ or $x = -3$.

b. $2x + 6 = 0$ or $x - 7 = 0$, so $x = -3$ or $x = 7$.

c. $3x + 4 = 0$ or $x + 1 = 0$, so $x = -\frac{4}{3}$ or $x = -1$.

d. $x = 0$ or $x + 6 = 0$ or $x + 9 = 0$, so $x = 0$ or $x = -6$ or $x = -9$.

3. To find the number that must be added, square half the coefficient of x.

a. $\left(\dfrac{18}{2}\right)^2 = 81$; $x^2 + 18x + 81 = (x + 9)^2$

b. $\left(\dfrac{-10}{2}\right)^2 = 25$; $x^2 - 10x + 25 = (x - 5)^2$

c. $\left(\dfrac{3}{2}\right)^2 = \dfrac{9}{4}$; $x^2 + 3x + \dfrac{9}{4} = \left(x + \dfrac{3}{2}\right)^2$

d. $\left(\dfrac{-1}{2}\right)^2 = \dfrac{1}{4}$; $x^2 - x + \dfrac{1}{4} = \left(x - \dfrac{1}{2}\right)^2$

e. $\left(\dfrac{1}{2} \cdot \dfrac{2}{3}\right)^2 = \dfrac{1}{9}$; $x^2 + \dfrac{2}{3}x + \dfrac{1}{9} = \left(x + \dfrac{1}{3}\right)^2$

f. $\left(\dfrac{-1.4}{2}\right)^2 = 0.49$; $x^2 - 1.4x + 0.49 = (x - 0.7)^2$

4. a.

$x^2 - 4x - 8 = 0$	The original equation.
$x^2 - 4x = 8$	Add 8 to both sides.
$x^2 - 4x + 4 = 12$	Add 4 to both sides to complete the square.
$(x - 2)^2 = 12$	Write the perfect square trinomial as a squared binomial.
$x - 2 = \pm\sqrt{12}$	Take the square root of both sides.
$x = 2 \pm \sqrt{12}$	Add 2 to both sides.

b.

$x^2 + 2x - 1 = -5$	The original equation.
$x^2 + 2x = -4$	Add 1 to both sides.
$x^2 + 2x + 1 = -3$	Add 1 to both sides to complete the square.
$(x + 1)^2 = -3$	Write the perfect square trinomial as a squared binomial.
$x + 1 = \pm\sqrt{-3}$	Take the square root of both sides.
$x = -1 \pm \sqrt{-3}$	Add -1 to both sides.

The number under the square root sign is negative, so there are no real roots.

c.

$x^2 + 10x - 9 = 0$	The original equation.
$x^2 + 10x = 9$	Add 9 to both sides.
$x^2 + 10x + 25 = 34$	Add 25 to both sides to complete the square.
$(x + 5)^2 = 34$	Write the perfect square trinomial as a squared binomial.
$x + 5 = \pm\sqrt{34}$	Take the square root of both sides.
$x = -5 \pm \sqrt{34}$	Add -5 to both sides.

d.

$5x^2 + 10x - 7 = 28$	The original equation.
$5x^2 + 10x = 35$	Add 7 to both sides.
$x^2 + 2x = 7$	Divide both sides by 5.
$x^2 + 2x + 1 = 8$	Add 1 to both sides to complete the square.
$(x + 1)^2 = 8$	Write the perfect square trinomial as a squared binomial.
$x + 1 = \pm\sqrt{8}$	Take the square root of both sides.
$x = -1 \pm \sqrt{8}$	Add -1 to both sides.

5. a. $y = a(x - 2)^2 - 31.5$

b. Solve the equation $0 = a(5 - 2)^2 - 31.5$; $a = 3.5$.

c. $y = 3.5(x - 2)^2 - 31.5$

d. The equation is of the form $y = a(x - 2)^2 + 32$. To find the value of a, substitute 5 for x and 14 for y to get $14 = a(5 - 2)^2 + 32$ and then solve for a. The value of a is -2, so the equation is $y = -2(x - 2)^2 + 32$.

6. a. Let w represent the width in meters. Then the length is $w + 4$, so the area equation is $w(w + 4) = 12$.

b.
$$w^2 + 4w = 12$$
$$w^2 + 4w + 4 = 12 + 4$$
$$(w + 2)^2 = 16$$
$$w + 2 = \pm 4$$
$$w = -2 \pm 4$$
$$w = -6 \text{ or } 2$$

The width cannot be negative, so it must be 2 meters.

c. The length is 4 meters more than the width, so the length is 6 meters.

7. a.

$y = x^2 + 6x + 10$	The original equation.
$y = x^2 + 6x + 9 - 9 + 10$	Add 0 in the form $9 - 9$ to complete the square for $x^2 + 6x$.
$y = (x + 3)^2 + 1$	Write the perfect square trinomial $x^2 + 6x + 9$ as a binomial squared.

b. $(-3, 1)$. The equations are equivalent, so their graphs are the same.

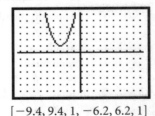

$[-9.4, 9.4, 1, -6.2, 6.2, 1]$

c.
$$x^2 + 6x + 10 = 0$$
$$x^2 + 6x = -10$$
$$x^2 + 6x + 9 = -10 + 9$$
$$(x + 3)^2 = -1$$
$$x + 3 = \pm\sqrt{-1}$$
$$x = -3 \pm \sqrt{-1}$$

There are no real roots. This indicates that the graph doesn't cross the x-axis.

8. a. The vertex is the highest point on the graph. Because the equation is in vertex form, you can see that the vertex is $(2.2, 26.9)$. This means 2.2 seconds after it is kicked, the ball reaches a maximum height of 26.9 yards (80.7 feet).

b. $t = 2.2 \pm \sqrt{-26.9 \cdot \frac{3}{-16}}$, $t \approx -0.046$ or

$t \approx 4.446$. The hang time is 4.446 seconds.

c. The initial height of the ball is the y-intercept of the graph. From the general form of the equation, $y = -\frac{16}{3}t^2 + 23.4\overline{6}t + 1.08\overline{6}$, you can see that the y-intercept is $1.08\overline{6}$, so the football is about 1 yard high when the punter kicks it.

d. The y-coordinate of the vertex is the maximum height of the ball, and the x-coordinate of the vertex is the time when the ball reaches this height. The y-intercept is the height of the ball when the punter kicks it. The positive x-intercept is the hang time. The other x-intercept has no real-world meaning.

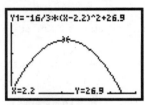

$[0, 5, 1, 0, 40, 10]$

9. a. $p = 2,500 - 5x$, where p represents the price in dollars per ticket and x represents the number of people in the group.

b. The cost for a group package is the number of people, x, times the cost per ticket, $2,500 - 5x$. If C represents the total cost of the group package, then $C = x(2,500 - 5x)$.

c.

$C = x(2,500 - 5x)$	Original equation.
$C = 2,500x - 5x^2$	Apply the distributive property.
$C = -5x^2 + 2,500x$	Apply the commutative property.
$C = -5(x^2 + 500x)$	Factor a -5 from the coefficients.
$C = -5(x^2 + 500x + 62,500 - 62,500)$	Add zero in the form $62,500 - 62,500$.
$C = -5(x^2 + 500x + 62,500) - 5(-62,500)$	Rewrite to get a perfect square trinomial.
$C = -5(x - 250)^2 + 312,500$	Express the trinomial as a squared binomial.

d. When $x = 20$, $C = 20(2,500 - 100) = 48,000$. So, the cost for 20 people is $48,000.

e.

$x(2,500 - 5x) = 200,000$	The original equation.
$2,500x - 5x^2 = 200,000$	Distribute x.
$500x - x^2 = 40,000$	Divide both sides by 5.
$x^2 - 500x = -40,000$	Multiply both sides by -1.
$x^2 - 500x + 250^2 = 250^2 - 40,000$	Complete the square on the left side.
$(x - 250)^2 = 22,500$	Write the left side as a binomial squared.
$x - 250 = \pm 150$	Take the square root of both sides.
$x = 250 \pm 150$	Add 250 to both sides.
$x = 100$ or	Evaluate.
$x = 400$	

f. Sample answer: The company will lose money if more than 400 people or fewer than 100 people per group go on the cruise. The vertex is $(250, 312500)$, so they will earn a maximum profit of $312,500 if 250 people are in the group.

10. a. $P(10) = 0.9$. This means that when there are 10 bears in the park, the population grows at a rate of 0.9 bear per year.

b. $P(b) = 0$ when $b = 0$ or 100. When there are no bears, the population does not grow. When there are 100 bears, the population does not grow.

c. The vertex lies halfway between the roots, 0 and 100, so the population is growing fastest when there are 50 bears.

d. Because the population does not grow when there are 100 bears, this value must be the maximum population.

e. It means that if bears were brought to the region to make a total of 120, the population would shrink, due to overpopulation.

11. a. $2x^3 + 5x^2 + 4x + 1$ **b.** $6x^3 - 11x^2 - 18x + 20$

12. a. $2x^2 + 4x + 2$ **b.** $3x^2 + 4x - 9$

   c. $-2x^2 - 2x$ **d.** $-3x^2 - 1$

EXERCISES

1. a. $5^2 - 4(3)(2) = 25 - 24 = 1$

   b. $(-3)^2 - 4(1)(-3) = 9 - (-12) = 9 + 12 = 21$

   c. $(-6)^2 - 4(-2)(-3) = 36 - 24 = 12$

   d. $9^2 - 4(9)(0) = 81 - 0 = 81$

2. a. $a = 2, b = 3, c = -7$

   b. $x^2 + 6x + 11 = 0; a = 1, b = 6, c = 11$

   c. $a = -3, b = -4, c = 12$

   d. $-4.9x^2 + 47x + 18; a = -4.9, b = 47, c = 18$

   e. $-16x^2 + 28x - 47 = 0; a = -16, b = 28, c = -47$

   f. $5x^2 - 6x - 7 = 0; a = 5, b = -6, c = -7$

3. a. $x = \dfrac{3 \pm \sqrt{(-3)^2 - 4(2)4}}{2(2)} = \dfrac{3 \pm \sqrt{-23}}{4}$.

   There are no real solutions.

   b. First rewrite in general form: $-2x^2 + 7x - 3 = 0$.
Then use the quadratic formula.

$$x = \frac{-7 \pm \sqrt{(7)^2 - 4(-2)(-3)}}{2(-2)}$$

$$= \frac{-7 \pm \sqrt{25}}{-4} = \frac{-7 \pm 5}{-4}; x = \frac{1}{2} \text{ and } x = 3$$

   c. This equation is most readily solved by completing the square.

$$x^2 - 6x - 8 = 0$$

$$x^2 - 6x = 8$$

$$x^2 - 6x + 9 = 17$$

$$(x - 3)^2 = 17$$

$$x - 3 = \pm\sqrt{17}$$

$$x = 3 \pm \sqrt{17}$$

   d. First subtract 5 from both sides of the equation to rewrite it in general form. Then use the quadratic formula.

$$x = \frac{-2 \pm \sqrt{(2)^2 - 4(3)(-6)}}{2(3)}; x = \frac{-2 \pm \sqrt{76}}{6}$$

$$= \frac{-2 \pm \sqrt{19}}{6} = \frac{-1 \pm \sqrt{19}}{3}$$

4. a. None

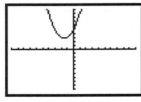

$[-10, 10, 1, -10, 10, 1]$

b. To use the quadratic formula, $a = 1, b = 3$, and $c = 5$.

$$x = \frac{-3 \pm \sqrt{(3)^2 - 4(1)(5)}}{2(1)}$$

$$= \frac{-3 \pm \sqrt{9 - 20}}{2} = \frac{-3 \pm \sqrt{-11}}{2}$$

There are no real square roots of negative numbers, so the equation has no real roots.

   c. If the discriminant, $b^2 - 4ac$, is negative, there are no real roots. If it is positive or zero, there are real roots.

5. a. $-4.9t^2 + 6.2t + 1.9 = 0$;

$$t = \frac{-6.2 \pm \sqrt{(6.2)^2 - 4(-4.9)(1.9)}}{2(-4.9)}; t \approx -0.255 \text{ sec}$$

or $t \approx 1.52$ sec. The ball hits the ground after 1.52 seconds.

   b. $-4.9t^2 + 6.2t + 1.9 = 3$. Rewrite the equation in the general form $-4.9t^2 + 6.2t - 1.1 = 0$, and then use the quadratic formula:

$$t = \frac{-6.2 \pm \sqrt{(6.2)^2 - 4(-4.9)(-1.1)}}{2(-4.9)}.$$ The ball is 3 meters above ground when $t \approx 0.21$ seconds and when $t \approx 1.05$ seconds.

   c. $-4.9t^2 + 6.2t + 1.9 = 4$. Rewrite the equation in the general form $-4.9t^2 + 6.2t - 2.1 = 0$, and then use the quadratic formula:

$$t = \frac{\sqrt{-6.2 \pm (6.2)^2 - 4(-4.9)(-2.1)}}{2(-4.9)};$$

$$t = \frac{-6.2 \pm \sqrt{-2.72}}{-9.8}.$$ This equation has no real solutions, so the ball is never 4 meters high.

6. Answers may vary. Sample answers:

   a. The expression is the quadratic formula with $a = 1, b = -14$, and $c = 49$, so the quadratic equation in general form is $x^2 - 14x + 49 = 0$. The expression is equal to 7.

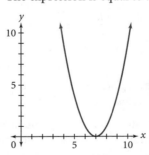

   b. The expression is the quadratic formula with $a = 2, b = -3$, and $c = 2$, so the quadratic equation in general form is $2x^2 - 3x + 2 = 0$. This expression is not equal to a real number because the number under the square root sign is negative.

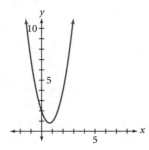

c. The expression is the quadratic formula with $a = 2$, $b = -3$, and $c = -2$, so the quadratic equation in general form is $2x^2 - 3x - 2 = 0$. The expression is equal to -0.5 and 2.

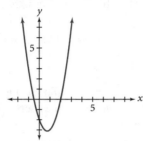

7. Find $b^2 - 4ac$ for each equation. If $b^2 - 4ac$ is negative, there are no x-intercepts (so the equation matches graph i). If it is zero, there is one x-intercept (so the equation matches graph iii). If it is positive, there are two x-intercepts (so the equation matches graph ii).

a. i   b. iii   c. ii

8. The average is the sum of the roots divided by 2. The sum is

$$\frac{-b + \sqrt{b^2 - 4ac}}{2a} + \frac{-b - \sqrt{b^2 - 4ac}}{2a}$$

$$= \frac{-b + (-b) + \sqrt{b^2 - 4ac} - \sqrt{b^2 - 4ac}}{2a}$$

$$= -\frac{2b}{2a} = -\frac{b}{a}$$

Dividing the result by 2 gives $\frac{-b}{2a}$. This is the x-coordinate of the vertex of the parabola.

9. To find how long the stone is in the air, you need to find the t-value when $h = 0$. So, you need to solve $-4.9t^2 + 17t + 2.2 = 0$. This equation is in general form with $a = -4.9$, $b = 17$, and $c = 2.2$. Substituting these values into the quadratic formula gives $t = \frac{-17 \pm \sqrt{17^2 - 4(-4.9)(2.2)}}{2(-4.9)}$. Evaluating this expression gives $t \approx -0.125$ and $t \approx 3.59$. The positive solution of 3.59 seconds makes sense in this situation. So, the stone is in the air about 3.59 seconds.

10. a.

Increase (x) (m)	Width (m)	Length (m)	Area (sq m)	Perimeter (m)
0	4	7	28	22
0.5	4.5	6.5	29.25	22
1.0	5	6	30	22
1.5	5.5	5.5	30.25	22
2.0	6	5	30	22

b. The perimeter does not change.

c. The area increases and then decreases.

d. $A = (4 + x)(7 - x)$, where x represents the amount of change.

e. The largest area occurs at the vertex of the parabola. The x-coordinate of the vertex is 1.5, the average of the x-intercepts -4 and 7. So, the largest rectangle has a width of $4 + 1.5$ or 5.5 inches and a length of $7 - 1.5$ or 5.5 inches. This rectangle is a square.

11. a. $\dfrac{x^2 - 5x + 6}{x - 3} = \dfrac{\cancel{(x - 3)}(x - 2)}{\cancel{x - 3}} = x - 2$

b. $\dfrac{x^2 + 7x + 6}{x + 1} = \dfrac{\cancel{(x + 1)}(x + 6)}{\cancel{x + 1}} = x + 6$

c. $\dfrac{2x^2 - x - 1}{2x + 1} = \dfrac{\cancel{(2x + 1)}(x - 1)}{\cancel{2x + 1}} = x - 1$

12. a.

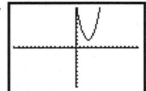

$[-15, 15, 1, -10, 10, 1]$

b.

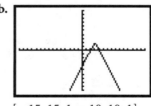

$[-15, 15, 1, -10, 10, 1]$

IMPROVING YOUR REASONING SKILLS

The square root recursive routine works for $x > -1$ to avoid square roots of negative numbers. The reciprocal recursive routine works if $x \neq -1$ or $x \neq 0$ to avoid division by zero. The radical form answers are $x = \frac{1 \pm \sqrt{5}}{2}$ (or $x \approx 1.618033989$ and $x \approx -0.6180339887$). A sample recursive routine is
0 [ENTER]; 1/(Ans − 1) [ENTER], [ENTER], ...

LESSON 10.8

EXERCISES

1. a. Perfect square; $47^2 = 2,209$

   b. Perfect cube: $18^3 = 5,832$

   c. Neither

   d. Perfect square; $101^2 = 10,201$

2. a.

$(2x)^3 = 5,832$	The volume equals the side length cubed.
$2x = 18$	Take the cube root of both sides.
$x = 8$	Divide both sides by 2.

   b.

$(3.5x)^3 = 21,952$	The volume equals the side length cubed.
$3.5x = 28$	Take the cube root of both sides.
$x = 8$	Divide both sides by 3.5.

   c.

$2(2.3x)^3 = 3,309$	The volume of each half equals the side length cubed.
$(2.3x)^3 = 1654.5$	Divide by 2.
$2.3x \approx 11.826$	Take the cube root of both sides.
$x \approx 5.142$	Divide both sides by 2.3.

3. a. $4x(x + 3)$ **b.** $2x(3x - 2)$

   c. $7x(2x^3 + x - 3)$ **d.** $3x^2(4x^3 + 2x + 1)$

4. a. Quadratic function   **b.** Linear function

   c. Exponential function   **d.** Cubic function

5. a. The graph has x-intercepts at -4, -2, and 1, so its equation includes the factors $(x + 4)$, $(x + 2)$, and $(x - 1)$. If you graph $y = (x + 4)(x + 2)(x - 1)$, you'll see that the x-value -3 corresponds to the y-value 4. You want the x-value -3 to correspond to the y-value 2, so you need to vertically shrink the graph of $y = (x + 4)(x + 2)(x - 1)$ by a factor of 0.5. The equation is $y = 0.5(x + 4)(x + 2)(x - 1)$.

   b. The graph has x-intercepts at -2 and 1. Because the graph does not cross the x-axis at $x = 1$, 1 is a double root. So, the equation contains the factors $(x + 2)$ and $(x - 1)^2$. If you graph $y = (x + 2)(x - 1)^2$, you'll see that the graph needs to be reflected over the x-axis to match the given graph. The equation is $y = -(x + 2)(x - 1)^2$.

6. a. Answers will vary. Three possibilities are $0^2 = 0^3 = 0$, $1^2 = 1^3 = 1$, and $8^2 = 4^3 = 64$.

   b. Possible answer: Start with any integer, a, and raise it to the 6th power. The result is both a perfect square and a perfect cube. (Because $a^6 = (a^3)^2 = (a^2)^3$, the square root of a^6 is a^3 and the cube root of a^6 is a^2. For example, $4^6 = 4,096$ is both a perfect square and a perfect cube. The square root of 4,096 is 64, which is 4^3, and the cube root of 4,096 is 16, which is 4^2.) Or enter $Y_1 = x^3$, $Y_2 = x^2$, and $Y_3 = x^6$ into your calculator and look at the table for integer X-values. Each value in the Y_3 column will be both a perfect square and a perfect cube. The square root of a Y_3-value will be the corresponding Y_1-value, and the cube root will be the corresponding Y_2-value.

7. a. If the width is w, the length is $w + 6$ and the height is $w - 2$, so the volume is given by the equation $V = w(w + 6)(w - 2)$.

   b. Three solutions to the equation $47 = w(w + 6)(w - 2)$ are shown on the graph. However, only one solution is a positive value. A table gives the answer: $w \approx 3.4$. Widths greater than 3.4 cm give volumes greater than 47 cm³.

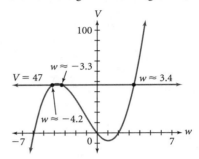

8. a. True. This can be determined by making a graph or a table.

   b. False. This can be determined from a graph or table or by substituting 2 for x in the equation.

   c. True. This can be determined by making a graph or a table.

   d. True. This can be determined from a graph or table or by checking to see if the values satisfy the equation.

9. a. Use a rectangular diagram or the distributive property to multiply one pair of factors. This gives $(x + 1)(x^2 + 5x + 6)$ or $(x^2 + 3x + 2)(x + 3)$. Then use another rectangular diagram or the distributive property to multiply the two expressions. The result is $x^3 + 6x^2 + 11x + 6$.

   b. Multiply the first two factors to get $(x^2 - 4)(x - 3)$. Then multiply again to get $x^3 - 3x^2 - 4x + 12$.

10. a. 50 cm   **b.** 70 cm

   c. $10 \cdot 50 \cdot 70 = 35,000$ cm³

   d. The width is 45 cm, and the length is 65 cm. The volume is $15 \cdot 45 \cdot 65 = 43,875$ cm³.

   e. $w = \dfrac{120 - 2x}{2} = 60 - x$

   f. $l = \dfrac{160 - 2x}{2} = 80 - x$

g. $V = x\left(\dfrac{120 - 2x}{2}\right)\left(\dfrac{160 - 2x}{2}\right) = x(60 - x)(80 - x)$

h. The roots are $x = 0$ cm, $x = 60$ cm, and $x = 80$ cm. These x-values make boxes with no volume.

i. Graph $Y_1 = x(60 - x)(80 - x)$ and $Y_2 = 48{,}488$ with a window of $[0, 60, 10, 0, 50000, 10000]$ to see that there are two solutions around $x = 23$. Use the table (TblStart $= 20$, ΔTbl $= 1$) to see one solution at 22 cm and another between 23 and 24 cm. For the solution with height 22 cm, the width is $60 - 22 = 38$ cm and the length is $80 - 22 = 58$ cm. Continue to zoom in on the table or the graph to approximate the other solution at $x \approx 23.265$ cm. For this solution, the height is approximately 23.265 cm, the width is approximately $60 - 23.265 = 36.735$ cm, and the length is approximately $80 - 23.265 = 56.735$ cm.

11. a. $11x^3 + 2x^2 + 2x + 12$ **b.** $5x^3 - 2x^2 - 12x - 12$

c. $-6x^2 - 13x + 20$ **d.** $10x^2 + x + 2$

e. $-16x^4 + 34x^3 - 28x^2 - 131x + 99$

CHAPTER 10 Review

EXERCISES

1. a. False. The right side should be $(x - 3)(x + 8)$.

b. False. The right side should be $2x^2 - 4x + 5$.

c. False. The right side should be $x^2 + 6x + 9$.

d. True

2. A reflection across the x-axis and a vertical stretch by a factor of 2, followed by a translation left 5 units and up 4 units

3. a. $y = -(x - 2)^2 + 3$; vertex form

b. $y = 0.5(x - 2)(x + 3)$; factored form

4. a. $y = -3(x - 1.5)^2 + 18.75$. Answers will vary. Sample window: $[0, 6, 1, 0, 25, 5]$.

b. $y = -1.6(x - 5)^2 + 30$. Answers will vary. Sample window: $[0, 10, 1, 0, 35, 5]$.

5. a. $2w + 9 = 0$ or $w - 3 = 0$, so $w = -4.5$ or $w = 3$.

b. $2x + 5 = 0$ or $x - 7 = 0$, so $x = -2.5$ or $x = 7$.

6. a. $y = (x - 1)^2 - 4$

b. Answers will vary. Possible answers:
$y = (x + 1.5)\left(x - \frac{1}{3}\right)$, $y = (2x + 3)(3x - 1)$.

7. a. $x^2 + 6x - 9 = 13$

$x^2 + 6x = 22$

$x^2 + 6x + 9 = 22 + 9$

$(x + 3)^2 = 31$

$x + 3 = \pm\sqrt{31}$

$x = -3 \pm \sqrt{31}$

b. $3x^2 - 24x + 27 = 0$

$3x^2 - 24x = -27$

$x^2 - 8x = -9$

$x^2 - 8x + 16 = -9 + 16$

$(x - 4)^2 = 7$

$x - 4 = \pm\sqrt{7}$

$x = 4 \pm \sqrt{7}$

8. a. $x = \dfrac{13 \pm \sqrt{(-13)^2 - 4(5)(18)}}{2(5)} = \dfrac{13 \pm \sqrt{-191}}{10}$.
There are no real-number solutions.

b. $x = \dfrac{-7 \pm \sqrt{7^2 - 4(-3)(9)}}{2(-6)} = \dfrac{-7 \pm \sqrt{157}}{-6}$

9. a. $f(60) = 0.0015(60)(150 - 60)$, or 8.1. When there are 60 fish in the tank, the population is growing at a rate of about 8 fish per week.

b. $f(x) = 0$ for $x = 0$ and $x = 150$. When there are no fish or 150 fish, the population does not grow.

c. The maximum growth rate corresponds to the vertex. The x-coordinate of the vertex is 75, the number halfway between the x-intercepts. So, when there are 75 fish, the population is growing fastest.

d. The population no longer grows once there are 150 fish, so this is the maximum number of fish the tank has to support.

e.

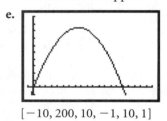

$[-10, 200, 10, -1, 10, 1]$

10. The roots are at 0 and 1.6 seconds, so start with the equation $y = x(x - 1.6)$. Then reflect the graph across the x-axis. When $x = 0.5$, $y = 0.55$, and we need the value of y to be 8.8. So, apply a vertical stretch with a factor of $\frac{8.8}{.55}$, or 16. The final equation is $y = -16x(x - 1.6)$.

11. a. The graph has no x-intercepts if $c > 9$. Possible solution methods: Find the c-values for which the discriminant is less than 0. To do this, solve the inequality $(-6)^2 - 4(1)c < 0$. The solution is $c > 9$. You can also find the answer by translating the graph of $y = x^2 - 6x$ vertically to see that for $c > 9$, the graph of $y = x^2 - 6x + c$ does not cross the x-axis.

b. The graph has one x-intercept if $c = 9$. Possible solution method: If the graph has one x-intercept, then the equation has a double root. So, $x^2 - 6x + c$ must be a perfect square trinomial. Completing the square gives the perfect square trinomial $x^2 - 6x + 9$, so $c = 9$.

c. The graph has one x-intercept if $c < 9$. Possible solution methods: Find the c-values for which the discriminant is greater than 0. To do this, solve the inequality $(-6)^2 - 4(1)c > 0$. The solution is $c < 9$. You can also find the answer by translating the graph of $y = x^2 - 6x$ vertically to see that for $c < 9$, the graph of $y = x^2 - 6x + c$ crosses the x-axis twice.

12. a. $x = -5 + \sqrt{31}$ and $x = -5 - \sqrt{31}$

    b. $x = 1$ and $x = \frac{5}{3}$

13. a. $x = -2, -1, 1,$ and 3;
    $y = 2(x - 3)(x + 2)(x + 1)(x - 1)$

    b. $x = -2$ (double root) and 3;
    $y = -3(x + 2)^2(x - 3)$

14. a. $(x + 3)(x + 4)$

$\times$	x	3
x	x^2	$3x$
4	$4x$	12

b. $(x - 7)^2$

$\times$	x	-7
x	x^2	$-7x$
-7	$-7x$	49

c. $(x + 7)(x - 4)$

$\times$	x	-4
x	x^2	$-4x$
7	$7x$	-28

d. $(x - 9)(x + 9)$

$\times$	x	-9
x	x^2	$-9x$
9	$9x$	-81

TAKE ANOTHER LOOK

$i = \sqrt{-1}$

$i^2 = -1$

$i^3 = (-1)i = -i$

$i^4 = 1$

$i^5 = i$

This pattern repeats every four powers.

$i^{10} = i^8 \cdot i^2 = -1$

$i^{25} = i^{24} \cdot i = i$

$i^{100} = 1$

CHAPTER 11

LESSON 11.1

EXERCISES

1. a. If you write the equation in point-slope form, $y = 7 + 0.8(x - 4)$, you can see that the slope is 0.8.

b. The equation is in slope-intercept form. The slope is -2.

c. If you write the equation in point-slope form, $y = 1 - 1.25(x - 3)$, you can see that the slope is -1.25.

d. The equation is in slope-intercept form. The slope is 2.

e. If you write the equation in intercept form, $y = -\frac{11}{4} + \frac{3}{2}x$, you can see that the slope is $\frac{3}{2}$.

f. If you write the equation in intercept form, $y = 6 - \frac{3}{2}x$, you can see that the slope is $-\frac{3}{2}$.

g. If you write the equation in intercept form, $y = -\frac{2}{3} + \frac{3}{2}x$, you can see that the slope is $\frac{3}{2}$.

h. If you write the equation in intercept form, $y = -\frac{7}{15} + \frac{2}{3}x$, you can see that the slope is $\frac{2}{3}$.

2. $y = 5 + \frac{3}{4}(x + 2)$

3. a. The slopes of the lines are 0.8 and -1.25. Because -1.25 is the negative reciprocal of 0.8 (that is, $-1.25 = -\frac{1}{0.8}$), the lines are perpendicular.

b. The slopes of the lines are -2 and 2. Because the slopes are not the same and they are not negative reciprocals, the lines are neither parallel nor perpendicular.

c. Rewriting the equations in intercept form gives the equations $y = -\frac{11}{4} + \frac{3}{2}x$ and $y = -\frac{2}{3} + \frac{3}{2}x$. Because both lines have the same slope, $\frac{3}{2}$, they are parallel.

d. Rewriting the equations in intercept form gives the equations $y = 6 - \frac{3}{2}x$ and $y = -\frac{7}{15} + \frac{2}{3}x$. Because the slopes, $-\frac{3}{2}$ and $\frac{2}{3}$, are negative reciprocals, the lines are perpendicular.

4. The polygon is a right trapezoid. The slopes of the sides are $\frac{2}{3}$, $-\frac{1}{5}$, $\frac{2}{3}$, and $-\frac{3}{2}$. The sides with slope $\frac{2}{3}$ are parallel, and the side with slope $-\frac{3}{2}$ is perpendicular to both of these sides.

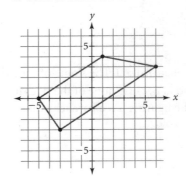

5. The polygon is a rectangle. The slopes of the sides are $\frac{1}{2}$, -2, $\frac{1}{2}$, and -2. The opposite sides have the same slope, so they are parallel. The adjacent sides have slopes that are negative reciprocals, so they are perpendicular.

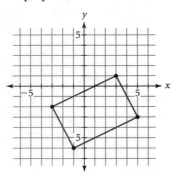

6. The polygon is a trapezoid. The slopes of the sides are 0, $-\frac{4}{3}$, undefined, and $-\frac{4}{3}$. Two sides have the same slope, so the figure has one pair of parallel sides.

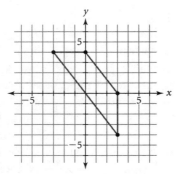

7. The polygon is a parallelogram. The slopes of the sides are 1, -3, 1, and -3. The opposite sides have the same slope, so they are parallel.

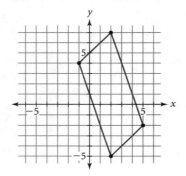

8. The polygon is a quadrilateral. The slopes of the sides are 4, $-\frac{1}{4}$, -3, and $\frac{4}{7}$. Because none of the sides have the same slope, the figure is not a parallelogram, rectangle, or trapezoid.

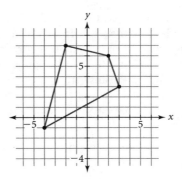

9. The polygon is a trapezoid. The slopes of the sides are 2, $-\frac{5}{2}$, $-\frac{1}{4}$, and $-\frac{5}{2}$. Two sides have the same slope, so the figure has one pair of parallel sides.

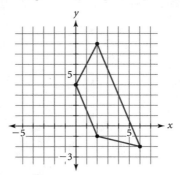

10. The polygon is a rectangle. The slopes of the sides are $-\frac{2}{3}$, $\frac{3}{2}$, $-\frac{2}{3}$, and $\frac{3}{2}$. The opposite sides have the same slope, so they are parallel. The adjacent sides have slopes that are negative reciprocals, so they are perpendicular.

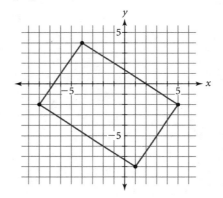

11. The polygon is a quadrilateral. The slopes of the sides are 1, -1, $\frac{5}{3}$, and $-\frac{5}{3}$. Because none of the sides have the same slope, the figure is not a parallelogram, rectangle, or trapezoid.

Discovering Algebra Solutions Manual
©2002 Key Curriculum Press

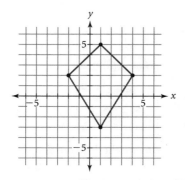

12. Possible answer: $(-2, 5)$, $(0, 6)$, $(2, 5)$, $(0, 1)$

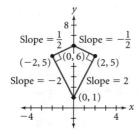

13. a. $\left(-\frac{2}{3}, 0\right)$ **b.** $(-1.\overline{3}, -0.58\overline{3})$

  c. $(0, -1)$

14. a. $2x^3 + 3x^2 - 2x$ **b.** $0.01x^2 - 4.41$

15. $\frac{6}{16}$ or $\frac{3}{8}$

16. a. 7 **b.** 1.5 **c.** -6.5 **d.** 24.5

LESSON 11.2

Exercises

1. 1.2

2. a. Because line m is perpendicular to line ℓ, its slope must be the negative reciprocal of the slope of ℓ. So, the slope of m is $\frac{-1}{1.2} = -\frac{5}{6} = -0.8\overline{3}$.

  b. -1

3. a. $\left(\frac{4 + (-3)}{2}, \frac{5 + (-2)}{2}\right) = (0.5, 1.5)$

  b. $\left(\frac{7 + 5}{2}, \frac{-1 + (-8)}{2}\right) = (6, -4.5)$

4. a. Rewrite the equation in intercept form:

  $Ax + By = C$

  $By = C - Ax$

  $y = \frac{C}{B} - \frac{A}{B}x$

  The slope of line ℓ is $-\frac{A}{B}$. The slope of a line perpendicular to ℓ is the negative reciprocal of $-\frac{A}{B}$, which is $\frac{B}{A}$.

  b. A line parallel to line ℓ has slope $-\frac{A}{B}$, the same slope as line ℓ.

5. $\left(\frac{a + c}{2}, \frac{b + d}{2}\right)$

6. Yes. Possible explanation: The slope of $\overline{AB}$ is 5 and the slope of $\overline{BC}$ is $\frac{-1}{5}$. Because the slopes are negative reciprocals, angle B is a right angle.

7. A horizontal line and a vertical line are perpendicular, but the product of their slopes is not -1. A horizontal line has a slope of 0, and a vertical line has an undefined slope, so the product of their slopes is undefined.

8. a. $\left(\frac{2 + 4}{2}, \frac{1 + 6}{2}\right) = (3, 3.5)$

  b. The slope of $\overline{AB}$ is $\frac{5}{2}$, so the slope of the perpendicular bisector is $-\frac{2}{5}$. The perpendicular bisector passes through $(3, 3.5)$. So the equation in point-slope form is $y = 3.5 - \frac{2}{5}(x - 3)$.

9. a. Midpoint of $\overline{AB}$: $\left(\frac{3 + 17}{2}, \frac{2 + 4}{2}\right) = (10, 3)$

  Midpoint of $\overline{BC}$: $\left(\frac{17 + 13}{2}, \frac{4 + 12}{2}\right) = (15, 8)$

  Midpoint of $\overline{CD}$: $\left(\frac{13 + 5}{2}, \frac{12 + 8}{2}\right) = (9, 10)$

  Midpoint of $\overline{DA}$: $\left(\frac{5 + 3}{2}, \frac{8 + 2}{2}\right) = (4, 5)$

  b. The polygon is a parallelogram. The sides of the polygon have slopes 1, $\frac{-1}{3}$, 1, and $\frac{-1}{3}$. Because the opposite sides have the same slope, they are parallel.

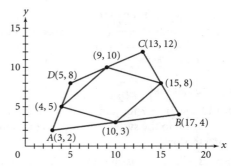

  c. The slopes of the diagonals are $\frac{3}{11}$ and -7. Because the slopes are not negative reciprocals, the diagonals are not perpendicular.

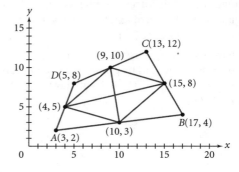

10. a. $D(7.5, -1)$, $E(-1, -1)$, $F(2.5, 6)$

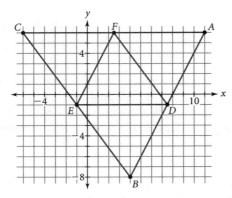

b. The slopes of $\overline{AB}$ and $\overline{FE}$ are both 2, so the segments are parallel.

c. Yes. The slopes of $\overline{BC}$ and $\overline{DF}$ are both $\frac{-7}{5}$, and the slopes of $\overline{CA}$ and $\overline{ED}$ are both 0.

d. The length of $\overline{ED}$ is $\frac{1}{2}$ the length of $\overline{CA}$.

e. The area of $\triangle DEF$ is $\frac{1}{4}$ the area of $\triangle ABC$.

f. The area of the new triangle would be $\frac{1}{4}$ the area of $\triangle DEF$, so it would be $\frac{1}{16}$ the area of $\triangle ABC$.

11. a. Let (x, y) represent the other endpoint. Then, $\frac{x+2}{2} = 7$ and $\frac{y+4}{2} = 4$. Solving these equations gives $x = 12$ and $y = 4$, so the endpoint is $(12, 4)$.

b. Let (x, y) represent the other endpoint. Then, $\frac{x+15}{2} = 9$ and $\frac{y+9}{2} = 7$. Solving these equations gives $x = 3$ and $y = 5$, so the endpoint is $(3, 5)$.

c. Let (x, y) represent the other endpoint. Then, $\frac{x+3}{2} = -1$ and $\frac{y+(-7.5)}{2} = -2$. Solving these equations gives $x = -5$ and $y = 3.5$, so the endpoint is $(-5, 3.5)$.

12. a. Solve the system $\begin{cases} 2x - 3y + 12 = 1 \\ x = 2y - 7 \end{cases}$ by substituting $2y - 7$ for x in the first equation. The solution to the system, $(-1, 3)$, is the point of intersection.

b. Answers will vary. Possible answer: The graph of any equation with point-slope form $y = 3 + m(x + 1)$, where m is any number, will pass through $(-1, 3)$. So, any two lines with equations in this form will intersect at $(-1, 3)$. An equation in this form and the vertical line $x = -1$ will also intersect at $(-1, 3)$.

c. Answers will vary. Possible answer: $y = (x + 1)^2 + 3$. (The graph of any equation in the form $y = a(x + 1)^2 + 3$ will have its vertex at $(-1, 3)$.)

13. a. Possible answers:

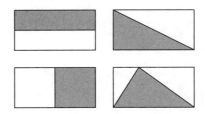

b. Answers will vary. Any method that uses only one line segment will form congruent polygons. Some other methods may also produce congruent polygons.

c. Yes. If you imagine a vertical segment through the upper vertex of the shaded triangle, the pair of triangles to the left of the segment are congruent and the pair of triangles to the right of the segment are congruent. Because the shaded section includes one triangle from each side of the segment and the unshaded section includes one triangle from each side of the segment, the areas of the shaded and unshaded sections are equal.

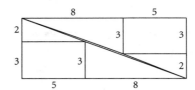

These triangles have the same area. These triangles have the same area.

So the area of the rectangle is divided in half.

IMPROVING YOUR GEOMETRY SKILLS

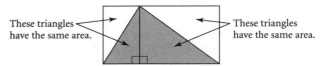

The slope of each small triangle's hypotenuse is $\frac{-2}{5}$ or -0.4. The slope of each large triangle's hypotenuse is $\frac{-3}{8}$ or -0.375. The slopes of these segments are close enough to fool the eye, but the segments do not lie on the same line. Instead, they create a parallelogram whose area is 1.

This and 59 other puzzles and paradoxes are collected in *One Equals Zero and Other Mathematical Surprises* by Nitsa Movshovitz-Hadar and John Webb, © Key Curriculum Press, 1998.

LESSON 11.3

EXERCISES

1. a. $\pm\sqrt{47}$

b. $(x - 4)^2 = 28$
$$x - 4 = \pm\sqrt{28}$$
$$x = 4 \pm \sqrt{28}$$

c. $(x + 2)^2 - 3 = 11$

$\qquad (x + 2)^2 = 14$

$\qquad\qquad x + 2 = \pm\sqrt{14}$

$\qquad\qquad\qquad x = -2 \pm \sqrt{14}$

d. $2(x - 1)^2 + 4 = 18$

$\qquad 2(x - 1)^2 = 14$

$\qquad\quad (x - 1)^2 = 7$

$\qquad\qquad x - 1 = \pm\sqrt{7}$

$\qquad\qquad\qquad x = 1 \pm \sqrt{7}$

2. a. ± 6.856 **b.** $-1.292, 9.292$

   c. $-5.742, 1.742$ **d.** $-1.646, 3.646$

3. a. You can draw a square with horizontal and vertical sides around the rectangle. The area of the rectangle is the area of the square minus the sum of the areas of the four triangles.

$$\text{Area} = 9 - \left(2 + 2 + \frac{1}{2} + \frac{1}{2}\right)$$
$$= 9 - 5$$
$$= 4 \text{ square units}$$

b. You can draw a square with horizontal and vertical sides around the rectangle. The area of the rectangle is the area of the square minus the sum of the areas of the four triangles.

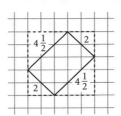

$$\text{Area} = 25 - \left(2 + 2 + 4\frac{1}{2} + 4\frac{1}{2}\right)$$
$$= 25 - 13$$
$$= 12 \text{ square units}$$

c. You can draw a rectangle with horizontal and vertical sides around the triangle. The area of the triangle is the area of the rectangle minus the sum of the areas of the three surrounding triangles.

$$\text{Area} = 6 - \left(2 + 1\frac{1}{2} + \frac{1}{2}\right)$$
$$= 6 - 4$$
$$= 2 \text{ square units}$$

d. 6 square units   **e.** 20 square units

f. 18 square units

4. The square has an area of 18 square units, so the side length is $\sqrt{18}$ units.

5. To find the length of each side, draw a square on the side and then find the area of the square. The side length is the square root of this area.

For the rectangle in 3a, a square on the short side has an area of 2 square units, so the length of the short side is $\sqrt{2}$ units. A square on the long side has an area of 8 square units, so the length of the long side is $\sqrt{8}$ units.

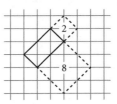

Polygon 3b: $\sqrt{8}$ units and $\sqrt{18}$ units

Polygon 3e: $\sqrt{50}$ units, $\sqrt{50}$ units, and $\sqrt{40}$ units

6. a–e. If you consider the horizontal side of each triangle to be the base, then each triangle has a base of length 9 units and a height of 4 units. So, the area of each triangle is $\frac{1}{2}(9)(4)$ or 18 square units.

7. a. 36 square units, 18 square units, and 18 square units

b. The length of each side is the square root of the area of the square constructed on it. So, the length of $\overline{AB}$ is 6 units, the length of $\overline{BC}$ is $\sqrt{18}$ units, and the length of $\overline{AC}$ is $\sqrt{18}$ units.

8. $(6, 11)$ and $(12, 7)$ or $(-2, -1)$ and $(4, -5)$.

9. a. $\overline{AC}$ is the hypotenuse. $\overline{AB}$ and $\overline{BC}$ are the legs.

b.

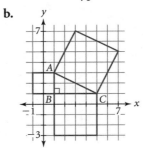

c. Area of square on $\overline{AB}$: four square units; area of square on $\overline{BC}$: 16 square units; area of square on $\overline{AC}$: twenty square units

d. Length of $\overline{AB}$: 2 units; length of $\overline{BC}$: 4 units; length of $\overline{AC}$: $\sqrt{20}$ units

e. The area of the largest square is equal to the sum of the areas of the two smaller squares.

10. a. City A: $47{,}000(1 + 0.045)^5 \approx 58{,}571$; the population will be 58,571 in 5 years.

City B: $56{,}000(1 - 0.012)^5 \approx 52{,}720$; the population will be 52,720 in 5 years.

b. $47{,}000(1 + 0.045)^{26} \approx 147{,}612$ and $47{,}000(1 + 0.045)^{27} \approx 154{,}254$, so the population will first exceed 150,000 in 27 years.

c. $56{,}000(1 - 0.012)^{-10} \approx 63{,}186$; the population was 63,186 ten years ago.

11. From the first clue, the equation must be in the form $y = a(x - b)(x - c)$. Using the second clue, the equation must be in the form $y = a(x + 7)(x - c)$. Look at the last clue. If the axis of symmetry passes through $(-4, -2)$, its equation must be $x = -4$. This line of symmetry is halfway between the x-intercepts, which are -7 and c. So, c must be -1. Now you know the equation must be in the form $y = a(x + 7)(x + 1)$. The third clue indicates that the point $(0, 14)$ is on the graph. Substituting these values into the equation gives $14 = 7a$, so $a = 2$. The equation is $y = 2(x + 7)(x + 1)$.

IMPROVING YOUR VISUAL THINKING SKILLS

Weaving under four, over one is the only way to get a $(1, -2)$-solution. (It might be called a $(1, 3)$-solution as well.) Under three, over one either creates diagonal stripes or creates rhombuses, not squares, which leave alternating white strands without any brown strands over them, so the mat would fall apart. Under two, over one creates diagonal stripes, not squares. Under five, over one creates stripes or rectangles that fall apart.

Under nine, over one is the $(1, -3)$-solution.

Some students may conjecture that the $(1, k)$-solution must go under k^2, over one. This is indeed true. The $(1, -4)$-solution goes under sixteen, over one. The $(1, -1)$-solution goes under one, over one. In general, imagine one square A in which a brown strand appears. In the next column to the right, the brown strand to which the first one is connected in a tilted square is k white strands lower. So, the appearance of the brown strand below A must be connected to a point k units to the right and 1 unit up. This will be an appearance of a brown strand only if each brown strand passes under k^2 white strands.

LESSON 11.4

EXERCISES

1. The area of the square on side c is equal to the sum of the areas of the squares on sides a and b. So, the area of the square on side a is $2601 - 2025$ or 576 cm^2.

2. Length of side $a = \sqrt{576}$ cm $= 24$ cm; length of side $b = \sqrt{2025}$ cm $= 45$ cm; length of side $c = \sqrt{2601}$ cm $= 51$ cm.

3. $a^2 + b^2 = c^2$
$$10^2 + b^2 = 20^2$$
$$b^2 = 20^2 - 10^2$$
$$b^2 = 400 - 100$$
$$b^2 = 300$$
$$b = \sqrt{300} \text{ cm}$$

4. a. The two legs are equal in length. The hypotenuse must be longer than either of them.

b. If c is the hypotenuse, then $c^2 = 8^2 + 8^2 = 128$, so $c = \sqrt{128}$ cm.

5. a. Each half is similar to a right triangle with side lengths 3, 4, and 5. The length of the longer leg is 18 ft (half of 36 ft). Let x represent the length of the shorter leg, which is the distance from the attic floor to the roof peak. To find x, solve the proportion $\frac{x}{18} = \frac{3}{4}$ to get $x = 13.5$. The distance from the attic floor to the roof peak is 13.5 ft.

b. The distance from the roof peak to the roof edge is the length of the hypotenuse of one of the two right triangles. If c represents this length, then $c^2 = 18^2 + 13.5^2 = 506.25$, so $c = \sqrt{506.25}$. This distance is $\sqrt{506.25}$ ft or 22.5 ft.

c. Each half of the roof is a rectangle with length 48 ft and width 22.5 ft (the length of the hypotenuse). The area of each half is 48 ft $\cdot$ 22.5 ft or 1080 ft^2, so the area of the entire roof is $2(1080$ ft$^2)$ or 2160 ft^2.

6. Al is right. Explanations will vary. As an example, $\sqrt{9 + 4} \neq \sqrt{9} + \sqrt{4}$.

7. a. Approximately 21.6 cm by 27.6 cm

b. If the diagonal length is c, then $c^2 = 21.6^2 + 27.6^2 = 1228.32$. So, the diagonal length is $\sqrt{1228.32}$ cm or about 35.0 cm.

c. Answers will vary but should be close to 35 cm.

d. Answers will vary. The two results should be approximately the same.

8. Answers will vary. If $x = 1$, then Michael is claiming that $1^2 + 4^2 = 5^2$, but $17 \neq 25$. You have to isolate x before you take the square root: $x^2 + 16 = 25$, $x^2 = 9$, $x = \pm 3$.

9. First, convert miles to feet: $1.2 \text{ mi} \cdot \frac{5280 \text{ ft}}{1 \text{ mi}} = 6336$ ft. Then, let c represent the distance and use the Pythagorean theorem:
$$c^2 = 6336^2 + 3000^2 = 49{,}144{,}896$$
$$c = \sqrt{49{,}144{,}896} \approx 7010.$$ The balloon is approximately 7010 ft away.

10. a.   **i.** Right triangle   **ii.** Right triangle

      iii. Not a right triangle   **iv.** Right triangle

b. Yes, the theorem works in reverse for these triangles.

11. a. $L_1 = \{1, 2, 3, \ldots, 26\}$

  b. $\text{Length}^2 = 27^2 - 1^2 = \sqrt{728}$, so length $= \sqrt{728}$ in. or about 26.98 in.

  c. $L_1^2 + L_2^2 = 27^2$, so $L_2 = \sqrt{(27^2 - L_1^2)}$.

  d. Using the calculator table, the length of the screen is about 26.926 inches, so the area is about 2 in. $\cdot$ 26.926 in. or 53.85 in^2.

  e. $L_3 = L_1 \cdot L_2$, or $L_3 = L_1 \cdot \sqrt{(27^2 - L_1^2)}$

  f. A model that works is $y = x\sqrt{27^2 - x^2}$, where x is the width and y is the area.

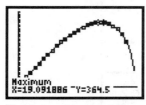

  $[0, 27, 5, -50, 450, 50]$

  g. Trace the graph or use a table to find that a 19-by-19 in. square gives the maximum area.

12. a. Answers will vary. Possible answer: The ratios $\frac{10}{5}$, $\frac{24}{12}$, and $\frac{26}{13}$ are all equal to 2, so the sides are proportional and the triangles are similar.

  b. Yes. Possible explanations: Similar polygons have congruent angles. Or, the side lengths 10, 24, and 26 satisfy the Pythagorean theorem, so the triangle is a right triangle.

13. a. If the slope is to be $\frac{5}{12}$, then the small right triangle in the sketch will be similar to a right triangle with side lengths 5, 12, and 13. The awning is the hypotenuse of this triangle. If a represents the length of the awning, then $\frac{13}{12} = \frac{a}{8}$, so $a = \frac{104}{12} = \frac{26}{3} = 8.\overline{6}$. So, the length of the awning will be $8.\overline{6}$ ft or 8 ft 8 in.

  b. Let s represent the short leg of the right triangle. Using the fact that the right triangle in the sketch is similar to a right triangle with side lengths 5, 12, and 13, $\frac{5}{12} = \frac{s}{8}$, so $s = 3\frac{1}{3}$ ft. The length of the support post is then 14 ft $-3\frac{1}{3}$ ft, which is $10\frac{2}{3}$ ft or 10 ft 8 in.

14. Let x represent the side length of the original deck. Then, $(x + 3)(x + 2) = 210$. Solve this equation for x.

$(x + 3)(x + 2) = 210$	The original equation.
$x^2 + 5x + 6 = 210$	Expand the left side.
$x^2 + 5x - 204 = 0$	Subtract 210 from both sides.
$x = -17$ or $x = 12$	Solve using the quadratic formula.

Only the positive solution makes sense in this situation. The original deck measured 12 ft by 12 ft.

LESSON 11.5

EXERCISES

1. a. $3\sqrt{3}$

  b. $\sqrt{5} \cdot \sqrt{2} \cdot \sqrt{5} = \sqrt{5} \cdot \sqrt{5} \cdot \sqrt{2} = \sqrt{25} \cdot \sqrt{2} = 5\sqrt{2}$

  c. $\sqrt{2}(\sqrt{2} + \sqrt{3}) = \sqrt{2}\sqrt{2} + \sqrt{2}\sqrt{3} = \sqrt{4} + \sqrt{6} = 2 + \sqrt{6}$

  d. $\sqrt{5} - \sqrt{2} + 3\sqrt{5} + 6\sqrt{2} = \sqrt{5} + 3\sqrt{5} - \sqrt{2} + 6\sqrt{2} = 4\sqrt{5} + 5\sqrt{2}$

  e. $\sqrt{3}(\sqrt{2}) + 5\sqrt{6} = \sqrt{6} + 5\sqrt{6} = 6\sqrt{6}$

  f. $\sqrt{2}(\sqrt{21}) + \sqrt{3}(\sqrt{14}) = \sqrt{42} + \sqrt{42} = 2\sqrt{42}$

  g. $\dfrac{\sqrt{35}}{\sqrt{7}} = \sqrt{\dfrac{35}{7}} = \sqrt{5}$

  h. $\sqrt{5}(4\sqrt{5}) = 4\sqrt{25} = 4 \cdot 5 = 20$

2. a. $a = \sqrt{91}$ **b.** $b = \sqrt{10}$

  c. $c = 4$ **d.** $d = \sqrt{13}$

3. For each part, you can use a rectangular diagram or the distributive property to expand the right side of the equation.

  a. The general form is $y = x^2 - 3$.

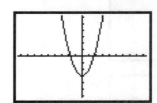

  $[-9.4, 9.4, 1, -6.2, 6.2, 1]$

  b. $y = x^2 + 2x\sqrt{5} + 5$

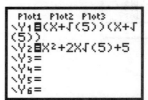

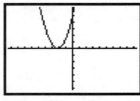

$[-9.4, 9.4, 1, -6.2, 6.2, 1]$

4. a. $x = \pm\sqrt{3} \approx \pm 1.732$ **b.** $x = -\sqrt{5} \approx -2.236$

5. a. The x-coordinate of the vertex is 0 (the value halfway between the x-intercepts $-\sqrt{3}$ and $\sqrt{3}$). To find the y-coordinate of the vertex, substitute 0 for x in the equation: $y = (0 + \sqrt{3})(0 - \sqrt{3}) = -3$. So the vertex is $(0, -3)$.

  b. The vertex of this graph is the x-intercept, so it is $(-\sqrt{5}, 0) \approx (-2.236, 0)$.

6. For each part, you can use the distributive property or a rectangular diagram to expand the right side of the equation.

  a. $y = x^2 - 112$

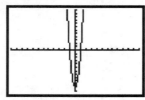

$[-120, 120, 10, -120, 120, 10]$

b. $y = 2x^2 + 2x\sqrt{6} - 72$

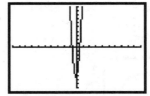

$[-100, 100, 10, -100, 100, 10]$

c. $y = x^2 + 6x + 7$

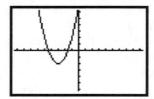

$[-9.4, 9.4, 1, -6.2, 6.2, 1]$

7. a. $x = \pm 4\sqrt{7} \approx \pm 10.583$

  b. $x = 2\sqrt{6} \approx 4.899$ and $x = -3\sqrt{6} \approx -7.348$

  c. $x = -3 - \sqrt{2} \approx -4.414$ and $x = -3 + \sqrt{2} \approx -1.586$

Discovering Algebra Solutions Manual
©2002 Key Curriculum Press

8. a. The x-coordinate of the vertex is 0 (the x-value halfway between the x-intercepts). To find the y-coordinate of the vertex, substitute 0 for x in the equation:
$y = (0 + 4\sqrt{7})(0 - 4\sqrt{7}) = -16\sqrt{49} = -112$.
So, the vertex is $(0, -112)$.

b. To find the x-coordinate of the vertex, average the x-intercepts: $\frac{2\sqrt{6} + (-3\sqrt{6})}{2} = \frac{-\sqrt{6}}{2}$. To find the y-coordinate of the vertex, substitute $\frac{-\sqrt{6}}{2}$ for x in the equation:

$$y = 2\left(-\frac{\sqrt{6}}{2} - 2\sqrt{6}\right)\left(-\frac{\sqrt{6}}{2} + 3\sqrt{6}\right)$$
$$= 2(-2.5\sqrt{6})(2.5\sqrt{6}) = -12.5\sqrt{36}$$
$$= -12.5 \cdot 6 = -75$$

So, the vertex is $\left(\frac{-\sqrt{6}}{2}, -75\right) \approx (-1.225, -75)$.

c. To find the x-coordinate of the vertex, average the x-intercepts: $\frac{-3 - \sqrt{2} - 3 + \sqrt{2}}{2} = \frac{-6}{2} = -3$. To find the y-coordinate of the vertex, substitute -3 for x in the equation:
$y = (-3 + 3 + \sqrt{2})(-3 + 3 - \sqrt{2})$
$= \sqrt{2}(-\sqrt{2}) = -\sqrt{4} = -2$. So, the vertex is $(-3, -2)$.

9. a. $4\sqrt{7} = \sqrt{16} \cdot \sqrt{7} = \sqrt{112}$
b. $5\sqrt{22} = \sqrt{25} \cdot \sqrt{22} = \sqrt{550}$
c. $18\sqrt{3} = \sqrt{324} \cdot \sqrt{3} = \sqrt{972}$
d. $30\sqrt{5} = \sqrt{900} \cdot \sqrt{5} = \sqrt{4500}$

10. a. $\sqrt{72} = \sqrt{36 \cdot 2} = \sqrt{36} \cdot \sqrt{2} = 6\sqrt{2}$
b. $\sqrt{27} = \sqrt{9 \cdot 3} = \sqrt{9} \cdot \sqrt{3} = 3\sqrt{3}$
c. $\sqrt{1800} = \sqrt{900 \cdot 2} = \sqrt{900} \cdot \sqrt{2} = 30\sqrt{2}$
d. $\sqrt{147} = \sqrt{49 \cdot 3} = \sqrt{49} \cdot \sqrt{3} = 7\sqrt{3}$

11.

$0 = 0.5x^2 - 6x + 8$	The original equation.
$0 \stackrel{?}{=} 0.5\left(6 - \sqrt{20}\right)^2$ $- 6(6 - \sqrt{20}) + 8$	Replace x with $6 - \sqrt{20}$.
$0 \stackrel{?}{=} 0.5\left(6 - \sqrt{20}\right)^2$ $- 36 + 6\sqrt{20} + 8$	Distribute the -6 over $6 - \sqrt{20}$.
$0 \stackrel{?}{=} 0.5(36 - 6\sqrt{20} - 6\sqrt{20} + 20)$ $- 36 + 6\sqrt{20} + 8$	Square the expression.
$0 \stackrel{?}{=} 18 - 3\sqrt{20} - 3\sqrt{20}$ $+ 10 - 36 + 6\sqrt{20} + 8$	Distribute the 0.5 over the expression in parentheses.
$0 \stackrel{?}{=} 18 + 10 - 36 + 8$	Combine the radical expressions.
$0 = 0$	Add and subtract.

12. a. The red line creates two right triangles, each with a leg length of $\frac{1}{2}(8)$ cm, or 4 cm, and a hypotenuse length of 8 cm. By the Pythagorean theorem, the length of the other leg is $4\sqrt{3}$ cm.

b. The height forms a right triangle with the answer from 12a as the hypotenuse length and a leg length of 4 cm (shown in black). By the Pythagorean theorem, the height (the length of the other leg) is $4\sqrt{2}$.

c. Approximately 566 ft

13. The pole is the hypotenuse of a right triangle in which one leg is the height of the box and the other is a diagonal of the base. The height of the box is 20 cm. To find the length of the diagonal of the base, use the Pythagorean theorem: $d^2 = 50^2 + 30^2 = 3400$, so $d \approx \sqrt{3400}$ cm. Now, use the Pythagorean theorem again to find the length of the pole: $p^2 = 20^2 + (\sqrt{3400})^2 = 3800$, so $p = \sqrt{3800}$ cm or $10\sqrt{38}$ cm.

14. Use the Pythagorean theorem to find each length, starting with a:

$a = \sqrt{2^2 + 2^2} = \sqrt{8} = 2\sqrt{2}$ cm

$b = \sqrt{2^2 + (\sqrt{8})^2} = \sqrt{4 + 8} = \sqrt{12} = 2\sqrt{3}$ cm

$c = \sqrt{(2 + \sqrt{12})^2 - (2)^2} = \sqrt{4 + 4\sqrt{12} + 12 - 4}$
$= \sqrt{4\sqrt{12} + 12} = \sqrt{8\sqrt{3} + 12}$ cm

15. a. $y = (x - 2)^2 + 3$ **b.** $y = -x^2 + 4$
c. $y = 3(x - 1)^2$

16. a. No x-intercepts   **b.** Two x-intercepts
c. One x-intercept

LESSON 11.6

EXERCISES

1. No, because $9^2 + 16^2 \neq 25^2$.

2. a. Possible answer:

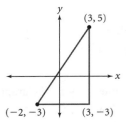

b. Horizontal length: $3 - (-2) = 5$ units; vertical length: $5 - (-3) = 8$ units

c. Using the Pythagorean theorem, the square of the distance is $5^2 + 8^2$ or 89, so the distance is $\sqrt{89}$ units.

3. Answers will vary. Possible answer: $(6, 3)$ and $(1, 7)$.

4. a. Slope of $\overline{AB}$ and $\overline{DC}$: $\frac{4}{5}$; slope of $\overline{AD}$ and $\overline{BC}$: $-\frac{2}{3}$

   b. Parallelogram

   c. Length of $\overline{AB} = \sqrt{(10 - 5)^2 + (6 - 2)^2}$
   $= \sqrt{25 + 16} = \sqrt{41}$ units
   Length of $\overline{DC} = \sqrt{(7 - 2)^2 + (8 - 4)^2}$
   $= \sqrt{25 + 16} = \sqrt{41}$ units
   Length of $\overline{AD} = \sqrt{(2 - 5)^2 + (4 - 2)^2}$
   $= \sqrt{9 + 4} = \sqrt{13}$ units
   Length of $\overline{BC} = \sqrt{(7 - 10)^2 + (8 - 6)^2}$
   $= \sqrt{9 + 4} = \sqrt{13}$ units

5. a. The coordinates of the Refreshment Stand are $(-5, 2)$. The coordinates of the Bumper Cars are $(-4, -3)$. Use the distance formula:

   $d = \sqrt{(-4 - (-5))^2 + (-3 - 2)^2}$
   $= \sqrt{1^2 + (-5)^2} = \sqrt{26}$

   The attractions are $\sqrt{26}$ units or about 0.5 mile apart.

   b. The coordinates of the Acrobats are $(-1, 4)$. The coordinates of the Hall of Mirrors are $(3, 1)$. Use the distance formula:

   $d = \sqrt{(3 - (-1))^2 + (1 - 4)^2}$
   $= \sqrt{4^2 + (-3)^2} = \sqrt{25} = 5$

   The attractions are 5 units or 0.5 mile apart.

6. The Roller Coaster is at $(-4, 5)$ and the Sledge Hammer is at $(2, -3)$. Use the midpoint formula:

   $\left(\frac{-4 + 2}{2}, \frac{5 + (-3)}{2}\right) = (-1, 1)$

   The sawdust spreader broke down at $(-1, 1)$.

7. a. 5 cm   b. 13 cm

8. a. $\sqrt{20 - x} = x$
   $20 - x = x^2$
   $0 = x^2 + x - 20$
   $0 = (x + 5)(x - 4)$
   $x = -5$ or $x = 4$

   b. Answers will vary. Possible answer: The graphs of $Y_1 = \sqrt{20 - x}$ and $Y_2 = x$ intersect once at $x = 4$.

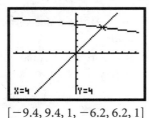

   $[-9.4, 9.4, 1, -6.2, 6.2, 1]$

c. $x = 4$ is a solution. Squaring both sides to solve the equation symbolically introduces an extra solution, $\sqrt{16} = 4$. But though -5 is a square root of 25, $x = -5$ is not a realistic solution, because a square root symbol indicates only the positive root.

9. a. $a = 63$

   b.
$\frac{1}{\sqrt{2}} = \frac{b}{7\sqrt{2}}$	The original equation.
$7\sqrt{2} \cdot \frac{1}{\sqrt{2}} = \frac{b}{7\sqrt{2}} \cdot 7\sqrt{2}$	Multiply both sides by $7\sqrt{2}$.
$7 = b$	Multiply and divide.

   c.
$\frac{\sqrt{3}}{2} = \frac{c}{\sqrt{12}}$	The original equation.
$\sqrt{12} \cdot \frac{\sqrt{3}}{2} = \frac{c}{\sqrt{12}} \cdot \sqrt{12}$	Multiply both sides by $\sqrt{12}$.
$\frac{\sqrt{36}}{2} = c$	Multiply and divide.
$\frac{6}{2} = c$	Evaluate the square root.
$3 = c$	Divide.

10. $3\sqrt{401}$ ft or approximately 60 ft 1 in.

LESSON 11.7

EXERCISES

1. a. $x = 27$ b. $x = 35$

   c.
$\frac{1}{4} = \frac{\sqrt{10}}{\sqrt{x}}$	The original equation.
$4 = \frac{\sqrt{x}}{\sqrt{10}}$	Invert both sides.
$16 = \frac{x}{10}$	Square both sides.
$160 = x$	Multiply both sides by 10.

   d.
$\frac{2}{x} = \frac{x}{8}$	The original equation.
$\frac{16}{x} = x$	Multiply both sides by 8.
$16 = x^2$	Multiply both sides by x.
$\pm 4 = x$	Take the square root of both sides.

2. Solve $\frac{1}{50} = \frac{3.6}{x}$. The cities are 180 miles apart.

3. a. For angle D, $o = 7$ and $h = 25$, so $\sin D = \frac{o}{h} = \frac{7}{25}$.

   b. For angle E, $a = 7$ and $h = 25$, so $\cos E = \frac{a}{h} = \frac{7}{25}$.

   c. For angle D, $o = 7$ and $a = 24$, so $\tan D = \frac{o}{a} = \frac{7}{24}$.

4. a. Yes. Possible explanation: Angle A is common to both triangles and angles B and D are both right angles, so angles C and D must also be congruent. Because all three angles are congruent, the triangles are similar.

   b. $\frac{8}{4} = 2$ c. 6 cm and 10 cm

   d. 24 cm² and 6 cm²   e. $\frac{24}{6} = \frac{4}{1}$

5. a. Solve $\frac{x}{6} = \frac{x+2}{7}$; $x = 12$

   b. Solve $\frac{x+1}{5} = \frac{x-2}{4}$; $x = 14$

   c. Solve $\frac{9}{0.25} = \frac{10+x}{1.25}$; $x = 35$

6. a. $\sqrt{60}$ m or approximately 7.75 m

   b. $\sqrt{15}$ m or approximately 3.87 m

7. a. $\frac{d}{w} = \frac{\text{length of adjacent leg}}{\text{length of hypotenuse}}$, so $\frac{d}{w}$ is the cosine of 65°.

   b. $\frac{h}{w} = \frac{\text{length of opposite leg}}{\text{length of hypotenuse}}$, so $\frac{h}{w}$ is the sine of 65°.

   c. $\frac{h}{d} = \frac{\text{length of opposite leg}}{\text{length of adjacent leg}}$, so $\frac{h}{d}$ is the tangent of 65°.

   d. $\cos 65° \approx 0.4226$; $\sin 65° \approx 0.9063$; $\tan 65° \approx 2.1445$

   e. $\tan 65° = \frac{h}{2.6}$, so $h = 2.6 \cdot \tan 65° \approx 5.57$. The pole is about 5.6 m high.

8. a. $\tan 28° = \frac{y}{x}$ or $y = x \cdot \tan 28°$

   b. Sample description: The graph is a direct variation.

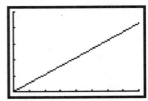

   [0, 200, 25, 0, 125, 25]

   c. $y = 100 \cdot \tan 28° \approx 53.17$

   d. $x = \frac{80}{\tan 28°} \approx 151$

9. a-b.

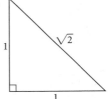

   c.

Trigonometric Functions for a 45° Angle

	Sine	Cosine	Tangent
Exact value of ratio	$\frac{1}{\sqrt{2}}$	$\frac{1}{\sqrt{2}}$	$\frac{1}{1}$
Decimal approximation of exact value	0.7071	0.7071	1.0000
Value by trigonometric function keys	0.7071	0.7071	1.0000

10. a–b.

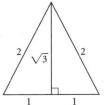

   c.

Trigonometric Functions for a 30° Angle

	Sine	Cosine	Tangent
Exact value of ratio	$\frac{1}{2}$	$\frac{\sqrt{3}}{2}$	$\frac{1}{\sqrt{3}}$
Decimal approximation of exact value	0.5000	0.8660	0.5774
Value by trigonometric function keys	0.5000	0.8660	0.5774

Trigonometric Functions for a 60° Angle

	Sine	Cosine	Tangent
Exact value of ratio	$\frac{\sqrt{3}}{2}$	$\frac{1}{2}$	$\frac{\sqrt{3}}{1}$
Decimal approximation of exact value	0.8660	0.5000	1.7321
Value by trigonometric function keys	0.8660	0.5000	1.7321

11. a. A rectangle

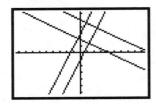

   [0, 200, 25, 0, 125, 25]

   b. $(1.2, 1.4)$, $(2.4, 3.8)$, $(0.8, 4.6)$, $(-0.4, 2.2)$

   c. $y = 11 - 8x$, $y = \frac{17}{7} + \frac{4}{7}x$

   d. The diagonals of a rectangle intersect at their midpoints. So, you can find the midpoint of the diagonal from $(1.2, 1.4)$ and $(0.8, 4.6)$. The diagonals intersect at $(1, 3)$.

12. $a = 10$
   $b = 26$
   $c = 13\sqrt{2} \approx 18.4$
   $d = 13\sqrt{3} - 13 \approx 9.52$

LESSON 11.8

EXERCISES

1. a. d **b.** A **c.** A **d.** $\frac{d}{c}$

   e. A **f.** A

2. a.

   b. Trigonometric ratios and inverse functions may vary. Possible answer: $\sin A = \frac{3}{5}$, so $A = \sin^{-1}\left(\frac{3}{5}\right) \approx 37°$; $\sin B = \frac{4}{5}$, so $B = \sin^{-1}\left(\frac{4}{5}\right) \approx 53°$.

   c. The angles should measure approximately 37° and 53°.

3. $\tan 42° = \frac{x}{49.5}$, so $x = 49.5 \cdot \tan 42° \approx 44.6$ m.

4. $\tan 25° = \frac{6.8}{b}$, so $b = \frac{6.8}{\tan 25°} \approx 14.6$ cm.

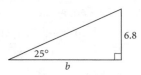

5. $\sin 28° = \frac{a}{20}$, so $a = 20 \cdot \sin 28° \approx 9.4$ cm.

$\cos 28° = \frac{b}{20}$, so $b = 20 \cdot \cos 28° \approx 17.7$ cm.

$\tan 64° = \frac{c}{2}$, so $c = 2 \cdot \tan 64° \approx 4.1$ cm.

$\cos 64° = \frac{2}{d}$, so $d = \frac{2}{\cos 64°} \approx 4.6$ cm.

$e^2 = 17^2 - 12^2 = 145$, so $e = \sqrt{145} \approx 12.0$ cm.

$\sin F = \frac{12}{17}$, so $F = \sin^{-1}\left(\frac{12}{17}\right) \approx 44.9°$.

$g^2 = 5^2 + 18^2 = 349$, so $g \approx \sqrt{349} \approx 18.7$ cm.

$\tan H = \frac{5}{18}$, so $H = \tan^{-1}\left(\frac{5}{18}\right) \approx 15.5°$.

6. a. 17 cm   **b.** $\frac{1}{2}(8)(15) = 60$ cm^2

   c. $P \approx 28°$ **d.** $Q \approx 62°$

   e. $P + Q + R = 180°$

7. $\tan 31° = \frac{height}{135}$, so height $= 135 \cdot \tan 31° \approx 81.1$ m.

8. Answers will vary. An average rise-to-run ratio for stairs is $\frac{7}{12}$. The answers provided are based on this ratio.

   a. Approximately 30°   **b.** Rise: 7; run: 12

   c. $\frac{7}{12}$ **d.** $\tan^{-1}\left(\frac{7}{12}\right) \approx 30.26°$

   e. $0.58\overline{3}$ or $\frac{7}{12}$

9. a. The tangent of the angle of elevation is 5% or 0.05, so the angle of elevation is $\tan^{-1}(0.05)$ or about 2.86°.

   b. The angle of elevation is $\tan^{-1}(0.15) = 8.5308$. $\sin(8.5308) = 0.14834$. The change in elevation is $0.14834(1000)$ or about 148 ft.

10. a. If ℓ represents the length of the rectangle, then $\tan 20° = \frac{5}{\ell}$. Solving this equation gives $\ell \approx 13.74$ cm. The area is then about 13.74 cm $\cdot$ 5 cm or 68.7 cm^2.

   b. Draw the height to the 8-cm side. This forms a right triangle with a 15° angle. The side opposite the 15° angle has a length of 4 cm. You can use the tangent function to find the height: $\tan 15° = \frac{4}{h}$, $h = \frac{4}{\tan 15°} \approx 14.93$ cm. The area of the original triangle is about $\frac{1}{2}(8$ cm$)(14.93$ cm$)$ or 59.7 cm^2.

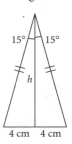

11. a. Approximately 19 ft   **b.** Approximately 51 ft

   c. Approximately 70 ft

12.
$$\begin{cases} y < 2 \\ x \geq -3 \\ y > -\frac{8}{3} - \frac{1}{3}x \\ y \geq -2 + x \end{cases}$$

13. Answers will vary. Possible answer:
$$y = -3 + \frac{x+7}{(x-2)(x+7)}.$$

CHAPTER 11 Review

EXERCISES

1. a. $8\sqrt{5}$ **b.** $4\sqrt{17}$ **c.** $123\sqrt{3}$ **d.** $\sqrt{15}$

   e. $4\sqrt{5} \cdot 4\sqrt{5} = 16\sqrt{25} = 16 \cdot 5 = 80$

   f. $\left(10\sqrt{17}\right)^2 = 10^2\left(\sqrt{17}\right)^2 = 100 \cdot 17 = 1700$

   g. $\sqrt{6} \cdot \sqrt{15} = \sqrt{90} = \sqrt{9 \cdot 10} = \sqrt{9}\sqrt{10} = 3\sqrt{10}$

   h. $4\sqrt{25} \cdot 4\sqrt{5} = 4 \cdot 5 \cdot 4\sqrt{5} = 80\sqrt{5}$

   i. $\sqrt{2} + \sqrt{3}$

   j. $\sqrt{2} + \sqrt{8} = \sqrt{2} + \sqrt{4 \cdot 2} = \sqrt{2} + \sqrt{4}\sqrt{2}$ $= \sqrt{2} + 2\sqrt{2} = 3\sqrt{2}$

   k. $\frac{\sqrt{18}}{\sqrt{3}} = \sqrt{\frac{18}{3}} = \sqrt{6}$

   l. $\sqrt{3} + \sqrt{27} = \sqrt{3} + \sqrt{9 \cdot 3} = \sqrt{3} + \sqrt{9}\sqrt{3}$ $= \sqrt{3} + 3\sqrt{3} = 4\sqrt{3}$

2. The area is 5 square units. Here are two possible strategies:

   i. Draw a square around the tilted square using the grid lines. Subtract the areas of the outer triangles from the area of the larger square: $9 - 4(1) = 5$.

ii. Use the distance formula to find the length of the side between $(1, 0)$ and $(3, 1)$:
$\sqrt{(3-1)^2 + (1-0)^2} = \sqrt{5}$. Square the side length to find the area: $\sqrt{5}^2 = 5$.

3. The slopes of the sides are $\frac{1}{2}$, -2, $\frac{1}{2}$, and -2. The slopes of each pair of adjacent sides are negative reciprocals, so the adjacent sides are perpendicular.

4. Answers will vary. Possible answer: Draw a 7-by-7 square on graph paper and remove triangles with areas of 5 square units (legs 2 units and 5 units) from each corner. The area of the remaining square is $49 - 4 \cdot 5 = 29$ square units.

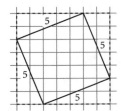

5. Answers will vary. Possible answer: Sides of 5 ft, 12 ft, and 13 ft satisfy the Pythagorean theorem and therefore a similar triangle with sides twice as long will form a right triangle. If the corner is a right angle, then the construction worker should be able to form a right triangle with the first 10 ft of the rope along one side of the corner, the next 24 ft of rope along the other side of the corner, and the remaining 26 ft as the hypotenuse.

6. **a.** $A(-4, 2)$, $B(0, 5)$, $C(6, -3)$, $D(2, -6)$

   b. Slope of $\overline{AB}$: $\frac{3}{4}$; slope of $\overline{BC}$: $\frac{-4}{3}$; slope of $\overline{CD}$: $\frac{3}{4}$; slope of $\overline{AD}$: $\frac{-4}{3}$.

   c. It is a rectangle. The slopes of opposite sides are the same, so they are parallel. The slopes of adjacent sides are negative reciprocals, so they are perpendicular.

   d.

   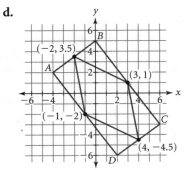

   e. Each side measures $\sqrt{31.25}$ units or about 5.59 units.

   f. The slopes are -0.5, -5.5, -0.5, and -5.5.

   g. It is a rhombus. The sides are all the same length, and opposite sides have the same slope, so they are parallel.

7. $a \approx 3.38$ m
   $b \approx 7.25$ m

8. **a.** Sample answer:

   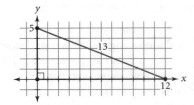

   b. Approximately $67°$

   c. Find $\sin^{-1}\left(\frac{12}{13}\right) \approx 67°$, $\cos^{-1}\left(\frac{5}{13}\right) \approx 67°$, and $\tan^{-1}\left(\frac{12}{5}\right) \approx 67°$.

   d. Answers will vary. Possible answer: Because the angle measures must add to $180°$, the angle opposite the 12-unit side has measure $180° - (90° + 67°)$ or $23°$.

9. **a.** $\sqrt{116}$ cm or about 10.77 cm

   b. $\sqrt{141}$ cm or about 11.87 cm

10. Answers will vary. Possible answer: If a triangle has base 8 cm and height 4 cm, its area is 16 sq. cm. If the triangle is enlarged by a factor of 3, its base will be 24 cm, its height will be 12 cm, and its area will be 144 sq. cm, which equals $3^2 \times 16$ sq. cm. For a triangle with base b and height h, the area is $A = \frac{1}{2}bh$. If the sides are enlarged by a factor of k, the base and height become kb and kh, and the area becomes $A = \frac{1}{2}(kb)(kh)$ or $A = \frac{1}{2}bh \cdot k^2$. So, the area is enlarged by a factor of k^2.

11. **a.** $y = 60 + 1.08(x - 40)$ or $y = 34 + 1.08(x - 16)$

    b. Approximately $50°$

    c. Approximately $38°$

12. **a.** $\begin{cases} 3a + 1.5p = 13.74 \\ 2a + 3p = 16.32 \end{cases}$, where a is the price per pound for dried apricots and p is the price per pound for dried papaya.

    b. Apricots: $2.79; papaya: $3.58

13. **a.** Inverse variation. Possible explanation: The product of x and y is constant; $xy = 2$ or $y = \frac{2}{x}$.

    b. Neither. Possible explanation: The product is not constant, so it is not an inverse variation. The y-value for $x = 0$ is not 0, so it is not a direct variation.

    c. Direct variation. Possible explanation: The ratio of y to x is constant; $y = 0.25x$.

    d. Neither. Possible explanation: The graph is not a curve, so the relationship is not an inverse variation. The line does not pass through the origin, so it is not a direct variation.

e. Inverse variation. Possible explanation: The product of the x- and y-coordinates for any point on the curve is 8; $xy = 8$ or $y = \frac{8}{x}$.

f. Direct variation. Possible explanation: The graph is a straight line through the origin; $y = 1.5x$.

14. a. Answers will vary. Possible answer: For $0 < x < 3$, f is nonlinear and increasing at a slower and slower rate. For $3 < x < 5$, f is linear and decreasing. For $5 < x < 7$, f is linear and increasing. For $7 < x < 9$, f is linear and constant (neither increasing nor decreasing). For $9 < x < 12$, f is nonlinear and decreasing at a slower and slower rate.

b. $0 \le y \le 5$ **c.** 3

d. 1, 5, 12   **e.** $7 \le x \le 9$

15. a. $27x^6y^3$ **b.** $5p^4q^2$ **c.** $\frac{x}{y^2}$ **d.** $\frac{m^2}{n^4} + \frac{1}{m^4}$

16. a. Mean: 108.4; median: 105; mode: 105

b. Five-number summary: 82, 99, 105, 112, 179

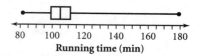

Running time (min)

c. Bin widths may vary.

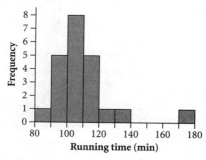

Running time (min)

d. Sample answers:

(1) About 75% of the new releases have running times of 112 minutes or less. (2) None of the new releases have running times between 140 and 169 minutes. (3) Most (18) of the running times are between 90 and 119 minutes.

17. a. $y = (x + 3)(x - 1)$ **b.** $y = (x + 1)^2 - 4$

c. $y = x^2 + 2x - 3$

18. a. Approximately $1197   **b.** Approximately $4102

19. a. 26   **b.** 2   **c.** 36   **d.** 128

e. -24

20. a. $62.39   **b.** $65.51

21. Answers will vary. Possible answers:

a. A reflection across the y-axis and a vertical shrink by a factor of 0.5

b. $(-x, 0.5y)$

22. a. $x = -5$ or $x = 2$ **b.** $x = 4$

c. $x = -3$ or $x = 10$ **d.** $x = \pm\sqrt{5}$

23. a. $y = (x + 2)^2 - 4$ **b.** $y = -0.5|x + 3|$

24. a. $35   **b.** $225

c. $\{0, 225\}$ ENTER; $\{\text{Ans}(1) + 1, \text{Ans}(2) + 35\}$ ENTER, ENTER, . . .

d. $y = 225 + 35x$ **e.** $645

f. 8

25. a.

Segment	Length	Slope
$\overline{AB}$	10	$\frac{3}{4}$
$\overline{BC}$	10	$-\frac{3}{4}$
$\overline{AC}$	16	0

b. Isosceles triangle. Two sides have equal length.

c. $D(2, 1)$

d. Right triangles. Possible explanation: $\overline{BD}$ has an undefined slope, so it is vertical; $\overline{AC}$ has a slope of 0, so it is horizontal.

e. A drawing should confirm 25a–d.

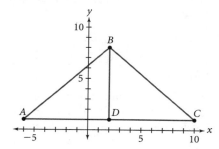

TAKE ANOTHER LOOK

For acute triangles, $a^2 + b^2 > c^2$. For obtuse triangles, $a^2 + b^2 < c^2$. Possible summary: If the angle opposite the longest side is *less than* 90°, then the square of the length of the longest side is *less than* the sum of the squares of the lengths of the other two sides. If the angle opposite the longest side is *equal to* 90°, then the square of the length of the longest side is *equal to* the sum of the squares of the lengths of the other two sides. If the angle opposite the longest side is *greater than* 90°, then the square of the length of the longest side is *greater than* the sum of the squares of the lengths of the other two sides.

Discovering Algebra Solutions Manual
©2002 Key Curriculum Press